W9-CUK-439

THEORY OF MOLECULAR EXCITONS

McGRAW-HILL SERIES IN ADVANCED CHEMISTRY

BAIR Introduction to Chemical Instrumentation
BENSON The Foundations of Chemical Kinetics
DAVIDSON Statistical Mechanics
DAVYDOV (*Trans.* Kasha and Oppenheimer) Theory of Molecular Excitons
DEAN Flame Photometry
DJERASSI Optical Rotatory Dispersion
ELIEL Stereochemistry of Carbon Compounds
FITTS Nonequilibrium Thermodynamics
HELFFERICH Ion Exchange
HILL Statistical Mechanics
HINE Physical Organic Chemistry
KIRKWOOD AND OPPENHEIM Chemical Thermodynamics
KOSOWER Molecular Biochemistry
LAITINEN Chemical Analysis
PITZER AND BREWER (*Revision of* Lewis and Randall) Thermodynamics
POPLE, SCHNEIDER, AND BERNSTEIN High-resolution Nuclear Magnetic Resonance
PRYOR Mechanisms of Sulfur Reactions
ROBERTS Nuclear Magnetic Resonance
ROSSOTTI AND ROSSOTTI The Determination of Stability Constants
WIBERG Laboratory Technique in Organic Chemistry

THEORY OF MOLECULAR EXCITONS

A. S. DAVYDOV

TRANSLATED FROM THE FIRST RUSSIAN EDITION BY

Michael Kasha
Professor of Chemistry, Florida State University

Max Oppenheimer, Jr.
Professor of Russian, State University of Iowa

McGRAW-HILL BOOK COMPANY, INC. 1962

New York San Francisco Toronto London

THEORY OF MOLECULAR EXCITONS

 Library of Congress Catalog Card Number 61-15914

THE MAPLE PRESS COMPANY, YORK, PA.

33363

TRANSLATORS' PREFACE

The exciton concept was introduced into solid-state physics by Frenkel in 1931, in connection with the transformation of excitation energy into heat in rare-gas solids. Not until Davydov's now-famous 1948 paper on the splitting of electronic terms in the naphthalene crystal was the concept applied to geometry-determined molecular problems. Since then the treatment of an impressive variety of problems has been published by Davydov and his colleagues and by numerous other researchers. The exciton model has now been used in treating general formulations of energy transfer, in the crystal splitting of electronic states which are nondegenerate in the isolated molecule, in the splitting of infrared bands and Raman lines in molecular crystals corresponding to nondegenerate vibrational modes in the isolated molecule, in the calculation of excited states of molecules consisting of two or more isolated or not-strongly-conjugated chromophoric units, in optical rotatory power of helical polymers containing nonconjugated chromophoric units, etc. Altogether, the range of problems covered suggests that the role of the exciton model may be as great in the fields of molecular physics and quantum chemistry as that of the molecular orbital model, the valence-bond model, or the charge-transfer model. Davydov's book summarizes many of the problems, and its perceptive treatment suggests many starting points for further extensions.

The translators are pleased to make this unique book available in English. In spite of widespread current interest in the topics covered, copies of the book in Russian are something of a rarity, and even its existence is unknown to many researchers.

We wish to give a few notes on our translation. Throughout the book we have translated:

"Combinational scattering spectra" as *combinational scattering* (*Raman*) *spectra*

"Partial vibrations" and "normal vibrations" as *normal vibrations*

"Long and intermediate axes" as *long and intermediate axes*

In the first case, the Russian terminology was preserved, but the more familiar terminology was introduced. In the last case, the author's usage was again preserved in preference to the more common "long and short axes."

We have not attempted to revise the form of the mathematical expressions except for the replacement of some half-dozen Cyrillic characters by Roman characters. A number of typographical errors among symbols in the original text have been corrected. A few fundamental corrections supplied by the author have been included.

This book was published originally under the title "Theory of the Absorption of Light in Molecular Crystals" by A. S. Davydov, Works of the Institute of Physics, Ukrainian Academy of Sciences, Kiev, Ukrainian S.S.R., 1951. We feel that the title we have adopted stresses the principal theme of the book—the resonance interaction of excited states of weakly coupled molecular systems.

To bring this edition more up to date, we have included two appendixes which cover principal literature on related topics to December, 1961.

We acknowledge with thanks the careful reading of the final proof and suggestions by Dr. Robin M. Hochstrasser.

Michael Kasha
Max Oppenheimer, Jr.

CONTENTS

INTRODUCTION

1. Molecular Crystals

For the theoretical description of the physical properties of a solid body, it is convenient to classify crystalline substances according to the magnitude of the ratio of the forces of interaction of the particles (atoms or molecules) of which the crystal is formed to the forces of interaction between the composite parts (electrons and atoms, respectively) of these particles. If the forces of interaction between the particles are significantly smaller than the forces of interaction between the composite parts of one particle, then when forming a solid body these particles preserve their individuality in the first approximation. We shall define such solid bodies as molecular crystals. Usually molecular crystals are composed of molecules between which van der Waals forces of attraction act within the crystal. If the energy of intermolecular interaction is close in order of magnitude to chemical energies (the bond energies of atoms in a molecule or of electrons in an atom), then the molecules lose their individuality, and the crystals can now be identified as of the valence, metallic, or ionic type.

Molecular crystals are formed from atoms of inert gases (Ne, A, Kr, and others) and from molecules with saturated bonds (H_2, CH_4, and others).† Molecular crystals have an especially wide occurrence among organic substances.

Molecular crystals are characterized by low melting and boiling points. Evaporation takes place by whole molecules. The heat of sublimation of typical molecular crystals amounts to several kcal/mole, i.e., is 10 to 20 times smaller than the dissociation energy of isolated molecules or than the dissociation energy of an ionic crystal lattice (Born, Ref. 1, p. 309).

Molecular crystals are electrical nonconductors. Almost all molecular crystals are diamagnetic (except, for example, crystals of O_2 and NO), inasmuch as they consist of closed-shell molecules having no resultant spin.

In this work we shall investigate the optical behavior of molecular

† Translators' note: Crystals formed of molecules containing unsaturated bonds (O_2, benzene, naphthalene) are also included in this category.

crystals and, more specifically, the problems of light absorption in molecular crystals.

2. Method and Aims of the Investigation

The theoretical examination of the question of light absorption by a solid body (as well as by other aggregates) leads to the solution of two problems: (1) the determination of the stationary states of the crystal and (2) the calculation of the transition probability, under the action of a light wave, from one state to another, or (a less complete but simpler problem) the determination of the selection rules for the optical transitions.

In general, the solution of these problems for any solid body cannot be completed in practice, inasmuch as the problem narrows down to solving the equations of the quantum mechanics of stationary states for a system with an enormous number of degrees of freedom. The solution of this type of problem can be achieved only by means of approximation methods. In this connection, the approximation method utilized depends upon (1) the region of wavelengths in which it is necessary to investigate the absorption and (2) the character of the solid body (metals or molecular, valence, or ionic crystals).

When investigating absorption in the infrared region of the spectrum, one can, with sufficiently good approximation, examine only the movement of the atomic nuclei in the lattice, utilizing classical mechanics. When investigating the absorption spectra in the visible and ultraviolet regions, coupled with vibrations of the nuclei, one must investigate the change in electronic states of the crystal, but in this case, it is necessary to utilize quantum mechanics. The methods used for the calculation of molecular crystals will be essentially different from the methods for solvng the same problems for other types of crystals.

When calculating the optical properties of molecular crystals, it is natural to start with the premise that these properties are determined basically by the optical behavior of isolated molecules and to consider the influence of their interaction as a perturbation. Such an assumption is useful from two points of view. First, it points out the method of solving the problem, namely, by utilizing quantum-mechanical perturbation theory. Second, it has great practical significance. If it is possible to determine how the optical properties of molecules change under the influence of intermolecular forces when molecules are united into crystals, then the investigation of the absorption spectra of crystals enables one to decipher the absorption spectrum of the free molecule, the structure of the crystal itself, and the nature of the molecular interaction.

It is known that the study of the character of the interaction of matter with radiation is one of the methods of investigating the structure of matter. It is sufficient merely to remember that the structure of atoms, and also, to a certain degree, of molecules, became known by virtue of the development of methods of spectroscopy for the gaseous state. The large amount of experimental information assembled served as a basis for creating quantum concepts and, later, quantum mechanics. In the spring of 1928, L. I. Mandelshtam and G. S. Landsberg[2] (for crystalline quartz) and C. V. Raman (for liquid benzene) discovered the *combinational scattering*† of light. This discovery soon took a prominent place as a means of investigating molecular structure. The combinational scattering (Raman scattering) enables one to obtain the vibrational frequencies of atoms in molecules and the frequencies of intermolecular vibrations in solid and liquid bodies. Vibrations of the latter type were first discovered by the Soviet physicists E. F. Gross and M. F. Vuks and named by them *low-frequency spectra.*[3]

One can expect that the study of absorption spectra and of light scattering of crystals also will be one of the methods for studying their structure and the forces of intermolecular interaction as well. However, in the visible and ultraviolet regions of the absorption spectrum, the majority of solid bodies at room temperature exhibit wide bands without evident structure. Salts of the rare-earth elements, salts of chromium and manganese, as well as a few others, form an exception: the absorption spectra of these substances show a large number of narrow bands. The anomalous behavior of the salts of rare-earth elements is conditioned by the following: When absorbing light, there is a change in the energy states of the $4f$ inner-shell electrons, which do not participate in valence bonds and are therefore protected by valence electrons from the effect of other atoms. The large number of absorption lines is explained by the splitting of the degenerate energy levels by the electric field (created by neighboring ions); the symmetry of this field is determined by the symmetry of the crystal. Splittings of this type are similar to the Stark effect and were qualitatively investigated by H. Bethe.[4]

J. Becquerel[5] first studied the spectra of the salts of rare-earth elements at the temperature of liquid air and showed that a significant narrowing of the absorption bands occurred when the temperature was lowered. At the same time, V. Kurbatov[6] showed that the color of a very large number of crystals changed upon immersion in liquid air. This demonstrates the change of the absorption spectra of crystals when the temperature is lowered.

Very significant are I. V. Obreimov's works,[7–9] in which it was shown that, when the temperature is lowered, the absorption bands of many molecular crystals become discrete.

These works supplied a basis for the systematic investigation of absorption and fluorescence spectra of molecular crystals.

† Translators' note: Commonly called Raman scattering.

The lowering of crystal temperature changes the absorption spectrum essentially. Eight wide absorption bands of benzene, superposed at room temperature, transform[10,11] at 78°K, into a series of separate absorption maxima each of which exhibits a complicated structure at 20.4°K.

As was shown by I. V. Obreimov and A. F. Prikhotko,[12] 3 wide and diffuse absorption bands of naphthalene at room temperature are transformed into 40 absorption bands at a temperature of 78°K and into more than 300 absorption bands[13] at a temperature of 20.4°K.

At low temperatures a discrete spectrum is observed even in those compounds which have a continuous spectrum in the gaseous state, making their analysis in this state impossible. As I. V. Obreimov showed,[8,9] the diffuse absorption spectrum of the vapor of azobenzene is broken up into a multitude of very sharp absorption bands in the crystal at the temperature of liquid hydrogen and helium. The continuous absorption spectrum of the vapors of iodobenzene, according to the data of E. M. Bronstein, acquires a distinct structure in the crystal at 20.4°K.

It is difficult to analyze the absorption spectra of complex molecules in the gaseous state because of the great vibrational and rotational structure. When studying the absorption spectra of the same substances in a crystalline state at low temperatures, it is apparently possible to decipher the absorption spectrum of the molecules. Owing to the small interaction forces between the molecules, one could expect only insignificant spectral changes in molecular crystals upon variation of the aggregate state. These changes can be limited to the displacement of the entire spectrum, to the disappearance of the rotational band structure, to the appearance of small lattice vibrations (Gross frequencies), and to the splitting of the absorption bands in the crystal. The last phenomenon has always been linked with the removal of degeneracy from degenerate states of free molecules. However, if the molecule did not have degenerate states, then presumably the splitting of terms could not take place.[14]

It is roughly these considerations which furnished I. V. Obreimov and A. F. Prikhotko the basis for their numerous investigations of absorption and fluorescence spectra of crystals.[12–18] However, these assumptions, which at first sight seemed obvious, required an experimental and theoretical basis. The author expresses his sincere gratitude to A. F. Prikhotko and I. V. Obreimov, who called his attention to the indispensability of analyzing this problem from the theoretical point of view.

Experience has fundamentally confirmed the correspondence between the spectra of the gas and crystal. However, until recently, a detailed verification could not be made, since there were insufficient experimental data available (especially concerning vapor spectra). It is true that the great pleochroism of molecular crystals has been well known for a comparatively long time. Thus, I. V. Obreimov[7,8] showed, taking azobenzene as an example, that the absorption spectrum for light in this crystal is markedly different for two mutually perpendicular directions of the electric vector of the impinging light wave. Furthermore, the pleochroism in the absorption spectra of crystals of anthracene,[17] phenanthrene,[16] and a series of others was observed. If we consider that almost all molecular crystals contain somewhat differently oriented molecules in one unit cell (most frequently, two or four molecules per cell), then it becomes clear that one cannot explain the pleochroism of the crystal without the assumption of changes in the absorption spectrum of the molecule.

There are very few theoretical works devoted to the investigation of absorption spectra of light in molecular crystals. The first investigations along this line were completed by J. I. Frenkel[19–21] and somewhat later by Peierls.[22] However, all these investigators examined only the cubic crystals of rare monatomic gases (neon, krypton, and others); therefore, a series of interesting physical results was lost in their work. In spite of this, the works of J. I. Frenkel are of great theoretical interest. Firstly, these works were the first to introduce the concept of the *exciton*, whose movement is equivalent to the migration of the excitation through the crystal from one atom to another. This concept turned out to be very fruitful and was utilized subsequently in a series of other works. Secondly, it was shown in these works that, in the ideal crystal, light can excite only the excitons with wave numbers equal to the wave number of the light wave. The violation of this condition is linked with the lattice vibrations. Thirdly, the works of J. I. Frenkel have posed and partially solved the problem of the transformation of absorbed light energy into heat.

The method of obtaining the energy states of a crystal from the states of isolated atoms was also utilized by D. I. Blokhintsev[23–25] in some of his works devoted to establishing a theory of light absorption in heteropolar crystals.

S. I. Vavilov[26–29] very successfully enlisted the phenomenon of *inductive resonance*, which leads to the migration of excitation energy from one molecule to another, to explain the changes in polarization and duration of the excited state of molecules in solutions. It was possible to prove experimentally the presence of energy migration in luminescent substances and in crystals which contain foreign atoms. In this connection, it was shown that the migration can take place over very significant distances, exceeding by a million times the distances between two neighboring molecules or atoms.[30,31]

In the present work, we shall show that the resonance interaction of molecules, which leads to the migration of energy in the crystal, plays an extremely essential role in explaining the peculiarities of absorption and luminescence spectra in molecular crystals.

We shall apply the exciton concepts to molecular crystals of any desired symmetry, which are composed of complicated polyatomic molecules. In this connection, we shall show that it is thereby possible to explain a series of absorption and fluorescence spectral peculiarities in molecular crystals. We shall see that taking into account the resonance interaction of molecules in the crystal leads to often basic, albeit small, changes in the spectrum of the isolated molecule. In particular, with the help of these concepts one can successfully explain the large pleochroism of molecular crystals. The resonance interaction between molecules sometimes leads to the appearance in the crystal of *crystal excited states,* which are distinct from the corresponding states in the gaseous phase. The appearance of special crystal excited states, which as a rule are strongly polarized, is experimentally confirmed by work performed in the laboratory under the direction of A. F. Prikhotko, Corresponding Member of the Academy of Sciences of the Ukrainian S.S.R.

We shall see that the intramolecular vibrations also vary under the action of intermolecular resonance forces. Therefore, the infrared spectra and the combinational scattering (Raman) spectra must also reflect the crystalline structure of a solid body. In the case of combinational scattering (Raman scattering), noticeable changes need be expected only for the vibrations which are simultaneously active in the infrared spectrum.

3. Scope of This Work

The following summary of the contents of the various chapters will facilitate reading this book.

Chapter I is of an auxiliary nature. Therein are stated the problems linked with the vibrations of atoms and molecules in a molecular lattice.

Chapters II and III contain the classical and quantal theory of absorption spectra in the infrared, visible, and ultraviolet regions, as well as several consequences related to the combinational scattering (Raman) spectra. We shall show that in crystals there occurs a splitting of energy terms into a number of components equal to the number of molecules in the unit cell. With the aid of group theory, the selection and polarization rules are established for certain crystals.

Starting with Chapter IV, we shall give the absorption theory, which considers the possibility of the movement of molecules in the lattice. Chapter IV formulates the problem. It states the circumstances under which the adiabatic method is applicable to systems with many degrees of freedom. Therein are shown the conditions under which either free or "localized" excitons appear in crystals at the instant light is absorbed.

Equations are derived which determine the movement of molecules in a crystal, when excited by free excitons.

Chapter V investigates the solutions of equations obtained in the zeroth-order approximation. It is shown that the zeroth-order approximation coincides with the case of rigidly fixed molecules. The limits within which the results obtained in Chapters II and III are applicable are thereby shown.

Chapter VI investigates the solutions of the same equations in the first approximation. This enables us to describe the processes of excitation of free excitons simultaneously with the excitation of lattice vibrations. Also examined are the problems of the structure of an absorption band and its dependence on temperature.

Chapter VII investigates the process of light absorption when "localized" excitons are formed. A comparison is made of the excitation energy upon formation of "localized" and free excitons.

Chapter VIII investigates the behavior of free and "localized" excitons subsequent to their formation. The necessary conditions are established for the appearance of fluorescence in solid bodies that do not contain admixtures.

Chapter IX investigates the application of the theory to several experimental data in the field of combinational scattering (Raman) spectra and infrared spectra, as well as absorption and fluorescence spectra in the visible and ultraviolet regions.

Chapter X applies exciton concepts to the calculation of excited energy states of certain individual polyatomic molecules.

CHAPTER I

TRANSLATIONAL AND ROTATIONAL VIBRATIONS OF MOLECULES IN A MOLECULAR LATTICE

4. Atomic Lattices

When investigating the movement of molecules in a molecular lattice, it is convenient in the beginning to consider the lattice as an atomic one and, subsequently, to take into account the fact that in a molecular lattice the atoms group themselves into molecules. The interaction forces between these molecules are considerably smaller than the interaction forces between the atoms which enter into the make-up of one molecule. The possibility of considering a lattice as such when investigating the movements of molecules is based on the fact that the displacements of atomic nuclei are essential for such movements. Considering the lattice in this manner is at times inadmissible when investigating the optical properties of molecular crystals in the visible and ultraviolet regions, the magnetic properties, and other properties.

Let us consider a crystal whose unit cell is determined by three noncoplanar vectors, $\mathbf{a}_1$, $\mathbf{a}_2$, and $\mathbf{a}_3$, and contains σ molecules, each of which has ρ atoms. Let us assume that the crystal has the form of an oblique-angled parallelepiped with axes $N_1\mathbf{a}_1$, $N_2\mathbf{a}_2$, and $N_3\mathbf{a}_3$, so that the general number of unit cells in the crystal is equal to $N = N_1N_2N_3$ (N assumed very large). In order to avoid the difficulties of considering the superficial layers of the crystal, we shall take as limiting conditions a cyclic system with large periods that correspond to the infinite repetition of the crystal in all directions.

Let us designate by $R_n^{x\alpha}$ the x component of the displacement of the atom which occupies the αth position in the nth cell; here $\alpha = 1, 2, \ldots,$ $\rho\sigma$ and $n = \mathbf{n} = n_1\mathbf{a}_1 + n_2\mathbf{a}_2 + n_3\mathbf{a}_3$ is the vector of the direct lattice.

In the decomposition of energy in powers of displacement from the equilibrium positions, if one limits oneself to quadratic terms, then the total energy of small vibrations about the equilibrium positions will have the form[1]

$$E = \tfrac{1}{2} \sum_{n\alpha x} \Big(m_\alpha |\dot{R}_n^{x\alpha}|^2 + \sum_{n'\alpha' x'} \lambda_{n-n'}^{x\alpha,x'\alpha'} R_n^{x\alpha} R_{n'}^{x'\alpha'} \Big). \tag{1.1}$$

In this circumstance, the equations of motion become

$$m_\alpha \ddot{R}_n^{x\alpha} + \sum_{n'\alpha'x'} \lambda_{n-n'}^{x\alpha,x'\alpha'} R_{n'}^{x'\alpha'} = 0. \tag{1.2}$$

Here m_α is the mass of the atom, occupying the αth site in the cell; the coefficients $\lambda_{n-n'}^{x\alpha,x'\alpha'}$ for the ideal lattice depend only on the difference $n - n'$, not on n and n' separately. These coefficients form a difference matrix in relation to the indices n and n'. Each element of this matrix is, in turn, in ultimate arrangement the matrix relative to the indices x, α.

Owing to the translational symmetry of the crystal, the equations (1.2) have the solutions

$$R_n^{x\alpha} = \mathbf{e}^{x\alpha}(\mathbf{q}) e^{i(\mathbf{qn}-\omega t)}. \tag{1.3}$$

We wrote (1.3) in the complex form. However, the displacements of atoms in the lattice are physically real magnitudes; therefore, one must take the real part of (1.3). The expressions (1.3) represent a running wave with a wave vector $\mathbf{q}$.

In order to satisfy the cyclical conditions, the wave vector $\mathbf{q}$ must have the discrete values

$$\mathbf{q} = \sum_{i=1}^{3} \frac{2\pi}{N_i} (\mathbf{a}_i)^{-1} \eta_i \tag{1.4}$$

where η_i are whole numbers which satisfy the inequalities

$$-\frac{N_i}{2} < \eta_i \leqslant \frac{N_i}{2}, \qquad i = 1, 2, 3,$$

and $(\mathbf{a}_i)^{-1}$ are the vectors of the reciprocal lattice

$$(\mathbf{a}_i)^{-1} = \frac{[\mathbf{a}_j \mathbf{a}_k]}{\mathbf{a}_1[\mathbf{a}_2 \mathbf{a}_3]}. \tag{1.5}$$

The vectors $\mathbf{e}^\alpha(\mathbf{q})$ characterize the vibrational directions in the running wave; they are defined as the solutions of the equations obtained after substitution of (1.3) into (1.2):

$$-\omega^2 m_\alpha \mathbf{e}^{x\alpha} + \sum_{n'x'\alpha'} \lambda_{n-n'}^{x\alpha,x'\alpha'} \mathbf{e}^{i\mathbf{q}(\mathbf{n}-\mathbf{n}')} e^{x'\alpha'} = 0. \tag{1.6}$$

Let us introduce the designation

$$L^{x\alpha,x'\alpha'}(\mathbf{q}) = \sum_{n'} \lambda_{n-n'}^{x\alpha,x'\alpha'} e^{i\mathbf{q}(\mathbf{n}-\mathbf{n}')}. \tag{1.7}$$

$L^{x\alpha,x'\alpha'}(\mathbf{q})$ is a continuous function of the wave number $\mathbf{q}$; this function does not depend on n, the indices of the cells.

The matrix $\lambda_{n-n'}^{x\alpha,x'\alpha'}$ is symmetrical in the indices n and $x\alpha$; that is,

$$\lambda_{n-n'}^{x\alpha,x'\alpha'} = \lambda_{n'-n}^{x'\alpha',x\alpha}. \tag{1.8}$$

Furthermore, it is also symmetrical in the indices x; that is,

$$\lambda_{n-n'}^{x\alpha,x'\alpha'} = \lambda_{n-n'}^{x'\alpha,x\alpha'}. \tag{1.8a}$$

From the symmetry properties [(1.8)] it follows that

$$L^{x\alpha,x'\alpha'}(\mathbf{q}) = L^{*,x'\alpha',x\alpha}(\mathbf{q}), \tag{1.9}$$
$$L^{x\alpha,x'\alpha'}(\mathbf{q}) = L^{*,x\alpha,x'\alpha'}(-\mathbf{q}). \tag{1.10}$$

For those crystals in which each atom is the center of symmetry, the coefficients $L^{x\alpha,x'\alpha'}(\mathbf{q})$ will be real.

With the help of (1.7), the equations of motion [(1.6)] may be written in the form

$$\sum_{x'\alpha'} L^{x\alpha,x'\alpha'}(\mathbf{q})\mathbf{e}^{x'\alpha'} - \omega^2 m_\alpha \mathbf{e}^{x\alpha} = 0. \tag{1.11}$$

The squares of the eigenfrequencies ω^2 are the roots of the equations of $3\sigma\rho$th order

$$|L^{x\alpha,x'\alpha'}(\mathbf{q}) - \omega^2(\mathbf{q})m_\alpha \delta_{x\alpha,x'\alpha'}| = 0. \tag{1.12}$$

Owing to the Hermitian nature [(1.9)] of the coefficients of this equation, the roots of the latter will be real and positive (they cannot be negative since the equilibrium positions correspond to an energy minimum) continuous functions of the wave number $\mathbf{q}$:

$$\omega_j^2 = \omega_j^2(\mathbf{q}), \qquad j = 1, 2, \ldots, 3\sigma\rho. \tag{1.13}$$

As is known, equation (1.12) has three roots, equal to zero when $\mathbf{q} = 0$; these solutions correspond to the acoustical class of vibrations. The remaining $3(\rho\sigma - 1)$ roots of (1.12) are different from zero when $\mathbf{q} = 0$; they correspond to the optical class of vibrations.

Each root [(1.13)] of equation (1.12) will correspond to its own sum total of solutions of the system of equations (1.11), which we shall distinguish by means of the index j; the latter runs through the values $1, 2, \ldots, 3\rho\sigma$:

$$\mathbf{e}_j^{x\alpha}(\mathbf{q}). \tag{1.14}$$

The vectors [(1.14)] form orthogonal systems, which may be normalized in the following manner:

$$\sum_{x\alpha} m_\alpha \mathbf{e}_j^{x\alpha}\mathbf{e}_{j'}^{x\alpha} = \sigma\rho\delta_{jj'}. \tag{1.15}$$

The arbitrary displacement of a desired atom of the lattice may be decomposed into a series according to solutions obtained:

$$R_n^{x\alpha} = (N_{\rho\sigma})^{-\frac{1}{2}} \sum_{jq} \mathbf{e}_j^{x\alpha}(\mathbf{q})(a_{qj}e^{i\mathbf{qn}} + a_{qj}^* e^{-i\mathbf{qn}}). \tag{1.16}$$

The coefficients $a_{qj} = a^{\circ}_{qj}e^{-i\omega t}$ characterize the amplitude of the jth class, which has a wave vector $\mathbf{q}$ and a vibrational direction that is determined by the index j. For $R_n^{x\alpha}$ to become physically real it is necessary to fulfill the conditions

$$a^*_{qj} = a_{-qj}. \tag{1.17}$$

The summation over $\mathbf{q}$ in (1.16) is carried out only for $q_x > 0$. Substituting (1.16) into (1.1), and taking into consideration that

$$\sum_n e^{i(\mathbf{q}-\mathbf{q}')\mathbf{n}} = N\delta_{\mathbf{q}\mathbf{q}'},$$

we obtain the total energy for lattice vibrations in the following form:

$$E = 2\sum_{qj} \omega_j^2 a_{qj} a^*_{qj}. \tag{1.18}$$

From the complex variables a_{qj} and a^*_{qj}, one can go over to the real canonical variables x_{qj} and P_{qj} with the aid of the transformation

$$a_{qj} = \frac{1}{\sqrt{2}}\left(x_{qj} + i\frac{P_{qj}}{\omega_{qj}}\right). \tag{1.19}$$

Then the total vibrational energy will be reduced to a sum of quadratic terms:

$$E = \tfrac{1}{2}\sum_{qj} (P^2_{qj} + \omega^2_{qj}x^2_{qj}). \tag{1.20}$$

The transition from classical to quantum mechanics is accomplished in the usual manner. It is necessary to consider the canonical variables of each vibration as noncommuting quantities which satisfy the commutation relationships

$$P_{qj}x_{q'j'} - x_{q'j'}P_{qj} = -ih'\delta_{qq'}\delta_{jj'}. \tag{1.21}$$

The quantum-mechanical equation which describes the movement of atoms in the lattice is reduced to the equations for a certain number ($3N\rho\sigma$) of independent oscillators, which are distinguished from each other by the quantities q and j. The wave function is decomposed into the product

$$\prod_{qj} \Psi(x_{qj}),$$

where $\Psi(x_{qj})$ satisfies the equation

$$\frac{d^2\Psi(x)}{dx^2} + \frac{2M_{qj}}{h^2}\left(E - \frac{M_{qj}\omega^2_{qj}x^2}{2}\right)\Psi(x) = 0.$$

The solution of this equation has the well-known form

$$\Psi_{N_{qj}}(x) = \frac{e^{-[x^2/2x_0{}^2]}}{\sqrt{x_0}} H_{N_{qi}}\left(\frac{x}{x_0}\right),$$

where N_{qj} represents whole numbers and where

$$x_0 = \sqrt{\frac{h}{M_{qj}\omega_{qj}}}.$$

The energy levels are

$$E_{N_{qj}} = h\omega_{qj}(N_{qj} + \tfrac{1}{2}).$$

Consequently, the total energy of the crystal is

$$E = \sum_{qj} (N_{qj} + \tfrac{1}{2})\omega_{qj}h, \tag{1.22}$$

and the wave function for the corresponding state is

$$\prod_{qj} \Psi_{N_{qj}}(x_{qj}).$$

The whole numbers N_{qj} determine the number of phonons which have wave number q and polarization j.

If we consider the canonical variables x_{qj} as independent, we can represent them by means of Hermitian matrices:

$$x_{N_{qj},N_{qj}+1} = x^*_{N_{qj}+1,N_{qj}} = \sqrt{\frac{h(N_{qj}+1)}{2\omega_{qj}}}\, e^{-i\omega_{qj}t},$$

$$x_{N_{qj},N_{qj}'} = 0, \qquad \text{if } N'_{qj} \neq N_{qj} + 1.$$

Consequently, x_{qj} has matrix elements different from zero only for such transitions in which N_{qj} decreases or increases by unity.

However, because they are independent variables, it is more convenient to consider the complex quantities a_{qj}, which can be represented by non-Hermitian matrices:

$$a_{N_{qj},N_{qj}+1} = \sqrt{\frac{h(N_{qj}+1)}{2\omega_{qj}}}\, e^{-i\omega_{qj}t}, \tag{1.23}$$

$$a^*_{N_{qj},N_{qj}-1} = \sqrt{\frac{hN_{qj}}{2\omega_{qj}}}\, e^{i\omega_{qj}t}. \tag{1.24}$$

These matrices are proportional to one and the same exponential factor when the matrix elements x_{qj} contain various time-dependent factors. The quantities a_{qj} satisfy the commutation relations

$$a_{qj}a^*_{qj} - a^*_{qj}a_{qj} = \frac{h}{2\omega_{qj}}. \tag{1.25}$$

5. Molecular Lattices. Internal and External (Lattice) Vibrations

A distinguishing characteristic of molecular crystals is that in such crystals the molecules preserve their individuality in the first approximation. This is because the interaction forces between molecules are small in comparison with the forces acting between the atoms of a single molecule. Therefore, all possible atomic vibrations in molecular crystals may be divided into two groups:

1. *Internal vibrations* of the atoms of a molecule relative to one another. In these vibrations, the center of gravity of the molecule is not displaced and there is no rotation of the molecule as a whole. As a result of the strong bonds between atoms in the molecule, these vibrations possess relatively large frequencies (300 to 3000 cm^{-1}). Temperature and other external agents exert little influence on these eigenfrequencies; therefore, these same frequencies (with small variations which will be investigated later) are preserved in various states of aggregation. In view of the small connection between the vibrations occurring in neighboring molecules, the frequencies of these vibrations are but little dependent on the wave number q.

2. *External vibrations*, or lattice vibrations, which appear because of rotational and translational degrees of freedom of the molecule. For the majority of molecular crystals, the frequencies of these vibrations rarely exceed 100 cm^{-1}. These vibrations are not encountered in vapors and solutions, and therefore, in the future, we shall simply call them lattice vibrations. The frequencies of these vibrations depend essentially on the wave vector q.

In reality both types of vibration are lattice vibrations and cannot, strictly speaking, be separated from each other. However, in molecular lattices the separation described above is entirely possible in the first approximation and results in a significant simplification when investigating vibrations.

At times, the influence of the crystalline lattice on the internal vibrations of the molecule leads to a change of selection rules and of polarization, as well as to a small displacement and splitting of the frequencies of internal vibrations. All these changes are relatively small (especially for vibrations with no change in dipole moment) and will be investigated in Chapter II. In the meantime, we shall consider that the internal vibrations of the molecules in the crystal are known.

As we saw in the preceding paragraph, there are $3\sigma\rho$ classes of vibrations, that is, $3\sigma\rho$ types of vibrations for each wave vector, in a molecular crystal which contains in the unit cell σ molecules, each having ρ atoms. Three classes of vibrations are acoustical, the remainder optical.

Out of all $3\sigma\rho$ classes of vibrations of the molecular crystals, 6σ classes belong to the lattice vibrations; out of these, $6\sigma - 3$ are optical classes and 3 are acoustical. Out of $6\sigma - 3$ optical classes of molecular vibrations $3(\sigma - 1)$ classes are translational vibrations and 3σ classes are rotational.

All remaining $(3\rho - 6)\sigma$ classes will be determined by the internal vibrations of the atoms in the σ molecules of the unit cell; they all belong to optical classes.

Figure 1 shows the dependence on the wave vector q of the various classes of vibrations in the molecular crystal.

Hereafter the term lattice vibration will mean only external vibrations. In other words, out of all classes of vibrations considered in Section 4, we shall concern ourselves only with the first 6σ classes (including the 3 acoustical ones). We can utilize all of the results obtained in Section 4, considering that the index j, which determines the type of vibration, runs only through the values

$$j = 1, 2, \ldots, 6\sigma. \tag{1.26}$$

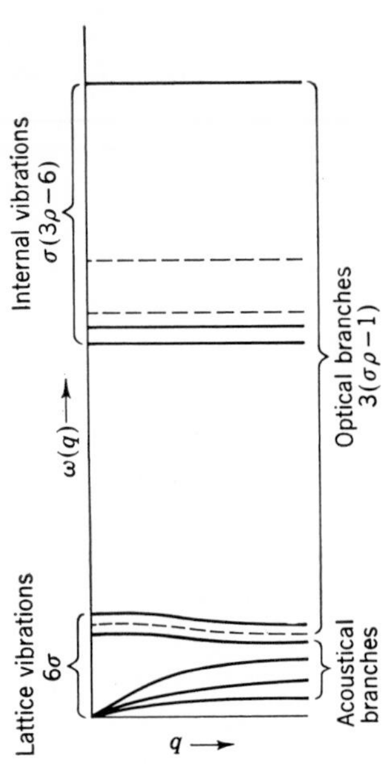

FIG. 1. Dependence of vibrational frequency on the wave vector for various classes of vibrations.

6. Classification of Lattice Vibrations According to Irreducible Representations of the Symmetry Group of a Crystal

At the present time it is hardly possible to calculate the external vibrations of a complicated polyatomic lattice. Therefore, we must utilize experimental data.

It is comparatively simple to classify lattice vibrations according to the irreducible representations of the symmetry group of the crystals and to establish the laws of behavior of these frequencies in various types of spectra [infrared and combinational scattering (Raman) spectra, etc.] and their polarizations as well. Furthermore, the lattice vibrations can be divided into rotational and translational ones. The vibrations of the translational type usually have small frequencies (especially in crystals of low melting point, i.e., those with weak binding forces between molecules).

Such a qualitative examination can be carried out by the methods of group theory and is extremely useful when analyzing experimental data.

By way of an example, let us consider molecular crystals having two molecules in a unit cell. Such crystals usually crystallize in the monoclinic system and belong to the space symmetry group C_{2h}^5.

The symmetry group C_{2h}^5 has four symmetry elements:

1. The identity element E.

2. Rotation by 180° about the monoclinic axis C_2. In this operation, the molecules in the unit cell change places.

3. Inversion i. Both molecules of the unit cell remain in their places.

4. Reflection σ in a plane perpendicular to the monoclinic axis. In this operation, both molecules of the unit cell exchange places.

The characters of the irreducible representations of the group C_{2h}^5, showing the transformation properties of the radius vector components r_a, r_b, and r_c, are given in Table 1. The table also shows the characters of the reducible representations: $\chi(T)$, the characters of all translational motions of the two molecules in the unit cell; $\chi(T_a)$, the characters of translational motions corresponding to the acoustical classes; $\chi(R)$, the characters of rotational motions of molecules in the lattice.

TABLE 1. CHARACTER TABLE FOR THE C_{2h}^5 SPACE GROUP; IRREDUCIBLE AND REDUCIBLE REPRESENTATIONS

C_{2h}^5	E	C_2	i	σ
A_g	1	1	1	1
r_b, A_u	1	1	−1	−1
B_g	1	−1	1	−1
r_a, r_c, B_u	1	−1	−1	1
$\chi(T)$	6	0	−6	0
$\chi(T_a)$	3	−1	−3	1
$\chi(R)$	6	0	6	0

Decomposing the characters $\chi(T)$ of the reducible representation $\Gamma(T)$ for translation into the irreducible representations of the group C_{2h}^5, we obtain

$$\Gamma(T) = 3A_u + 3B_u. \tag{1.27}$$

In order to obtain only the relative motions of both molecules belonging to the optical class, it is often necessary to separate from all possible translations the translations of the lattice as a whole. (The lattice translations correspond to the extreme acoustical vibrations.) If the reducible representation of the translations of the lattice as a whole is designated by $\Gamma(T_a)$, then

$$\Gamma(T_a) = A_u + 2B_u. \tag{1.28}$$

Subtracting (1.28) from (1.27), we obtain the representation $\Gamma(T_o)$ of the optical class of frequencies corresponding to the progressive shifts of the molecules relative to each other:

$$\Gamma(T_0) = 2A_u + B_u. \tag{1.29}$$

Utilizing the characters of the reducible representations $\Gamma(R)$ of the molecular rotations in the lattice, we obtain the decomposition of this representation into irreducible components:

$$\Gamma(R) = 3A_g + 3B_g. \tag{1.30}$$

In this manner, the six possible rotational vibrations in the lattice are divided into two groups: three vibrations belong to the totally symmetrical representation A_g and three vibrations belong to the irreducible representation B_g. As a result of the small intermolecular forces in molecular crystals, the frequencies corresponding to the vibrations of symmetry A_g and B_g are little distinguished from each other.

The presence of lattice vibrations in the combinational scattering (Raman) spectra was first discovered by E. F. Gross and M. F. Vuks.[3] There are now many works covering the investigation of these vibrations. Among these we may mention the works of Gross and collaborators,[33,34] of Vuks,[35] of Raskin,[36] of Nedungadi,[37] and of Rousset.[38] The frequencies of crystal vibrations in single crystals of naphthalene were especially thoroughly studied in reference to combinational scattering (Raman scattering). Six vibrations, distributed in three pairs of similar frequencies (38, 47; 72, 78; and 107, 121 cm^{-1}), were found. All these frequencies belong to rotational vibrations of the molecules. The presence of approximately the same pairs of rotational-vibrational frequencies (54, 46; 76, 74; and 109, 127 cm^{-1}) was confirmed in the more recent work of Rousset.[38]

CHAPTER II

THE INFLUENCE OF THE INTERACTION FORCES BETWEEN MOLECULES OF A MOLECULAR LATTICE ON THE INTRAMOLECULAR VIBRATIONS†

7. Free Vibrations

In this chapter we shall examine the approximation method of accounting for the influence of the crystal lattice on the internal vibrations of molecules. This problem is of great interest (1) because its rigorous solution by the method set forth in Chapter I is infeasible in practice even where the interaction forces between the atoms making up a molecule and between the molecules are known and (2) because very often investigators are specifically concerned with the problem of the change in molecular vibrational frequencies (calculated or experimentally determined when investigating gases at low pressures) when molecules enter into a crystal lattice.

The theory of such changes must relate them to the interaction forces of molecules in the lattice and with the structure of the crystal. This, on the basis of the study of spectra [in particular combinational scattering (Raman) and infrared], will enable us to deduce certain features of the crystal structure. It is evident that spectral methods of investigating the crystal structure are extremely useful for verifying and supplementing results obtained by other means.

It is known that, when investigating the vibrations of atoms relative to each other, we can, with great approximation, utilize the laws of classical mechanics, which are simpler and more obvious. In the following chapters we shall give the more rigorous quantum-mechanical theory and show the limits within which the approximation results obtained here are applicable.

Thus we shall proceed from the assumption that we know the frequencies and symmetry properties of the normal vibrations of each molecule taken separately. Let us consider the changes of the normal vibrations of σN molecules when they are united into a molecular crystal containing

† A short summary of the principles in this chapter was published by the author.[39]

σ molecules in the unit cell and when they are rigidly fixed in equilibrium positions corresponding to the equilibrium state of the crystal.

If each molecule possesses ρ atoms, the molecule will have $3\rho - 6$ internal normal vibrations. A crystal containing σN molecules will have $\sigma N(3\rho - 6)$ "internal" vibrations (the molecules being fixed). In the zeroth approximation, such a crystal may be considered the aggregate of completely noninteracting molecules. In this case, all $\sigma N(3\rho - 6)$ vibrations of the crystal break down into $3\rho - 6$ different σN multiply degenerate vibrations, if, that is, the normal vibrations of the separated molecule do not include degenerate vibrations. In the converse case, the number of different vibrations of the crystal in the zeroth approximation decreases, and their multiplicity increases proportionately.

In reality, however, the molecules of a crystal interact with each other, and consequently, the vibrations of separated molecules cannot be considered as independent. As we have already shown, the problem is reduced to determining the changes introduced by the interaction of normal molecular vibrations.

By taking into account the specific resonance character of vibrational interaction, the solution of this problem can be significantly simplified. By way of example, let us consider the interaction of two normal vibrations having frequencies ω_{10} and ω_{20} and an interaction energy of the dipole type $\gamma a_1 a_2$, where a_1 and a_2 are coordinates of the corresponding normal vibrations. The equations of motion of such a system will have the form

$$\begin{aligned} \ddot{a}_1 + \omega_{10}^2 a_1 + \frac{\gamma}{m} a_2 &= 0, \\ \ddot{a}_2 + \omega_{20}^2 a_2 + \frac{\gamma}{m} a_1 &= 0. \end{aligned} \tag{2.1}$$

Solving this system of equations by substituting

$$a_i = a_i^{\circ} e^{i\omega t},$$

we obtain two values for the frequency ω:

$$\omega_{1,2}^2 = \tfrac{1}{2}\left[\omega_{10}^2 + \omega_{20}^2 \pm \sqrt{(\omega_{10}^2 - \omega_{20}^2)^2 + 4\left(\frac{\gamma}{m}\right)^2}\right]. \tag{2.2}$$

If $\omega_{10} = \omega_{20}$, then

$$\omega_{1,2}^2 = \omega_{10}^2 \pm \frac{\gamma}{m}. \tag{2.3}$$

Consequently, if the normal frequencies coincide (resonance), the correction to the square of the frequency will be of the first order relative to the bond coefficient γ/m. Therefore, if

$$|\omega_{10}^2 - \omega_{20}^2| \gg \frac{\gamma}{m}, \tag{2.4}$$

then

$$\omega_1^2 = \omega_{10}^2 + \frac{(\gamma/m)^2}{\omega_{10}^2 - \omega_{20}^2}; \qquad \omega_2^2 = \omega_{20}^2 - \frac{(\gamma/m)^2}{\omega_{10}^2 - \omega_{20}^2}. \tag{2.5}$$

Consequently, if the normal frequencies do not coincide, the corrections to the frequencies will be quadratic relative to the bond coefficient γ/m. Therefore, if the inequality [(2.4)] is fulfilled, it is possible not to take into account the changes of frequencies caused by the interaction of vibrations.

We shall assume that the following inequality is fulfilled:

$$|\omega_0^2 - \omega_i^2| \gg \frac{\gamma_{oi}}{m}, \qquad i = 1, 2, \ldots, 3\rho - 6 \tag{2.6}$$

and consider σN vibrations of the crystal, corresponding to the frequency ω_0 in the zeroth approximation. Let us designate by $a_{n\alpha}$ the normal coordinate of the molecular vibration in the molecule occupying the αth site of the nth cell. Then in the isolated molecule, this coordinate will satisfy the equation

$$\ddot{a}_{n\alpha} + \omega_0^2 a_{n\alpha} = 0 \tag{2.7}$$

where ω_0 is the normal vibrational frequency (vibrational frequency of the free molecule).

Initially we shall consider the case in which a change of the electric dipole moment of the molecule corresponds to the vibration with frequency ω_0. In this case the interaction between molecules will have a dipole-dipole character. The total energy of σN vibrations will be

$$E = \tfrac{1}{2} \Big\{ \sum_{n\alpha} \dot{a}_{n\alpha}^2 + \omega_0^2 \sum_{n\alpha} a_{n\alpha}^2 + \sum_{n\alpha, m\beta}{}' R_{n\alpha,m\beta}^{-3} [\mathbf{P}_{n\alpha}\mathbf{P}_{m\beta} - 3(\mathbf{P}_{m\beta}\mathbf{r}_{n\alpha,m\beta})(\mathbf{P}_{n\alpha}\mathbf{r}_{n\alpha,m\beta})] \Big\}, \tag{2.8}$$

where

$$\mathbf{P}_{n\alpha} = e\sqrt{f}\,\mathbf{e}_\alpha a_{n\alpha} \tag{2.8a}$$

is the effective dipole moment of the molecule $n\alpha$; $\mathbf{e}_\alpha$ is the unit vector of the direction of the dipole moment of the molecule occupying the site α in the unit cell and is determined by the type of vibrations in the molecule and by the orientation of the molecule relative to the crystallographic axis of the crystal (the vector, here, assumed to be known); e is the electronic charge; $\mathbf{r}_{n\alpha,m\beta}$ is the unit vector in the direction of the line connecting the molecules $n\alpha$ and $m\beta$; and f is the oscillator strength, which here, in accord with Ladenburg,[40] is introduced as a certain factor, allowing for the correction of the quantum behavior of the oscillator.

The equations of motion of the system of oscillators with energy given by (2.8) will be

$$\ddot{a}_{n\alpha} + \omega_0^2 a_{n\alpha} + \sum_{\substack{m\beta \\ m\beta \neq n\alpha}} \gamma_{n\alpha,m\beta} a_{m\beta}[(\mathbf{e}_\alpha \mathbf{e}_\beta) - 3(\mathbf{e}_\beta \mathbf{r}_{n\alpha,m\beta})(\mathbf{e}_\alpha \mathbf{r}_{n\alpha,m\beta})] = 0, \tag{2.9}$$

where

$$\gamma_{n\alpha,m\beta} = \frac{fe^2}{2R^3_{n\alpha,m\beta}}. \tag{2.9a}$$

The solutions of this system of equations may be looked for in the form of running waves:

$$a_{n\alpha} = a_\alpha e^{i(\mathbf{kn}-\omega t)}, \tag{2.10}$$

where a_α is the amplitude of the vibrations and $\mathbf{k}$ is the wave vector running through N discrete values as a result of the cyclic conditions (with large period). We assume that the crystal, in the form of an oblique-angled parallelepiped with axes $N_1\mathbf{a}_1$, $N_2\mathbf{a}_2$, and $N_3\mathbf{a}_3$, repeats itself endlessly in all directions ($N = N_1N_2N_3$ and is very large). Then

$$\mathbf{k} = \sum_{i=1}^{3} \frac{2\pi}{N_i} \mathbf{a}_i^{-1} \eta_i, \tag{2.11}$$

where η_i is a whole number satisfying the inequality

$$-\frac{N_i}{2} < \eta_i \leqslant \frac{N_i}{2} \qquad i = 1, 2, 3, \tag{2.12}$$

and the $\mathbf{a}_i^{-1}$ are the vectors of the reciprocal lattice.

Substituting (2.10) in (2.9), we obtain

$$(\omega_0^2 - \omega^2) a_\alpha + \sum_{\beta=1}^{\sigma} \Gamma_{\alpha\beta}(\mathbf{k}) a_\beta = 0, \tag{2.13}$$

where

$$\Gamma_{\alpha\beta}(\mathbf{k}) = \sum_m \gamma_{n\alpha,m\beta} e^{i\mathbf{k}(\mathbf{m}-\mathbf{n})}[(\mathbf{e}_\alpha \mathbf{e}_\beta) - 3(\mathbf{e}_\alpha \mathbf{r}_{n\alpha,m\beta})(\mathbf{e}_\beta \mathbf{r}_{n\alpha,m\beta})]. \tag{2.14}$$

If $\alpha \neq \beta$, then the summation over m includes $m = n$; if $\alpha = \beta$, then the summation includes only $m \neq n$.

The matrix [(2.14)] is Hermitian:

$$\Gamma_{\alpha\beta}(\mathbf{k}) = \Gamma^*_{\beta\alpha}(\mathbf{k}).$$

However, for those crystals in which each molecule is a center of symmetry, this matrix is real and symmetric relative to the indices α and β. The system of homogeneous equations [(2.13)] has nontrivial solutions if the determinant composed of the coefficients of these equations is equal to zero:

$$\Delta(\omega^2) \equiv |\Gamma_{\alpha\beta}(\mathbf{k}) + (\omega_0^2 - \omega^2)\delta_{\alpha\beta}| = 0. \tag{2.15}$$

The preceding equation determines σ roots of ω^2, as functions of the wave vector $\mathbf{k}$:

$$\omega_\mu^2 = \omega_\mu^2(\mathbf{k}), \qquad \mu = 1, 2, \ldots, \sigma. \tag{2.16}$$

In this manner, as a result of the interaction between molecules, instead of one degenerate frequency ω_0 of the vibrations, one obtains, generally speaking, μ different (some of them may coincide) quasi-continuous bands of frequencies (corresponding to the number of molecules in the unit cell) or classes of frequencies. Each of these bands of frequencies will consist of N closely spaced frequencies distinguished by various values of the wave number $\mathbf{k}$; these values satisfy the conditions given by (2.11).

For the sake of greater concreteness, let us examine, by way of example, crystals having two molecules per unit cell. In this case, the equation (2.15) takes the form

$$\begin{vmatrix} \omega_0^2 - \omega^2 + \Gamma_{11}(\mathbf{k}) & \Gamma_{12}(\mathbf{k}) \\ \Gamma_{21}(\mathbf{k}) & \omega_0^2 - \omega^2 + \Gamma_{11}(\mathbf{k}) \end{vmatrix} = 0. \tag{2.17}$$

Its solution is

$$\begin{aligned} \omega_1^2(\mathbf{k}) &= \omega_0^2 + \Gamma_{11}(\mathbf{k}) + \Gamma_{12}(\mathbf{k}), \\ \omega_2^2(\mathbf{k}) &= \omega_0^2 + \Gamma_{11}(\mathbf{k}) - \Gamma_{12}(\mathbf{k}). \end{aligned} \tag{2.18}$$

We obtain, with the aid of (2.13), two systems of coefficients a_α corresponding to the two roots of (2.18):

μ	a_1^μ	a_2^μ
1	1	1
2	1	-1

(2.18*a*)

These determine the solutions [(2.10)].

8. Forced Vibrations. Absorption in the Infrared Region Corresponding to the Excitation of Intramolecular Vibrations in Crystals

Let us now consider the forced vibrations arising in a crystal under the influence of a plane electromagnetic wave:

$$\mathbf{E} = \mathbf{E}_0 e^{i(\mathbf{Qr} - \omega t)}, \tag{2.19}$$

where $\mathbf{Q}$ is the wave vector of the electromagnetic wave and ω is its frequency.

To clarify the optical behavior of a crystal, it is necessary to determine the electric moment of a crystal:

$$\mathbf{P} = \mathbf{P}_0 e^{i\omega t},$$

the electric moment induced by the electromagnetic wave [(2.19)]. This moment is expressed in terms of the dipole moment $\mathbf{P}_{n\alpha}$ of separate molecules in the following way (all molecules being identical):

$$\mathbf{P}_0 = e\sqrt{f} \sum_{n\alpha} a'_\alpha \mathbf{e}_\alpha e^{i\mathbf{k}\mathbf{n}}, \tag{2.20}$$

where a'_α satisfies a system of nonhomogeneous equations

$$(\omega_0^2 - \omega^2) a'_\alpha + \sum_{\beta=1}^{\sigma} \Gamma_{\alpha\beta}(\mathbf{k}) a'_\beta = M_\alpha, \tag{2.21}$$

where

$$M_\alpha = e\sqrt{f}\, \mathbf{E}_0 \mathbf{e}_\alpha \sum_n \frac{e^{i(\mathbf{Q}-\mathbf{k})\mathbf{n}}}{N}. \tag{2.21a}$$

Here, owing to the fact that the wavelength of light is great in comparison with the distance between molecules, we disregard the difference of the phases of the light wave's action on the molecules occurring in a unit cell.

Particular solutions of the equations (2.21) may be represented in the form

$$a'_\alpha = \frac{\sum_\beta A_{\beta\alpha} M_\beta}{\Delta(\omega^2)}, \tag{2.22}$$

where $A_{\alpha\beta}$ is the minor of the determinant $\Delta(\omega^2)$, corresponding to the element

$$\Gamma_{\alpha\beta}(\mathbf{k}) + (\omega_0^2 - \omega^2)\delta_{\alpha\beta}.$$

Since

$$\sum_n e^{i(\mathbf{Q}-\mathbf{k})\mathbf{n}} = N\delta(\mathbf{Q} - \mathbf{k}),$$

it becomes immediately apparent that, under the influence of the electromagnetic wave, only the eigenfrequencies

$$\omega_\mu^2 = \omega_\mu^2(\mathbf{Q}) \tag{2.23}$$

may be excited. These frequencies correspond to the value of the wave vector $\mathbf{k} = \mathbf{Q}$, since only for these values of the squares of the frequencies is the numerator of (2.22) different from zero and the denominator equal to zero. Thus the values of the frequencies are the resonance points of our system. At the resonance points, the amplitude [(2.22)] is infinite.

This result is obtained because the model we are considering is too idealized. We do not take into account the transformation of energy to the lattice vibrations (see Section 11). This transition of energy is equivalent to the damping of the vibrations we have considered. The damping of vibrations causes the amplitude to remain finite and within the region of resonance.

Because the wavelength of infrared radiation is very great, the wave vector $\mathbf{Q}$ is small, and we can set $\mathbf{Q} = 0$. Thus we come to the conclusion that under the influence of an impinging electromagnetic wave, only limited wave frequencies may be excited in each band of frequencies [(2.16)]. Substituting in (2.20) the solution obtained in (2.22), we may determine the electric moment arising in the system:

$$\mathbf{P}_\mu = \mathbf{P}_{0\mu} e^{-i\omega_\mu t}, \tag{2.24}$$

where

$$\mathbf{P}_{0\mu} = e\sqrt{f}\,N \sum_\alpha \mathbf{e}_\alpha \frac{\sum_\beta A_{\alpha\beta} M_\beta}{\Delta(\omega_\mu^2)}, \tag{2.25}$$

$$\mu = 1, 2, \ldots, \sigma.$$

In particular, for crystals containing two molecules per unit cell, we obtain

$$\mathbf{P}_1 = \mathbf{P}_{01} e^{-i\omega_1 t}, \qquad \mathbf{P}_{01} = -\frac{e^2 f N \Gamma_{12}}{\Delta(\omega_1^2)} (\mathbf{e}_1 + \mathbf{e}_2), \tag{2.26}$$

$$\mathbf{P}_2 = \mathbf{P}_{02} e^{-i\omega_2 t}, \qquad \mathbf{P}_{02} = -\frac{e^2 f N \Gamma_{12}}{\Delta(\omega_2^2)} (\mathbf{e}_1 - \mathbf{e}_2). \tag{2.27}$$

Consequently, for the frequency ω_1 determined by (2.18) for $\mathbf{k} = 0$, the electric moment of the system is proportional to the sum of the electric moments of the two molecules occurring in the unit cell; but for the frequency ω_2, the electric moment is proportional to their difference.

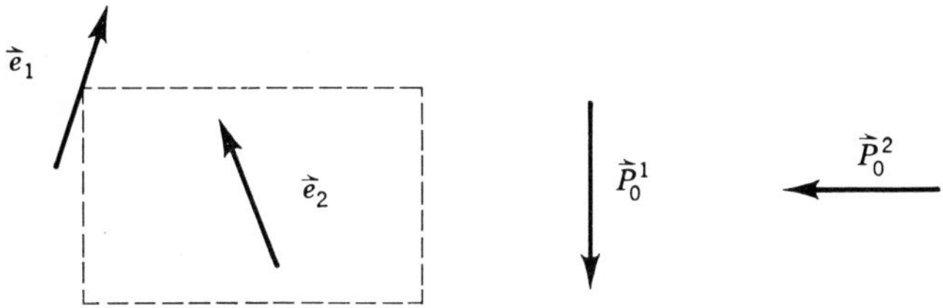

FIG. 2. Projection of electric moments of two molecules (left) and resultant moments of entire system (right) onto *ab* plane of monoclinic crystal, with two molecules per unit cell.

Figure 2 shows the possible position of the projection onto the plane *ab* of a monoclinic crystal of the electric moments of the two molecules $\mathbf{e}_1$

and $\mathbf{e}_2$ of the unit cell of the crystal, as well as the projection onto the same plane of the direction of the vectors of the resultant electric moment of the entire system. Thus, because of the resonance interaction of the intramolecular vibrations, the infrared absorption and emission bands must double in comparison with the corresponding bands for the gas, and they must be strongly polarized. The ratio of the intensities of the absorption bands will be

$$\frac{I(\omega_1)}{I(\omega_2)} = \frac{(\mathbf{e}_1 + \mathbf{e}_2)^2}{(\mathbf{e}_1 - \mathbf{e}_2)^2}. \tag{2.28}$$

If such an interaction did not exist, only one frequency would be absorbed, and the strong polarization would be absent for $\mathbf{e}_1$ not parallel to $\mathbf{e}_2$. It is interesting to note that if the dipole moments of the normal molecular vibrations of two molecules in a unit cell are parallel to each other, then the electric moment of the system will differ from zero only for (2.26). Here the polarization of the absorption bands of the crystal will coincide with the polarization of the absorption bands of the free molecule, and the position of the absorption bands of the crystal will be displaced relative to their position in the spectrum of the free molecule.

Investigations of the infrared absorption of molecular crystals in polarized light are extremely complex and comparatively crude. In order to detect the effect described above, one must conduct experiments at the lowest temperatures possible and with the smallest possible thicknesses of the absorbing substance. Nevertheless, in the experiments of Elliott and Ambrose,[41] there was observed a noticeable pleochroism (at room temperature) of the infrared absorption of naphthalene crystals when the wave fell perpendicular to the plane *ab* of the crystal (for the cases in which the direction of the electric vector of the wave is parallel to the axes *b* and *a* of the crystal) in the region 2 to 4 μ, corresponding to the intramolecular vibrations of the crystal.

9. Intramolecular Crystal Vibrations in Which the 2*l*-pole Moment of the Molecule Changes

In Sections 7 and 8 we considered the interaction between molecules that occurs upon excitation of intramolecular vibrations of the dipole type. We shall now consider the general case in which, to the normal frequency ω_0, there corresponds the formation of a $2l$-pole moment of a molecule (for $l = 1$, a dipole moment; for $l = 2$, a quadrupole, etc.). Let us designate the corresponding moment of the molecule occupying the αth place in the nth cell by

$$P_{n\alpha}^{2l} = \varkappa a_{n\alpha} \mathbf{e}_{n\alpha}^{2l},$$

where $\mathbf{e}_{n\alpha}^{2l}$ is a unit tensor of the corresponding rank characterizing the transformation properties of a given multipole of the molecule, and $\varkappa$ is the coefficient of proportionality between the multipole moment and the value of the normal coordinate $\alpha_{n\alpha}$ of the intramolecular vibration. Since we consider the molecules rigidly fixed in the lattice, the axes of the tensor will have a constant orientation relative to the crystallographic axes of the crystal, the only change being that of the normal coordinate $\alpha_{n\alpha}$, of the intramolecular vibration, characterizing the magnitude of the corresponding multipole.

Let $D^{2l}_{n\alpha,m\beta}$ determine the interaction between two $2l$-pole moments of molecules $n\alpha$ and $m\beta$. It is essential that $D^{2l}_{n\alpha,m\beta}$ be inversely proportional to the $(2l + 1)$ power of the distance between molecules:

$$D^{2l}_{n\alpha,m\beta} \sim R^{-(2l+1)} \tag{2.29}$$

For the case in which $l = 1$ (dipole-dipole interaction),

$$D^{2}_{n\alpha,m\beta} = \gamma_{n\alpha,m\beta}[(\mathbf{e}_\alpha \mathbf{e}_\beta) - 3(\mathbf{e}_\alpha \mathbf{r}_{n\alpha,m\beta})(\mathbf{e}_\beta \mathbf{r}_{n\alpha,m\beta})]. \tag{2.29a}$$

The magnitudes entering into (2.29*a*) are determined in Section 8.

We must, however, keep in view that besides the interaction between molecules [(2.29)] (occurring at the moment of excitation of the molecules), there is an interaction even before excitation. It is precisely this interaction (van der Waals forces and exchange repulsion forces) which determines the configuration of molecules in the crystal in its normal state. Upon excitation of intramolecular vibrations, this interaction also changes; therefore, in a more rigorous theory, it must be taken into account. Let us designate this type of interaction energy by the letter V. We assume that this energy depends on, besides the distances and the mutual orientations of the molecules (here fixed), the vibrational state, i.e., on the normal intramolecular coordinates $a_{n\alpha}$. When the normal coordinate $a_{n\alpha}$ changes, the force

$$F_{n\alpha} = -\frac{\partial V}{\partial a_{n\alpha}}$$

will act upon the molecule $n\alpha$. If the displacements from the equilibrium positions are small, this force may be decomposed into a power series of normal coordinates:

$$F_{n\alpha} = -\left(\frac{\partial V}{\partial a_{n\alpha}}\right)_0 - \sum_{m\beta}\left(\frac{\partial^2 V}{\partial a_{n\alpha}\,\partial a_{m\beta}}\right)_0 a_{m\beta} + \cdots. \tag{2.30}$$

The first, constant, term of the force [(2.30)] will result in a small displacement of the equilibrium position for the intramolecular vibrations. The second term in (2.30) is, generally speaking, also small and falls off with distance not slower than R^{-6}. It is therefore expedient to take

(2.30) into account only when the interaction between excited molecules is not lower than quadrupole-quadrupole.

When taking (2.30) and the $2l - 2l$-pole character of the interaction between excited molecules into account, the equations of the vibrations of $N\sigma$ molecules may be written in the form of the following system of nonhomogeneous equations:

$$\ddot{a}_{n\alpha} + \Omega_0^2 a_{n\alpha} + \sum_{\substack{m\beta \\ m\beta \neq n\alpha}} M^{2l}_{n\alpha,m\beta} a_{m\beta} = -\left(\frac{\partial V}{\partial a_{n\alpha}}\right)_0, \tag{2.31}$$

where

$$\Omega_0^2 = \omega_0^2 + \left(\frac{\partial^2 V}{\partial a_{n\alpha}^2}\right)_0, \tag{2.31a}$$

$$M^{2l}_{n\alpha,m\beta} = D^{2l}_{n\alpha,m\beta} + \left(\frac{\partial^2 V}{\partial a_{n\alpha}\,\partial a_{m\beta}}\right)_0. \tag{2.31b}$$

The solution of the system of equations [(2.31)] can be searched for in the form

$$a_{n\alpha} = a^{\circ}_{n\alpha} + a_\alpha e^{i(\mathbf{kn}-\omega t)}, \tag{2.32}$$

where the wave vector $\mathbf{k}$ runs through the same N discrete values as in (2.11).

The magnitudes $a^{\circ}_{n\alpha}$ determine the constant displacements; they are calculated with the aid of a system of nonhomogeneous equations:

$$\Omega_0^2 a^{\circ}_{n\alpha} + \sum_{m\beta} M^{2l}_{n\alpha,m\beta} a^{\circ}_{m\beta} = -\left(\frac{\partial V}{\partial a_{n\alpha}}\right)_0. \tag{2.33}$$

These magnitudes are, generally speaking, very small and will not interest us.

The amplitudes a_α now satisfy the system of homogeneous equations

$$\epsilon a_\alpha + \sum_{\beta=1}^{\sigma} \Gamma^{2l}_{\alpha\beta}(\mathbf{k}) a_\beta = 0, \tag{2.34}$$

where

$$\epsilon = \Omega_0^2 - \omega^2, \tag{2.34a}$$

$$\Gamma^{2l}_{\alpha\beta}(\mathbf{k}) = \sum_m M^{2l}_{n\alpha,m\beta} e^{i\mathbf{k}(\mathbf{m}-\mathbf{n})}. \tag{2.34b}$$

Here the summation over m has the same meaning as in (2.14).

From the conditions of solubility of the system of equations [(2.34)],

$$\Delta^{2l}(\epsilon) \equiv \left|\Gamma^{2l}_{\alpha\beta}(\mathbf{k}) - \epsilon\delta_{\alpha\beta}\right| = 0, \tag{2.35}$$

we shall obtain the algebraic equation of the σth degree relative to ϵ. The roots of this equation will give σ functions,

$$\epsilon_\mu = \epsilon_\mu(\mathbf{k}),$$

and consequently, also σ quasi-continuous bands of frequencies:

$$\omega_\mu^2 = \omega_0^2 + \left(\frac{\partial^2 V}{\partial a_{n\alpha}^2}\right)_0 + \epsilon_\mu(\mathbf{k}), \qquad \mu = 1, 2, \ldots, \sigma. \tag{2.36}$$

Thus, in the crystal, splitting and displacement of the frequencies of normal molecular vibrations take place. In the particular case of crystals with two molecules per unit cell,

$$\omega_1^2(\mathbf{k}) = \omega_0^2 + \left(\frac{\partial^2 V}{\partial a_{n\alpha}^2}\right)_0 + \Gamma_{11}(\mathbf{k}) + \Gamma_{12}(\mathbf{k}),$$

$$\omega_2^2(\mathbf{k}) = \omega_0^2 + \left(\frac{\partial^2 V}{\partial a_{n\alpha}^2}\right)_0 + \Gamma_{11}(\mathbf{k}) - \Gamma_{12}(\mathbf{k}).$$

Thus the splitting in the crystal of the molecular frequency ω_0 into σ quasi-continuous bands of frequencies [(2.36)] applies generally to all types of vibrations of the molecule. However, the distance between bands and the width of the bands of frequencies, which is determined by the magnitudes of $\Gamma_{\alpha\beta}^{2l}(\mathbf{k})$, will decrease with the increase in the vibrational multipole index. This was to be expected, since the resonance interaction between molecules falls off rapidly with an increase of the multipole index of the vibrations.

The investigation which has been conducted permits us to draw a rather interesting conclusion. In a crystal, splitting of the molecular frequency ω_0 into σ quasi-continuous bands of frequencies occurs, and the polarization character changes essentially. The magnitudes of the splittings and the widths of the bands of vibrational frequencies are significantly larger when accompanied by a change in the molecular dipole moment (in which case they appear in the infrared spectrum) than are the corresponding magnitudes for those vibrations which do not result in changes in the molecular electric moment.

10. Influence of the Interaction Forces between Molecules on Combinational Scattering (Raman Scattering)

As is well known, spectra of combinational scattering (Raman scattering) of light play an important role in the spectral study of the structure of matter. The value of this method consists in the possibility of investigating intramolecular vibrations in the visible and ultraviolet regions of the spectrum but not in the experimentally difficult infrared region. Recently, thanks to the discovery by E. Gross and M. Vuks[3] of the low-frequency spectrum, one can also utilize combinational scattering (Raman scattering) to elucidate the structure of molecular crystals and liquids.

Naturally, it is of great interest to investigate the change in the combinational scattering (Raman) spectrum upon transformation of the molecules from a gaseous to a liquid or solid state. Repeated efforts were made to take into account these changes by means of examining the influence on the spectrum of the field created by the van der Waals forces. One of the first theoretical studies in this direction was that of Buchheim.[42] This study was not without basic defects and has already attracted criticism.[43]

We must accept as significantly more successful the effort undertaken in this connection by M. V. Volkenstein.[43] However, even Volkenstein's calculation is not without a series of defects, even within the framework of a classical model.

When investigating intermolecular interaction, Volkenstein considered the interaction of only one pair of molecules. Since, generally speaking, the changes of intramolecular vibrations resulting from interaction with surrounding molecules are not additive, such consideration was insufficient. Furthermore, Volkenstein did not consider the forces of repulsion between molecules and took into account only the van der Waals attraction for the energy, for which he used the expression

$$V = -\frac{1}{R^6}\left(\frac{2}{3kT}\,\mu_1^2\mu_2^2 + \mu_1^2\alpha_2 + \mu_2^2\alpha_1 + \tfrac{3}{4}I\alpha_1\alpha_2\right),$$

where μ_1 and μ_2 are the molecular dipole moments, α_1 and α_2 are the polarizabilities, I is the ionization potential, and T is the temperature.

The first term of this formula has meaning only for gas molecules, since it is obtained by averaging the interaction of the dipoles over all possible orientations. This term is not applicable to liquids and is even less applicable to solids. Its use may be justified only at sufficiently high temperatures, but then the term is small; as a result of heat fluctuations the change of frequencies is mainly determined by the change of intermolecular distances, which, in the calculation, are assumed to be fixed. Since the main change of combinational scattering (Raman) frequencies is, according to Volkenstein, determined by precisely the orientational interaction, one must be wary of the results obtained.

A much more essential observation is that, when calculating the influence of the interaction forces between molecules on the intramolecular vibrations, one must take into account the interaction forces between excited vibrations. Here the so-called resonance forces of interaction between molecules occur. When the molecules are excited with a concomitant change in dipole moment (i.e., vibrations active in the infrared spectra), these resonance forces vary only as the inverse fourth power (and not the seventh, as do the van der Waals forces) and, therefore, surpass by a hundredfold the van der Waals forces.

If vibrations which are also simultaneously active in the infrared spectrum participate in the combinational scattering (Raman scattering), it is inadmissible to ignore the forces of the resonance type. In molecules not having a center of symmetry, many frequencies are simultaneously active in both spectra. The forces of the resonance type (quadrupole-quadrupole) will be comparable with the van der Waals forces only in the study of the influence of intermolecular forces on the combinational scattering (Raman) spectrum of molecules having a center of symmetry. However, in this case, the interaction effect will be very small, as was shown in the preceding paragraph. In particular, the magnitude of the line splittings must be small in combinational scattering (Raman scattering) of crystals containing few molecules per unit cell.

Nedungadi[44] carried out a thorough investigation of the intramolecular vibrations of the naphthalene monocrystal. When studying the polarization of the lines of combinational scattering (Raman scattering) it became evident that in the crystal there occurs a splitting of the lines 512 and 1576 cm^{-1}. Here the difference of frequencies between the split components of both lines equals 4 to 5 cm^{-1}. A similar splitting was also observed for the lines 1384 and 3058 cm^{-1}. Nedungadi considers that the splitting effect is a general property of internal vibrations; however, the splitting of components is in many cases so small that it cannot be observed. These deductions find a theoretical confirmation in our work.

In crystals which consist of molecules not having a center of symmetry, one must expect great changes for the vibrations simultaneously active (in the isolated molecule) in the infrared and combinational scattering (Raman) spectra. Owing to the quasi-crystalline structure of liquids, the splitting of frequencies must be smeared out, and as a result, the lines will be wide. Since molecules with a dipole moment do not have a center of symmetry, the displacement and splitting of frequencies must be greater for such molecules than for molecules possessing a center of symmetry. The presence of a permanent moment is not essential for a widening of the lines connected with the splitting of vibrations of free molecules. The only indispensable requirement is that an induced moment occur with the vibration. We must, however, keep in mind that another essential cause for the widening of lines also exists and shall be described in the following section.

11. Several Generalizations

In the three preceding sections, we suggested a few simplifications in order to facilitate calculation. Let us consider how the results obtained there will vary if we discard these simplifications and which of the simplifications are of little importance.

1. We proposed that the frequency of normal molecular vibrations ω_0 under study satisfies the inequality [(2.6)]. This allowed us to consider only the interaction of molecular vibrations of frequency ω_0.

Let us now assume that there are two normal frequencies, ω_{01} and ω_{02}, located sufficiently close together so that the inequality [(2.6)] is not fulfilled. It is now necessary to consider the interaction of each of the normal frequencies (ω_{01} and ω_{02}) of the molecule, together with vibrations of types ω_{01} and ω_{02} of other molecules. In place of the system of σN equations, we shall obtain the system of $2\sigma N$ connected equations (here, for simplification, we assume $V = 0$):

$$\ddot{a}^1_{n\alpha} + \omega^2_{01}a^1_{n\alpha} + \sum_{\substack{m\beta \\ m\beta \neq n\alpha}} [D^{2l}_{n\alpha,m\beta}(11)a^1_{m\beta} + D^{2l}_{n\alpha,m\beta}(12)a^2_{m\beta}] = 0,$$

$$\ddot{a}^2_{n\alpha} + \omega^2_{02}a^2_{n\alpha} + \sum_{\substack{m\beta \\ m\beta \neq n\alpha}} [D^{2l}_{n\alpha,m\beta}(22)a^2_{m\beta} + D^{2l}_{n\alpha,m\beta}(21)a^1_{m\beta}] = 0.$$

Solving this system of equations by substituting

$$a^1_{n\alpha} = a^1_\alpha e^{i(\mathbf{kn}-\omega t)}, \qquad a^2_{n\alpha} = a^2_\alpha e^{i(\mathbf{kn}-\omega t)},$$

we obtain the system of 2σ equations

$$(\omega^2_{01} - \omega^2)a^1_\alpha + \sum_\beta [\Gamma^{2l}_{\alpha\beta}(11)a^1_\beta + \Gamma^{2l}_{\alpha\beta}(12)a^2_\beta] = 0,$$

$$(\omega_{02} - \omega^2)a^2_\alpha + \sum_\beta [\Gamma^{2l}_{\alpha\beta}(22)a^2_\beta + \Gamma^{2l}_{\alpha\beta}(21)a^1_\beta] = 0.$$

This system will have nontrivial solutions if the determinant, composed of the coefficients of the unknowns, is equal to zero. We shall obtain an algebraic equation of the 2σth degree with respect to ω^2:

$$\Delta(\omega^2) = 0.$$

The solution of the latter yields 2σ bands of frequencies:

$$\omega^2_\mu = \omega^2_\mu(\mathbf{k}), \qquad \mu = 1, 2, \ldots, 2\sigma.$$

Thus, in this case also, to each of the normal molecular frequencies will formally correspond its own σ bands of frequencies. However, the width and distance between them will depend not only on the vibrations connected with one of the normal frequencies, but also on the vibrations corresponding to another normal frequency. In particular, one can also expect noticeable displacements and splittings of the combinational scattering (Raman) frequencies in molecules having a center of symmetry, if the molecule possesses a frequency in the infrared spectrum which happens to coincide with or is close to the Raman frequency (see Section 35).

2. A second, more essential point was our assumption that the molecules were rigidly fixed in the lattice points (i.e., that the mass of the molecule was infinitely large). This allowed us to exclude from consideration the connection between the intramolecular vibrations and the external vibrations (rotations and translations) of the molecules. This

assumption is sometimes very crude and results in the loss of several physically interesting possibilities. These we shall briefly (and incompletely) indicate here, leaving a more detailed examination for later sections, in which we shall develop the general quantum-mechanical theory of light absorption in the infrared, visible, and ultraviolet regions.

Upon excitation of the intramolecular vibrations, the forces of interaction with the surrounding molecules change. The change in interaction forces results in a local lattice deformation in the region of the vibrating molecule and, consequently, in an excitation of external vibrations (lattice vibrations). Thus, when taking into account the possibility of the displacement of molecules from their equilibrium positions, it is impossible to consider intramolecular vibrations as independent from lattice vibrations.

The transfer of energy from intramolecular vibrations to lattice vibrations is equivalent to the damping (vibrations with friction) of intramolecular vibrations. As a result, in the resonance points $\omega_\mu = \omega_\mu(0)$ of the expression (2.22), the amplitudes will now be finite, and the resonance curve will have a finite width. Consequently, the absorption bands will be wide. The widening of absorption bands will be simultaneously accompanied by a decrease in the width of the bands and a decrease in the distances between the bands of frequencies caused by the splitting of normal frequencies. Therefore, the above-mentioned polarization effects will be less noticeable.

The width of the absorption bands will be greater as energy is more rapidly transferred to the lattice vibrations. This last process depends on the correlation of two magnitudes: (*a*) the time of transfer τ_t of intramolecular vibrations from molecule to molecule, which is inversely proportional to the group velocity of running vibrational waves [(2.23)]; (*b*) the time of displacement τ_d of molecules into new equilibrium positions, which depends on the masses of the molecules and on the change of the interaction forces when intramolecular vibrations occur.

If $\tau_t > \tau_d$, a local lattice deformation occurs. This results in a transfer of the energy of intramolecular vibrations to the lattice vibrations, and vice versa, at high temperatures.

If $\tau_t < \tau_d$, the intramolecular vibrational state is transmitted from molecule to molecule at such speed that the displacements of the molecules from their equilibrium positions cannot attain significant magnitude. The probability of transfer of energy of intramolecular vibrations to lattice vibrations will be small.

3. The results obtained in this chapter may also be extended to spectra in the visible and ultraviolet regions, since it is well known that a rough picture of the interaction of molecules (atoms) with light may be obtained by having a certain virtual oscillator correspond to each quantized transition in the molecule. The interaction of molecules upon the absorption of light will then be reduced to the interaction of a system of oscillators.

CHAPTER III

QUANTUM THEORY OF ABSORPTION AND COMBINATIONAL SCATTERING (RAMAN) SPECTRA IN MOLECULAR CRYSTALS (ZEROTH APPROXIMATION)†

12. Energy Terms of a Molecular Crystal with Fixed Molecules

We shall begin the investigation of absorption spectra of molecular crystals by means of quantum-mechanical methods, assuming that the molecules are rigidly fixed in equilibrium positions (temperature of the crystal near zero, and mass of molecules very great). In Chapter IV the limits of applicability of such an approximation will be shown.

Let us examine, as we did in Chapter II, a molecular crystal containing σ identical molecules in a unit cell. We further consider the stationary energy states of the isolated molecule, i.e., the wave functions $\bar{\varphi}^f_{\text{mol}}$ and the energy levels $\bar{E}^f_{\text{mol}}$, to be known. The symbol f determines the character and number of the excited state. This may be one of the vibrational excited states, a purely electronic excitation, or an electronic-vibrational excitation.

In order not to complicate calculations, we at first assume that the molecules do not have degenerate states. For many molecules of a low symmetry class (which will chiefly interest us), this is actually the case. It is not very difficult to extend the generalization of the theory to the case of degenerate excited states. If there are degenerate levels in a molecule, the degeneracy may be removed when the molecule is situated in a crystal of suitable symmetry. This results in a splitting of molecular terms, similar to the splitting of atomic terms already studied by H. Bethe.[4] Splitting of this type is analogous to the splitting of atomic terms in an electric field. It is essential in ionic crystals but cannot play a significant part in molecular crystals consisting of neutral, nondipolar molecules. Study of this type of splitting does not come within the scope of our work. Therefore, we shall limit ourselves to examining the nondegenerate energy states in an isolated molecule, and we shall show that

† The results of the first two sections of this chapter have been published by the author in a somewhat less general form.[45]

even in this case, as a result of the presence in the unit cell of several differently oriented molecules, a characteristic splitting of the bands of light absorption by crystals appears.

The wave functions φ^f_{mol} of the molecule will depend on the relative coordinates of the nuclei of the molecule and on the coordinates and spins of electrons that make up the molecule. For the sake of brevity, all these coordinates will henceforth be called *internal coordinates* of the molecule and will be designated by the letter r. As is known for molecules, one can always separate the group of electrons whose energy states determine the light absorption in the long-wave spectral region and whose wave functions overlap weakly with the wave functions of the remaining electrons. We shall call these electrons *optical*. In many organic compounds these electrons are the so-called π electrons. Let us assume that each molecule possesses S optical electrons.

We shall designate by $H_{n\alpha}$ the operator for the energy of the molecule occupying the αth place in the nth cell of the crystal and by $V_{n\alpha,m\beta}$ the operator for the energy of interaction between the molecules $n\alpha$ and $m\beta$. The wave functions Φ and the energy levels E of the stationary states of the entire crystal are then determined from the quantum-mechanical equation:

$$\Big(\sum_{n\alpha} H_{n\alpha} + \tfrac{1}{2} \sum_{n\alpha,m\beta}{}' V_{n\alpha,m\beta} - E\Big)\, \Phi = 0. \tag{3.1}$$

Here the summation is carried out over all σN molecules that make up the crystal. The prime of the second sum shows that the term for which simultaneously $m = n$ and $\alpha = \beta$ is absent in the sum. The wave function Φ depends on the internal coordinates r of all the molecules of the crystal and of the coordinates determining the spatial locations of the molecules; we consider the latter coordinates fixed.

If the interaction between molecules is small, it may be neglected in the zeroth approximation. Then the wave function of the normal state of the crystal may be presented in the form of antisymmetrized products of the wave functions of $\bar{\varphi}^{\circ}_{n\alpha}$ normal states of isolated molecules.

$$\Phi_0 = [(S\sigma N)!]^{-\frac{1}{2}} \sum_{\nu} (-1)^{\nu} P_{\nu} \Psi_0, \tag{3.2}$$

where

$$\Psi_0 = \prod_{n\alpha} \bar{\varphi}^{\circ}_{n\alpha}. \tag{3.3}$$

$\bar{\varphi}^{\circ}_{n\alpha}$ is the nonantisymmetrized wave function for a separate molecule, and P_{ν} is one of $(S\sigma N)!$ possible permutations of electrons. The permutations are numbered arbitrarily but in such a manner that each succeeding one is obtained from the preceding by permutation of one pair of electrons; the summation is carried out over all possible permutations of the electrons.

With the aid of (3.2) and (3.1), the usual methods [substitution of (3.2) in (3.1), multiplication by the complex conjugate of function (3.3), and integration over all internal coordinates of the molecules] enable us to obtain the energy of the normal state of the crystal in the first approximation:

$$E^\circ = \sum_{n\alpha} \Big\{ \bar{E}^\circ_{n\alpha} + \tfrac{1}{2} \sum_{m\beta}{}' \Big[\int |\bar{\varphi}^\circ_{n\alpha}(\mathrm{I})|^2 V_{n\alpha,m\beta} |\bar{\varphi}^\circ_{m\beta}(\mathrm{II})|^2 \, d\tau - \sum_{\mu} \int \bar{\varphi}^{\circ *}_{n\alpha}(\mathrm{I}) \bar{\varphi}^\circ_{n\alpha}(\mathrm{II}) V_{n\alpha,m\beta} \bar{\varphi}^{\circ *}_{m\beta}(\mathrm{II}) \bar{\varphi}^\circ_{m\beta}(\mathrm{I}) \, d\tau \Big] \Big\}, \tag{3.4a}$$

where $\bar{\varphi}_{n\alpha}(\mathrm{I})$ and $\bar{\varphi}_{m\beta}(\mathrm{II})$ are the wave functions of the molecules $n\alpha$ and $m\beta$ when the electrons are in a certain arbitrary position in the molecules, and $\bar{\varphi}_{n\alpha}(\mathrm{II})$ and $\bar{\varphi}_{m\beta}(\mathrm{I})$ are the same functions upon permutation between the molecules $n\alpha$ and $m\beta$ of any pair of electrons. The sum over μ covers all possible permutations between the molecules $n\alpha$ and $m\beta$ of pairs of electrons.†

The expression (3.4*a*) is derived by assuming that the wave functions $\bar{\varphi}^\circ_{n\alpha}$ of isolated molecules do not change when a crystal is formed. In reality, of course, these functions do change as a result of the mutual polarization of the molecules. As is well known, this change is the cause of van der Waals attraction between molecules.

Therefore, to allow for this effect, somewhat different wave functions should be substituted for the wave functions $\bar{\varphi}^\circ_{n\alpha}$ in (3.3):

$$\bar{\varphi}^\circ_{n\alpha} \rightarrow \varphi^\circ_{n\alpha} = c^\circ \bar{\varphi}^\circ_{n\alpha} + v_{n\alpha}. \tag{3.3a}$$

To find a correction for the wave function, the variational method of quantum mechanics could be utilized. For this purpose, one must resolve $v_{n\alpha}$ into a series over the full system of orthogonal functions $\bar{\varphi}^f_{n\alpha}$ for an isolated molecule

$$v_{n\alpha} = \sum_{f \neq 0} c^f \bar{\varphi}^f_{n\alpha} \tag{3.3b}$$

and use instead of (3.3) the wave functions of (3.3*a*); then instead of (3.4*a*), we obtain the new expression

$$E^\circ = \sum_{n\alpha} \Big\{ E^\circ_{n\alpha} + \tfrac{1}{2} \sum_{m\beta}{}' \Big[\int |\varphi^\circ_{n\alpha}(\mathrm{I})|^2 V_{n\alpha,m\beta} |\varphi^\circ_{m\beta}(\mathrm{II})|^2 \, d\tau - \sum_{\mu} \int \varphi^{\circ *}_{n\alpha}(\mathrm{I}) \varphi^\circ_{n\alpha}(\mathrm{II}) V_{n\alpha,m\beta} \varphi^{\circ *}_{m\beta}(\mathrm{II}) \varphi^\circ_{m\beta}(\mathrm{I}) \, d\tau \Big] \Big\}, \tag{3.4}$$

where

$$E^\circ_{n\alpha} = (c^\circ)^2 \bar{E}^\circ_{n\alpha} + \sum_{f \neq 0} (c^f)^2 \bar{E}^f_{n\alpha}. \tag{3.4b}$$

† If each molecule has S electrons, the number of terms in this sum will be equal to S^2.

The unknown coefficients c^f for molecular crystals must be small magnitudes, and $c^\circ \approx 1$. These coefficients are determined from the minimum condition for (3.4), relative to the variation of these coefficients.

However, inasmuch as the wave functions $\bar{\varphi}^\circ_{n\alpha}$ for the isolated molecules are usually unknown, the solution of the problem formulated by us does not have practical meaning. It is more convenient to consider that the energies [(3.4*b*)] and the functions [(3.3*a*)], corrected in this manner, enter into the integral [(3.4)] determining the energy of the system's normal state. These energies and functions take into account the mutual polarization of the molecules and, consequently, are functions not only of the internal coordinates of the molecules, but also of their mutual distances and orientations. In other words, instead of (3.4*a*), we will use (3.4), considering that the values $E^\circ_{n\alpha}$ and $\varphi^\circ_{n\alpha}$ entering into (3.4) are known.

If one of the molecules of the crystal (for instance $n\alpha$) passes to the fth excited state, and if all molecules are sufficiently distant from each other, such an excited state of the crystal will be described by the wave function†

$$\chi^f_{n\alpha} = [(S\sigma N)!]^{-1/2} \sum_{\nu} (-1)^\nu p_\nu \Psi^f_{n\alpha}, \tag{3.5}$$

where

$$\Psi^f_{n\alpha} = \varphi^f_{n\alpha} \prod_{\substack{m\beta \\ m\beta \neq n\alpha}} \varphi^\circ_{m\beta}. \tag{3.6}$$

When the molecules are drawn together to the distances corresponding to the normal location of the molecules in the crystal, the excitation will no longer be localized in the molecule $n\alpha$ but will be transmitted from one molecule to another. The transmission of the excitation from molecule to molecule is analogous to the spreading over the crystal of excitation waves, or *excitons* according to the terminology first introduced by J. I. Frenkel[20,21] and now universally recognized.

The crystal states, differing only in the site of the molecular excitation, belong to one and the same energy of the crystal. In other words, the wave functions [(3.5)], which differ from each other by their indices $n\alpha$, form a degenerate system of functions in the zeroth approximation. Therefore, the wave function of the excited state of the crystal (in the zeroth approximation) may be written in the form of a superposition of states [(3.5)].

$$\Phi^f = (\sigma N)^{-1/2} \sum_{n\alpha} a_{n\alpha} \chi^f_{n\alpha}, \tag{3.7}$$

where $|a_{n\alpha}|^2/\sigma N$ determines the probability of the molecule $n\alpha$ being in an excited state for a given location of the molecules in a crystal. In the

† Here also it is assumed that the functions $\varphi^f_{n\alpha}$ and $\varphi^\circ_{n\alpha}$ take into account the effect of mutual polarization of the molecules.

ideal crystal lattice formed from identical molecules, the probability that precisely molecule $n\alpha$ will turn out to be excited does not depend on the indices $n\alpha$; that is,

$$|a_{n\alpha}|^2 = \text{const.} \tag{3.8}$$

Substituting (3.7) into (3.1), multiplying by $\chi^f_{m\beta}$, and integrating over internal molecular variables, gives a system of algebraic equations for determining $a_{n\alpha}$ and the energy E^f of a system which is in an excited state:

$$\sum_{n\alpha}' M^f_{n\alpha,m\beta} a_{n\alpha} - \epsilon^f a_{m\beta} = 0. \tag{3.9}$$

Here the summation covers all molecules except the $m\beta$th; the matrix element

$$M^f_{n\alpha,m\beta} = \int \varphi^{f*}_{m\beta}(\mathrm{I})\varphi^{\circ}_{m\beta}(\mathrm{I})V_{n\alpha,m\beta}\varphi^{\circ*}_{n\alpha}(\mathrm{II})\varphi^{f}_{n\alpha}(\mathrm{II})\,d\tau - \sum_{\mu}\int \varphi^{f*}_{m\beta}(\mathrm{I})\varphi^{\circ}_{m\beta}(\mathrm{II})V_{n\alpha,m\beta}\varphi^{\circ*}_{n\alpha}(\mathrm{II})\varphi^{f}_{n\alpha}(\mathrm{I})\,d\tau \tag{3.10}$$

determines the exchange of excitation between the $n\alpha$th and $m\beta$th molecules.

$$\begin{aligned} E^f = \epsilon^f + E^f_{m\beta} + \sum_{n\alpha}' \Big\{ E^{\circ}_{n\alpha} &+ \int |\varphi^f_{m\beta}(\mathrm{I})|^2 V_{n\alpha,m\beta}|\varphi^{\circ}_{n\alpha}(\mathrm{II})|^2\,d\tau \\ &- \sum_{\mu}\int \varphi^{f*}_{m\beta}(\mathrm{I})\varphi^{\circ}_{m\beta}(\mathrm{II})V_{n\alpha,m\beta}\varphi^{\circ*}_{n\alpha}(\mathrm{II})\varphi^{f}_{n\alpha}(\mathrm{I})\,d\tau \\ &+ \tfrac{1}{2}\sum_{m\beta}\Big[\int |\varphi^{\circ}_{m\beta}(\mathrm{I})|^2 V_{n\alpha,m\beta}|\varphi^{\circ}_{n\alpha}(\mathrm{II})|^2\,d\tau \\ &- \sum_{\mu}\int \varphi^{\circ*}_{m\beta}(\mathrm{I})\varphi^{\circ}_{m\beta}(\mathrm{II})V_{n\alpha,m\beta}\varphi^{\circ*}_{n\alpha}(\mathrm{II})\varphi^{\circ}_{n\alpha}(\mathrm{I})\,d\tau\Big]\Big\}. \end{aligned} \tag{3.11}$$

The prime in the sum indicates that the summation is carried out over all molecules except the $m\beta$th.

By subtracting the energy of the normal state [(3.4)] from (3.11), we obtain the excitation energy of the crystal:

$$\Delta E^f = \Delta E^f_{m\beta} + D^f_{m\beta} + \epsilon^f, \tag{3.12}$$

where

$$\Delta E^f_{m\beta} = E^f_{m\beta} - E^{\circ}_{m\beta}$$

is the excitation energy of one molecule,† and the expression

$$D^f_{m\beta} = \sum_{n\alpha}' \Big[\int |\varphi^f_{m\beta}(\mathrm{I})|^2 V_{n\alpha,m\beta}|\varphi^{\circ}_{n\alpha}(\mathrm{II})|^2\,d\tau - \int |\varphi^{\circ}_{m\beta}(\mathrm{I})|^2 V_{n\alpha,m\beta}|\varphi^{\circ}_{n\alpha}(\mathrm{II})|^2\,d\tau - \text{exchange terms}\Big] \tag{3.13}$$

† Generally speaking, this energy differs from the excitation energy of an isolated molecule because, as a result of mutual polarization of molecules in a crystal, their energy levels change. However, in molecular crystals, as we have previously shown, this change must occur in the second approximation of the theory and will be insignificant.

determines the difference in the interaction energy between the excited and normal $m\beta$ molecule and all the remaining molecules.

Thus the excitation energy [(3.12)] of a crystal differs from the excitation energy of a molecule by the two terms $D_{m\beta}$ and ϵ.

To calculate ϵ, one must solve the system of equations (3.9), which are homogeneous relative to $a_{n\alpha}$. By virtue of the translational symmetry of the crystal, the system of equations (3.9) can be reduced to a simpler system with the aid of the substitution

$$a_{n\alpha} = B_\alpha e^{i\mathbf{kn}}, \tag{3.14}$$

where $\mathbf{k}$ is the wave vector characterizing the excitation wave in the crystal and running through N discrete values.

$$\mathbf{k} = \sum_{i=1}^{3} \frac{2\pi}{N_i} \mathbf{a}_i^{-1} \nu_i.$$

Here ν_i are whole numbers satisfying the inequality

$$-\frac{N_i}{2} < \nu_i \leqslant \frac{N_i}{2}, \qquad i = 1, 2, 3,$$

and $\mathbf{a}_i^{-1}$ are vectors of the reciprocal lattice.

The coefficients B_α [(3.14)] satisfy the system of equations

$$\sum_{\alpha=1}^{\sigma} L^f_{\alpha\beta}(\mathbf{k}) B_\alpha - \epsilon^f B_\beta = 0, \tag{3.15}$$

where

$$L^f_{\alpha\beta}(\mathbf{k}) = \sum_n{}' M^f_{n\alpha,m\beta} e^{i\mathbf{k}(\mathbf{m}-\mathbf{n})}. \tag{3.16}$$

The prime in the sum [(3.16)] indicates that if $\alpha \neq \beta$ the summation is carried out over all the values of n, including $n = m$, but that if $\alpha = \beta$ then the summation is over all $n \neq m$.

The conditions under which the system of equations (3.15) has nontrivial solutions leads to the equation of the σth degree relative to ϵ:

$$\Delta(\epsilon) \equiv |L^f_{\alpha\beta}(\mathbf{k}) - \epsilon^f \delta_{\alpha\beta}| = 0. \tag{3.17}$$

After solving the (3.17), we obtain σ values of ϵ, as functions of the wave number $\mathbf{k}$:

$$\epsilon^f_\mu = \epsilon^f_\mu(\mathbf{k}), \qquad \mu = 1, 2, \ldots, \sigma. \tag{3.18}$$

The energy distances between the values ϵ^f_μ, corresponding to various μ, are determined by the matrix elements $L^f_{\alpha\beta}(\mathbf{k})$, which, with the aid of (3.16), are expressed through the matrix elements for the transfer of excitation between two molecules. In molecular crystals, these matrix elements are small, even for neighboring molecules (~0.01 ev and less).

For a rough calculation of the matrix elements of (3.10), we can utilize the decomposition in a power series of inverse distances between molecules $R_{n\alpha,m\beta}^{-1}$ of the classical interaction energy $V_{n\alpha,m\beta}$. If we limit ourselves merely to the first term of the series (i.e., dipole-dipole interaction), then

$$V_{n\alpha,m\beta} = -\frac{e^2}{R_{n\alpha,m\beta}^3}\sum (2z_{n\alpha}^i z_{m\beta}^j - x_{n\alpha}^i x_{m\beta}^j - y_{n\alpha}^i y_{m\beta}^j), \qquad (3.19)$$

where $x_{n\alpha}^i,\ y_{n\alpha}^i,\ z_{n\alpha}^i$ and $x_{m\beta}^j,\ y_{m\beta}^j,\ z_{m\beta}^j$

are the coordinates of electrons i and j in two molecules, relative to the systems of coordinates located in the centers of the molecules, so that the line linking the centers of the molecules coincides with the z axes of both systems.

If we substitute (3.19) in (3.10), we are immediately convinced that, for dipole transitions in the molecules, only the first integral, which determines the resonance interaction between two molecules, will have practical meaning. With this approximation, we obtain the matrix element [(3.10)] in the following form:

$$M_{n\alpha,m\beta}^f = -\frac{e^2}{R_{n\alpha,m\beta}^3}\left|\int \varphi_{n\alpha}^{f*}\mathbf{r}\varphi_{n\alpha}^{\circ}\,d\tau\right|^2 (2\cos\Theta_{m\beta}^z\cos\Theta_{n\alpha}^z - \cos\Theta_{m\beta}^x\cos\Theta_{n\alpha}^x - \cos\Theta_{m\beta}^y\cos\Theta_{n\alpha}^y), \qquad (3.20)$$

where $e\int\varphi_{n\alpha}^{f*}\mathbf{r}\varphi_{n\alpha}^{\circ}\,d\tau$ is the matrix element of the electric moment vector determining the quantum transition within the molecule, and $\cos\Theta_{m\beta}^x$ and $\cos\Theta_{n\alpha}^x$ are the cosines, formed by the electrical moment vectors in the molecules $m\beta$ and $n\alpha$, respectively, with the axes of the coordinates.

The square of the matrix element for the transition may be expressed through the oscillator strength F_{f0} for the corresponding transition and through the cyclic frequency of the transition ω with the aid of the known formula

$$\left|\int \varphi^*\mathbf{r}\varphi\,d\tau\right|^2 = \frac{F_{0f}h}{2\mu\omega},$$

where μ is the mass of the electron. Then the expression (3.20) assumes the form

$$M_{n\alpha,m\beta}^f = -\frac{e^2hF_{0f}}{2\mu\omega R_{n\alpha,m\beta}^3}(2\cos\Theta_{m\beta}^z\cos\Theta_{n\alpha}^z - \cos\Theta_{m\beta}^x\cos\Theta_{n\alpha}^x - \cos\Theta_{m\beta}^y\cos\Theta_{n\alpha}^y). \qquad (3.20a)$$

For dipole forbidden transitions, $\int\varphi_{n\alpha}^{f*}\mathbf{r}\varphi_{n\alpha}\,d\tau = 0$. In this case, an interaction of a higher order (quadrupole-quadrupole, etc.) must be taken into account in the decomposition of (3.19). It is then not possible to discard the second term in (3.10), since in certain cases it will have a value identical with the first term in order of magnitude.

Thus, to the molecular excitation energy $E^f_{m\beta}$ in the crystal, μ quasi-continuous bands of excited states will correspond:

$$\Delta E^f_\mu(\mathbf{k}) = \Delta E^f_{m\beta} + D^f_{m\beta} + \epsilon^f_\mu(\mathbf{k}). \tag{3.21}$$

By substituting the μ values of ϵ from (3.18) in the equations (3.15), we obtain μ systems of coefficients B^μ_α, which determine μ wave functions for excited states of the crystal, corresponding to the fth excitation of the molecule

$$\Phi^f_\mu(\mathbf{k}) = (\sigma N)^{-1/2} \sum_{n\alpha} B^\mu_\alpha \chi^f_{n\alpha} e^{i\mathbf{kn}}. \tag{3.22}$$

To determine the selection and polarization rules for quantum transition from a normal state Φ° to an excited state $\Phi^f_\mu(\mathbf{k})$ of the crystal under the action of light, we must calculate the matrix element

$$(\mu f|\mathbf{r}|o) = \int \Phi^{f*}_\mu(\mathbf{k})\mathbf{r}\Phi^\circ \, d\tau. \tag{3.23}$$

Here we have disregarded the wave vector Q of light for the same reasons as in Section 8.†

After substituting the values for the wave functions into (3.23), we obtain

$$(\mu f|\mathbf{r}|o) = (\sigma N)^{-1/2} \sum_n e^{i\mathbf{kn}} \sum_\alpha B^\mu_\alpha \int \varphi^{f*}_{n\alpha}\mathbf{r}\varphi^\circ_{n\alpha} \, d\tau. \tag{3.24}$$

The integrals entering into (3.24) do not depend on n; therefore, the matrix element [(3.24)] will differ from zero only when

$$\mathbf{k} = 0. \tag{3.25}$$

Thus the transitions may occur only at the points of quasi-continuous zones of energy $\epsilon_\mu(\mathbf{k})$, which correspond to the values $\mathbf{k} = 0$. This agrees with the classical statement: Only the bounding (limiting) frequencies are excited by light.

Thus the matrix element [(3.24)] must have the form

$$N^{-1/2}(\mu f|\mathbf{r}|o) = \sigma^{-1/2} \sum_\alpha B^\mu_\alpha \int \varphi^{f*}_{n\alpha}\mathbf{r}\varphi^\circ_{n\alpha} \, d\tau. \tag{3.26}$$

For a further investigation of the matrix element [(3.26)], we need to know the values of the system of coefficients B^μ_α for each μ.

13. Application of Group Theory for Determining the Selection and Polarization Rules of Split Components upon Absorption and Combinational Scattering (Raman Scattering) of Light in Crystals Which Contain Two Molecules per Unit Cell

The solution of equation (3.17) to determine $\epsilon^f_\mu(\mathbf{k})$ and the coefficients B^μ_α is comparatively simple in the case of a small number of molecules in

† A more rigorous investigation, which considers $Q \neq 0$, will be carried out in Sections 21 to 23.

a unit cell. To establish a qualitative picture, it is sufficient to obtain the values of the coefficients B^μ_α in (3.22) and to determine the symmetry properties of the wave functions [(3.22)] by utilizing group theoretical methods. After determining the symmetry of the wave functions for the energy bands distinguished by the designation μ, we can establish the selection rules and polarization of the corresponding transitions under the action of light.

In lieu of the immediate solution of equations (3.15) and (3.17), we may use the following method to find the coefficients B^μ_α.

Let us write the wave functions [(3.22)] for the case of two molecules per unit cell and $\mathbf{k} = 0$:

$$\begin{aligned} \Phi^f_1 &= (2N)^{-\frac{1}{2}} \sum_n (\chi^f_{n_1} B^1_1 + \chi^f_{n_2} B^1_2) \\ \Phi^f_2 &= (2N)^{-\frac{1}{2}} \sum_n (\chi^f_{n_1} B^2_1 + \chi^f_{n_2} B^2_2) \end{aligned} \tag{3.27}$$

The functions [(3.27)] must be orthogonal to each other and normalized; i.e., they must satisfy the conditions

$$\int \Phi^{f*}_i \Phi^f_j \, d\tau = \delta_{ij}. \tag{3.28}$$

Furthermore, by virtue of (3.28),

$$|B^\mu_2| = |B^\mu_1|. \tag{3.29}$$

Utilizing (3.27), we shall, with the aid of (3.28), obtain the following equations:

$$\begin{aligned} |B^1_1|^2 + |B^1_2|^2 &= 2 \\ |B^2_1|^2 + |B^2_2|^2 &= 2 \\ B^1_1 B^2_1 + B^1_2 B^2_2 &= 0 \end{aligned} \tag{3.30}$$

Equations (3.30) and (3.29) satisfy the system of coefficients

μ	B^μ_1	B^μ_2
1	1	1
2	1	-1

(3.31)

Thus the wave functions [(3.27)] will have the form

$$\begin{aligned} \Phi^f_1 &= (2N)^{-\frac{1}{2}} \sum_n (\chi^f_{n_1} + \chi^f_{n_2}), \\ \Phi^f_2 &= (2N)^{-\frac{1}{2}} \sum_n (\chi^f_{n_1} - \chi^f_{n_2}). \end{aligned} \tag{3.32}$$

Inasmuch as the wave functions $\varphi^0_{m\beta}$ for the normal state of the molecules belong to the totally symmetrical representation, the symmetry properties of the wave functions $\chi^f_{n\alpha}$ entering into (3.32) will be determined by the symmetry properties for the wave functions $\varphi^f_{n\alpha}$ of the fth excited state of the molecule. To determine the irreducible representations according to which the functions [(3.32)] transform, we must know the irreducible representations of the wave functions for the excited states of the molecules entering into the crystal.

a. Crystals of the Naphthalene Type. To illustrate the use of group theory, let us examine a monoclinic crystal belonging to the space group C_{2h}^5 and containing two molecules in a unit cell. The space symmetry group C_{2h}^5—the fifth group of the monoclinic-prismatic class—is very often encountered among organic crystals. This group has four symmetry elements: screw axes of the second order C_2, parallel to the b axis of the crystal; centers of symmetry i situated in the center, the corners, and the centers of the sides of the faces ab and of the plane parallel to the

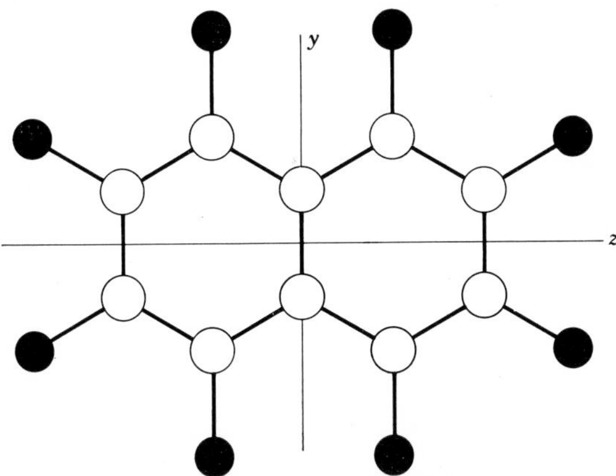

FIG. 3. Coordinate axes for the naphthalene molecule.

face ab and $c/2$ distant from it; glide planes σ perpendicular to the b axis; and identity element E. The characters of the irreducible representations of this group are given in Table 1 (see Section 6, Chapter I).

The minimum number of two molecules per unit cell in group C_{2h}^5 is realized when the molecules possess a center of symmetry. Then, when the centers of symmetry of a crystal and a molecule coincide, the symmetry operations of the crystal will transpose one molecule to the place of another or will leave them in place.

Crystals of this type include naphthalene $C_{10}H_8$, anthracene $C_{14}H_{10}$, biphenyl $(C_6H_5)_2$, ethylene C_2H_4, paradichlorobenzene $C_6H_4Cl_2$, and others.

By way of example, let us examine a crystal of naphthalene. All qualitative results obtained in this case will apply equally to other crystals of this type.

The naphthalene molecule has a planar structure which is schematically depicted in Figure 3. The carbon atoms are indicated by white circles and the hydrogen atoms by black ones. The molecule belongs to the point symmetry group D_{2h}. The characters of the irreducible representations of this group, together with the designation of the transformation properties for the components of the radius vector (x, y, z), are given in Table 2.

TABLE 2. CHARACTER TABLE FOR THE D_{2h} POINT GROUP, INCLUDING NUMBER OF NORMAL VIBRATIONAL MODES AND THEIR SELECTION RULES FOR NAPHTHALENE

D_{2h}	E	C_2^x	C_2^y	C_2^z	i	σ^x	σ^y	σ^z	N	Infrared	Combinational scattering (Raman)
A_{1g}	1	1	1	1	1	1	1	1	9	Forbidden	Permitted
B_{1g}	1	−1	−1	1	1	−1	−1	1	4	Forbidden	Permitted
A_{2g}	1	1	−1	−1	1	1	−1	−1	8	Forbidden	Permitted
B_{2g}	1	−1	1	−1	1	−1	1	−1	3	Forbidden	Permitted
A_{1u}	1	1	1	1	−1	−1	−1	−1	4	Forbidden	Forbidden
z, B_{1u}	1	−1	−1	1	−1	1	1	−1	7	Permitted	Forbidden
x, A_{2u}	1	1	−1	−1	−1	−1	1	1	4	Permitted	Forbidden
y, B_{2u}	1	−1	1	−1	−1	1	−1	1	8	Permitted	Forbidden

The number of intramolecular vibrations N belonging to each irreducible representation are also noted in this table. The last two columns show whether the corresponding vibrations are forbidden or permitted in the infrared and the combinational scattering (Raman scattering) spectra.

As the author has shown,[46] the excited states for π electrons in the naphthalene molecule may belong to four irreducible representations, A_{1g}, A_{2g}, B_{1u}, and B_{2u}, of the symmetry group D_{2h}. The normal states of these molecules belong to the totally symmetrical irreducible representation A_{1g}. Optical transitions (of the dipole type) from a normal state are permitted only to the excited states B_{1u} and B_{2u} (with polarization along the long and intermediate molecular axes, respectively). The transitions to the states A_{1g} and A_{2g} are forbidden.

These results are obtained by the methods of group theory and do not depend on the approximation method of calculating the molecular energy terms themselves.

Knowing the symmetry of the wave functions of the electronic transitions in the molecule, one can determine, with the aid of group theory, the symmetry properties of the corresponding wave functions of the crystal and, consequently, can determine the selection rules and the polarization of the spectral lines of the crystal.

The wave function of the normal state of the crystal will transform as the totally symmetrical representation A_g of group C_{2h}^5 (Table 1):

$$\Phi^\circ \sim A_g. \tag{3.33}$$

Naturally, the character of the excited states of the crystal will depend on the type of the corresponding excited molecular state. Therefore, for the upper index f of the wave functions of the crystal Φ_μ^f we substitute the symbol for that irreducible representation of the molecular symmetry group to which the corresponding molecular transition pertains.

Let us take into consideration the fact that the identity operation E and the inversion i coincide in the molecule and the crystal. The transposition of the molecules with indices 1 and 2 and the subsequent turn by 180° of the molecule around its intermediate axis correspond to the crystal symmetry operations C_2 and σ (i.e., the operation C_2^y of the molecule, and correspondingly, the reflection in the plane, perpendicular to the same axis is the operation σ^y of the molecule). Then, utilizing the table of characters of the irreducible representations for the symmetry group of the molecule, we obtain the following transformation properties of the wave function of the crystal $\Phi_1^{B_{1u}}$:

$$E\Phi_1^{B_{1u}} = \Phi_1^{B_{1u}} \qquad c_2\Phi_1^{B_{1u}} = -\Phi_1^{B_{1u}}$$
$$i\Phi_1^{B_{1u}} = -\Phi_1^{B_{1u}} \qquad \sigma\Phi_1^{B_{1u}} = \Phi_1^{B_{1u}}.$$

If we compare the results obtained with the character table, we are satisfied that the wave function of the crystal $\Phi_1^{B_{1u}}$ transforms like the irreducible representation B_u of the crystal symmetry group. This may be written in abbreviated form:

$$\Phi_1^{B_{1u}} \sim B_u. \tag{3.34}$$

We similarly establish the transformation properties of the remaining functions, which determine the excited electronic states of the crystal:

$$\begin{aligned} \Phi_1^{A_{1g}}, \Phi_2^{A_{2g}} &\sim A_g \\ \Phi_1^{A_{2g}}, \Phi_2^{A_{1g}} &\sim B_g \\ \Phi_1^{B_{2u}}, \Phi_2^{B_{1u}} &\sim A_u \\ \Phi_1^{B_{1u}}, \Phi_2^{B_{2u}} &\sim B_u. \end{aligned} \tag{3.35}$$

Using group theory, we may at once show the selection rules and polarization of the corresponding optical dipole transitions in the crystal. All transitions from a normal state to excited states of a crystal are forbidden with wave functions $\Phi_1^{A_{1g}}$, $\Phi_2^{A_{2g}}$, $\Phi_1^{A_{2g}}$, and $\Phi_2^{A_{1g}}$. The transitions to all other levels are permitted. Thus the transitions in the crystal are forbidden if they correspond to forbidden transitions in the molecule, and they are permitted if they correspond to permitted transitions in the molecule, for the case of two molecules per unit cell.

Two permitted transitions in the crystal correspond to each permitted transition in the molecule. In other words, the energy term of the molecule in a crystal is split into two terms, which differ from each other in polarization. One term, pertaining to the irreducible representation A_u of the crystal, is polarized in such a fashion that the vibrations of the electric vector have a direction parallel to the b axis of the crystal. The other term is in the plane perpendicular to the b axis. The splitting of molecular terms is caused by the nonidentical spatial orientation of anisotropic molecules in a crystal and by the resonance interaction between molecules.

Similarly, results pertaining to the infrared spectra may be obtained. The absorption is permitted for molecular vibrations pertaining to the irreducible representations A_{2u}, B_{1u}, and B_{2u} of the molecule. To each type of molecular vibration in the crystal, two vibrations with a different polarization will correspond. Table 3 shows the irreducible representations to which the split intramolecular crystal vibrations belong and their polarizations.

TABLE 3. CORRELATION TABLE FOR SYMMETRY SPECIES OF INFRARED ACTIVE NAPHTHALENE VIBRATIONS IN THE MOLECULE (D_{2h}) AND THE CRYSTAL (C^5_{2h})

Molecular vibration	Wave function for crystal vibration	Irreducible representation	Direction of vibration in crystal
A_{2u}	$\Phi_1^{A_{2u}}$ $\Phi_2^{A_{2u}}$	B_u A_u	$\perp b$ $\parallel b$
B_{1u}	$\Phi_1^{B_{1u}}$ $\Phi_2^{B_{1u}}$	B_u A_u	$\perp b$ $\parallel b$
B_{2u}	$\Phi_1^{B_{2u}}$ $\Phi_2^{B_{2u}}$	A_u B_u	$\parallel b$ $\perp b$

It must be noted that, in a crystal, molecular vibrations in the isolated molecule belonging to an irreducible representation A_{1u} will also occur in the infrared absorption spectrum. In the naphthalene molecule there are four such vibrations, and they are forbidden not only in the infrared spectrum, but also in the combinational scattering (Raman) spectrum. To each of these vibrations, in a crystal there will correspond two vibrations with wave functions

$$\Phi_1^{A_{1u}} \sim A_u \qquad \text{vibration parallel to } b \text{ axis,}$$
$$\Phi_2^{A_{1u}} \sim B_u \qquad \text{vibration perpendicular to } b \text{ axis.}$$

However, inasmuch as the separations between split components are proportional in the first approximation to the squares of the dipole moments for the corresponding molecular vibrations (in the given case they are equal to zero), these separations must be very small. Therefore, in the absorption spectrum, the split components corresponding to the molecular vibrations of the A_{1u} type apparently cannot be permitted.

The vibrations occurring in combinational scattering (Raman scattering) of light may also be analyzed in the same manner. Table 4 shows the irreducible representations to which the split components of vibrations in an isolated molecule belong.

TABLE 4. CORRELATION TABLE FOR SYMMETRY SPECIES OF COMBINATIONAL SCATTERING (RAMAN ACTIVE) NAPHTHALENE VIBRATIONS IN THE MOLECULE (D_{2h}) AND THE CRYSTAL (C_{2h}^5)

Molecular vibration	Crystal wave function	Irreducible representation
A_{1g}	$\Phi_1^{A_{1g}}$ $\Phi_2^{A_{1g}}$	A_g B_g
B_{1g}	$\Phi_1^{B_{1g}}$ $\Phi_2^{B_{1g}}$	B_g A_g
A_{2g}	$\Phi_1^{A_{2g}}$ $\Phi_2^{A_{2g}}$	B_g A_g
B_{2g}	$\Phi_1^{B_{2g}}$ $\Phi_2^{B_{2g}}$	A_g B_g

From this table we may infer that each type of vibration occurring in the combinational scattering (Raman) spectrum of an isolated molecule splits in the crystal into two vibrations. One of these belongs to the totally symmetrical type A_g. The separation between split components of the vibrations must be small, since the corresponding vibrations do not have dipole moments.

Nedungadi's[44] experiments confirm the results obtained here.

b. Crystals of the Calcite Type. Let us now consider crystals of the calcite type, which possess a rhombohedral lattice with a spatial symmetry group D_{3d}^6 and contain two molecules per unit cell. Crystals of many carbonates of divalent metals ($CaCO_3$, $MgCO_3$, etc.) possess this type of lattice. The infrared spectra of such crystals have been repeatedly investigated.[47–49]

It has been established that, in the wavelength region 3 to 15 μ, infrared spectra of such crystals are identical. This was explained by the fact that in this wavelength region, the spectrum is determined by the vibrations of separate atoms within the ionic molecule CO_3^{--}.

The binding of particles within the ion CO_3^{--} is significantly firmer than the binding between ions in the lattice. Therefore, we may consider this ion an independent molecule. Furthermore, we may apply the methods developed above for molecular crystals in studying the change of intramolecular vibrations of this ion when it enters into an ionic crystal. The ion CO_3^{--} represents a plane equilateral triangle, in the center of which lies a C atom (Figure 4); consequently, it may be related to the symmetry group D_{3h}. The molecule possesses the following symmetry elements: 1 threefold rotation axis C_3, 1 improper rotation axis S_3, 3 twofold axes C_2 ($\perp C_3$), 3 reflection planes σ_v (crossing C_3), and 1 reflection plane σ_h ($\perp C_3$). Table 5 lists the characters of the irreducible representations for this group and shows the characters for the transformations of coordinates x, y, z.

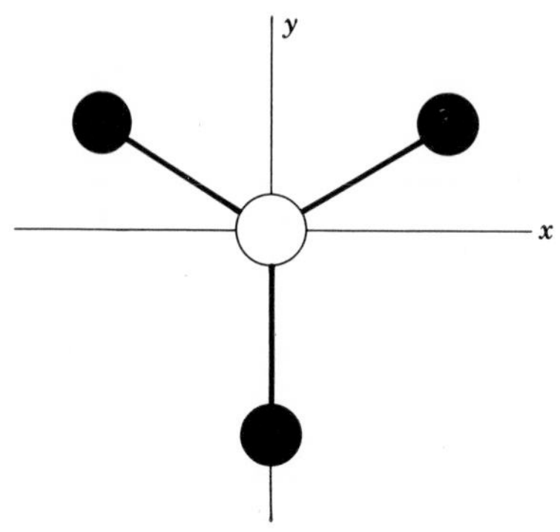

FIG. 4. Coordinate axes for the carbonate ion molecule.

Altogether, six internal vibrations, of which two pairs are doubly degenerate, are possible in the carbonate ion. The last three columns of Table 5 indicate the N numbers of the internal vibrations for each irreducible representation, as well as the selection rules in the infrared spectrum and in the combinational scattering (Raman) spectrum. The vibration A_1', which is inactive in the infrared spectrum, has, according to calculations (Ref. 50, p. 178), a frequency of 1069 cm^{-1} (9.42 μ). The vibration A_2'', which is active in the infrared spectrum and which has an electric moment perpendicular to the plane of the molecule, has a frequency of 879 cm^{-1} (11.4 μ). Two degenerate vibrations E', with an electric moment lying in the plane of the molecule, have frequencies of 1415 cm^{-1} (7.06 μ) and 680 cm^{-1} (14.7 μ), respectively.

TABLE 5. CHARACTER TABLE FOR THE D_{3h} POINT GROUP, INCLUDING NUMBER OF NORMAL VIBRATIONAL MODES AND THEIR SELECTION RULES FOR THE CARBONATE ION

D_{3h}	E	σ_h	$2C_3^z$	$2S_3$	$3C_2$	$3\sigma_v$	N	Infrared	Combinational scattering (Raman)
A_1'	1	1	1	1	1	1	1	Forbidden	Permitted
A_2'	1	1	1	1	-1	-1	0	Forbidden	Permitted
A_1''	1	-1	1	-1	1	-1	0	Forbidden	Permitted
z, A_2''	1	-1	1	-1	-1	1	1	Permitted	Forbidden
$x + iy$, E'	2	2	-1	-1	0	0	2	Permitted	Forbidden
E''	2	-2	-1	1	0	0	0	Permitted	Forbidden

The ions of CO_3^{--} are located in the lattice in such a way that their planes are parallel to each other (Figure 5) and perpendicular to the main axis, which coincides with the diagonal of a rhombohedron. Figure 5 shows only the ions of CO_3^{--}; the carbon atoms are indicated by white circles, the oxygen atoms by black ones.

The calcite crystal belongs to the space group D_{3d}^6, whose characters of irreducible representation are listed in Table 6.

TABLE 6. CHARACTER TABLE FOR THE D_{3d}^6 SPACE GROUP

D_{3d}^6	E	$2S_3^z$	$2C_3$	i	$3C_2$	$3\sigma_v$
A_{1g}	1	1	1	1	1	1
A_{1u}	1	−1	1	−1	1	−1
A_{2g}	1	1	1	1	−1	−1
z, A_{2u}	1	−1	1	−1	−1	1
E_g	2	−1	−1	2	0	0
x, y, E_u	2	1	−1	−2	0	0

Of the symmetry operations for the crystal, the following operations apply to the radicals. In operation S_3^z, operation S_3 is applied to the radical and the radicals change places and turn by 60° about the z axis. In operation C_3, operation C_3^z is applied to the radicals. In operation i, operation S_3 is applied to the radical and the radicals change places and turn by 60°. In operation C_2, operation C_2 is applied to the radicals. In operation σ_v, operations σ_v are applied to the radicals and the radicals change places.

If we use these rules governing the application of crystal symmetry operations, as well as the tables of characters of the irreducible representations of the molecule (Table 5) and of the crystal (Table 6), we shall find the irreducible representations governing the transformation of the wave functions [(3.32)] for the excited states of the crystal. The results obtained are brought together in Table 7.

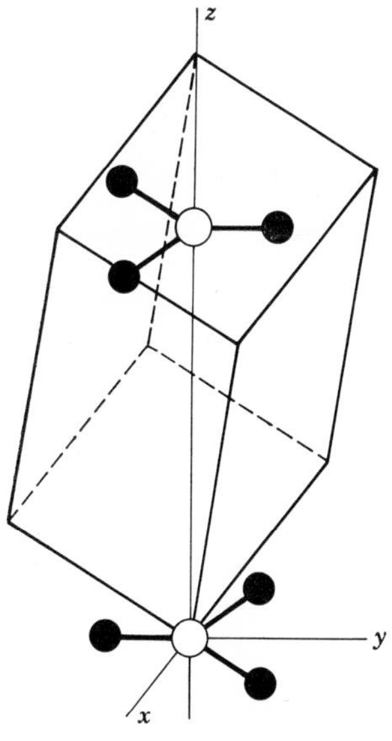

FIG. 5. Disposition of the carbonate ions in the calcite crystal.

Since the intramolecular vibrations of the ion CO_3^{--} belong only to the irreducible representations A_1', A_2'', and E', we shall now be interested only in the splitting of vibrations corresponding to these irreducible representations (first three lines of Table 7).

According to Table 7, vibration A_1', forbidden in the ion, remains forbidden in the infrared spectrum as well. Furthermore, the permitted vibration A_2'' with vibrational direction along the z axis (perpendicular to the plane of CO_3^{--}) is also permitted, with like polarization, in the infrared spectrum of the crystal. Finally, the degenerate vibrations E', permitted in the free ion (with a vibrational direction in the plane of the radical), remain degenerate in the crystal as well and possess the same polarization.

TABLE 7. CORRELATION TABLE FOR SYMMETRY SPECIES OF CARBONATE ION VIBRATIONS IN THE MOLECULE (D_{3h}) AND THE CRYSTAL (D_{3d}^6)

Radical	Wave function of crystal	Irreducible representation	Vibration in infrared	Symmetry of vibration in combinational scattering (Raman)
A_1'	$\Phi_1^{A_1'}$ $\Phi_2^{A_1'}$	A_{1g} A_{1u}	Forbidden Forbidden	Totally symmetrical Forbidden
A_2''	$\Phi_1^{A_2''}$ $\Phi_2^{A_2''}$	A_{2u} A_{2g}	$\parallel z$ Forbidden	Forbidden Forbidden
E'	$\Phi_1^{E'}$ $\Phi_2^{E'}$	E_u E_g	$\perp z$ Forbidden	Forbidden Asymmetrical
A_2'	$\Phi_1^{A_2'}$ $\Phi_2^{A_2'}$	A_{2g} A_{2u}	Forbidden $\parallel z$	Forbidden Forbidden
A_1''	$\Phi_1^{A_1''}$ $\Phi_2^{A_1''}$	A_{1u} A_{1g}	Forbidden Forbidden	Forbidden Totally symmetrical
E''	$\Phi_1^{E''}$ $\Phi_2^{E''}$	E_g E_u	Forbidden $\perp z$	Asymmetrical Forbidden

Thus, despite the splitting of vibrational terms into two components, the character of the infrared spectrum does not change qualitatively in the crystal; new absorption bands do not appear and their polarization does not change.

The same deductions may also be made for the combinational scattering (Raman) spectrum: the spectral character of the crystal and of the isolated radical (calculated) must coincide.

This result is caused by a particular orientation of the molecules in the crystal. If the molecular ions in the crystal had another mutual orientation, it would be necessary to expect qualitative changes in the spectrum. This takes place when the same ion CO_3^{--} enters into another type of lattice (aragonite). This case will be analyzed in Section 14*b*.

14. Crystals Containing Four Molecules per Unit Cell

Normalization and orthogonalization [(3.29)] conditions for the wave functions for excited states, as well as equation (3.8), lead to the system

TABLE 8. COEFFICIENTS B_α^μ FOR THE CASE OF FOUR MOLECULES PER UNIT CELL

μ	B_1^μ	B_2^μ	B_3^μ	B_4^μ
1	1	1	1	1
2	1	−1	1	−1
3	1	−1	−1	1
4	1	1	−1	−1

of values for the B_α^μ coefficients given in Table 8. The wave functions for the excited states of a crystal will be:

$$\begin{aligned}\Phi_1^f &= (4N)^{-1/2}(\chi_{n_1}^f + \chi_{n_2}^f + \chi_{n_3}^f + \chi_{n_4}^f)\\ \Phi_2^f &= (4N)^{-1/2}(\chi_{n_1}^f - \chi_{n_2}^f + \chi_{n_3}^f - \chi_{n_4}^f)\\ \Phi_3^f &= (4N)^{-1/2}(\chi_{n_1}^f - \chi_{n_2}^f - \chi_{n_3}^f + \chi_{n_4}^f)\\ \Phi_4^f &= (4N)^{-1/2}(\chi_{n_1}^f + \chi_{n_2}^f - \chi_{n_3}^f - \chi_{n_4}^f)\end{aligned} \tag{3.36}$$

Among crystals containing four molecules per unit cell, we first of all consider the crystals of the space symmetry group C_{2h}^5. The molecules in the unit cell of crystals of this type may be arranged in two possible ways.[51]

1. If the molecules do not have a center of symmetry, all four molecules can change places during crystal symmetry operations. Crystals of this type comprise phenanthrene, β-naphthol, and others.

2. If the molecules do have a center of symmetry, they may occupy two pairs of independent centers of symmetry in the crystal, and the crystal symmetry operations may transpose among themselves only those molecules which belong to the same pair. Crystals of this type comprise stilbene, azobenzene, and others.

We shall consider examples of crystals with molecules not possessing a center of symmetry and of crystals formed by molecules having a center of symmetry.

a. Crystals of the Phenanthrene Type. The molecule of phenanthrene $C_{14}H_{10}$ (Figure 6) belongs to the point symmetry group C_{2v}. It possesses the following symmetry elements: a twofold rotation axis C_2^y, a reflection plane σ^x coinciding with the molecular plane, and a symmetry plane σ^z perpendicular to the z axis. The characters of the irreducible representations for this group, together with the transformation properties of the components of the radius vector (x, y, z), are shown in Table 9. This table also gives the number of intramolecular vibrations, N, belonging to each irreducible representation.

Operation E coincides in the crystal and in the molecule. Operation C_2 for the crystal corresponds to a transposition of molecule 1 and molecule 3 and of molecule 2 and molecule 4 and to a subsequent application of operation C_2^y to the molecule. Operation i of the crystal corresponds

TABLE 9. CHARACTER TABLE FOR THE C_{2v} POINT GROUP, INCLUDING NUMBER OF NORMAL VIBRATIONAL MODES AND THEIR SELECTION RULES FOR PHENANTHRENE

	C_{2v}	E	C_2^y	σ^x	σ^z	N	Infrared	Combinational scattering (Raman)
y	A_1	1	1	1	1	23	Permitted	Permitted
	A_2	1	1	−1	−1	11	Forbidden	Permitted
z	B_1	1	−1	1	−1	22	Permitted	Permitted
x	B_2	1	−1	−1	1	10	Permitted	Permitted

to the transposition of molecules 1 and 4 and of 2 and 3 and to the subsequent application of operation σ^z to the molecule. Operation σ of the crystal corresponds to a transposition of molecules 1 and 2 and of 3 and 4, as well as to a subsequent application of the σ^x operation of the molecule.

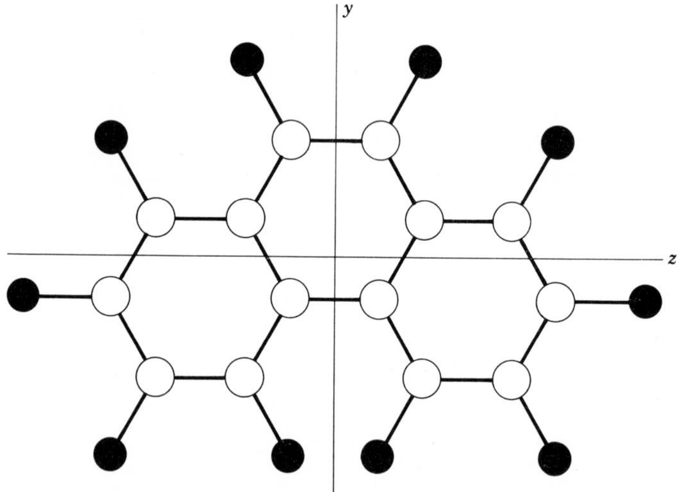

FIG. 6. Coordinate axes for the phenanthrene molecule.

If we use tables of characters of the irreducible representations for the symmetry groups of the molecule (C_{2v}) (Table 9) and of the crystal (C_{2h}^5) (Table 1), we can establish for the crystal symmetry group the irreducible representations, according to which the wave functions for the intramolecular vibrations transform.

Table 10 shows the irreducible representations for wave functions of vibrational states of the phenanthrene crystal, the direction of the electric moment of the vibrations if the corresponding vibration is permitted in the infrared spectrum, the symmetry of vibrations permitted in the combinational scattering (Raman) spectrum, and those irreducible representations for the molecular symmetry group to which the given excited states of the crystal belong.

TABLE 10. CORRELATION TABLE FOR SYMMETRY SPECIES OF PHENANTHRENE VIBRATIONS IN THE MOLECULE (C_{2v}) AND THE CRYSTAL (C_{2h}^5)

Molecule	Wave function of crystal	Irreducible representation	Infrared	Combinational scattering (Raman)
A_1	$\Phi_1^{A_1}$	A_g	Forbidden	Totally symmetrical
	$\Phi_2^{A_1}$	A_u	$\parallel b$	Forbidden
	$\Phi_3^{A_1}$	B_g	Forbidden	Asymmetrical
	$\Phi_4^{A_1}$	B_u	$\perp b$	Forbidden
A_2	$\Phi_1^{A_2}$	A_u	$\parallel b$	Forbidden
	$\Phi_2^{A_2}$	A_g	Forbidden	Totally symmetrical
	$\Phi_3^{A_2}$	B_u	$\perp b$	Forbidden
	$\Phi_4^{A_2}$	B_g	Forbidden	Asymmetrical
B_1	$\Phi_1^{B_1}$	B_u	$\perp b$	Forbidden
	$\Phi_2^{B_1}$	B_g	Forbidden	Asymmetrical
	$\Phi_3^{B_1}$	A_u	$\parallel b$	Forbidden
	$\Phi_4^{B_1}$	A_g	Forbidden	Totally symmetrical
B_2	$\Phi_1^{B_2}$	B_g	Forbidden	Asymmetrical
	$\Phi_2^{B_2}$	B_u	$\perp b$	Forbidden
	$\Phi_3^{B_2}$	A_g	Forbidden	Totally symmetrical
	$\Phi_4^{B_2}$	A_u	$\parallel b$	Forbidden

The wave functions for the excited states of the π electrons in the phenanthrene molecule belong to the irreducible representations A_1 and B_1. Transitions from the normal level to both types of excited levels are permitted (there are no forbidden transitions) in the molecule. In the crystal, each of the molecular terms is split into four levels, and transitions under the action of light will be permitted in only two of the four split bands and will be induced by a light wave with an electric-vector direction along the b axis and perpendicular to the b axis.

b. Crystals of the Aragonite Type. The crystals of this type possess a rhombic lattice with a V_h^{16} space group (four molecules per unit cell). This structure is typical of many crystalline salts of inorganic acids. The infrared spectra of these crystals have been investigated repeatedly (unfortunately at a temperature not lower than 0°C). Table 11 gives the characters of irreducible representations for the V_h^{16} space group.

TABLE 11. CHARACTER TABLE FOR THE V_h^{16} SPACE GROUP

V_h^{16}	E	C_2^x	C_2^y	C_2^z	i	σ^x	σ^y	σ^z
A_{1g}	1	1	1	1	1	1	1	1
B_{1g}	1	−1	−1	1	1	−1	−1	1
A_{2g}	1	1	−1	−1	1	1	−1	−1
B_{2g}	1	−1	1	−1	1	−1	1	−1
A_{1u}	1	1	1	1	−1	−1	−1	−1
z, B_{1u}	1	−1	−1	1	−1	1	1	−1
x, A_{2u}	1	1	−1	−1	−1	−1	1	1
y, B_{2u}	1	−1	1	−1	−1	1	−1	1

Figure 7 shows schematically the arrangement of molecules in the aragonite crystal.[52] When applying the symmetry operations of the crystal, the following operations apply to the ions of CO_3^{--}. In operation C_2^x, operation C_2 is applied to the ion, and then the transposition of ion 1 and ion 4 and of ion 2 and ion 3 takes place. In operation C_2^y,

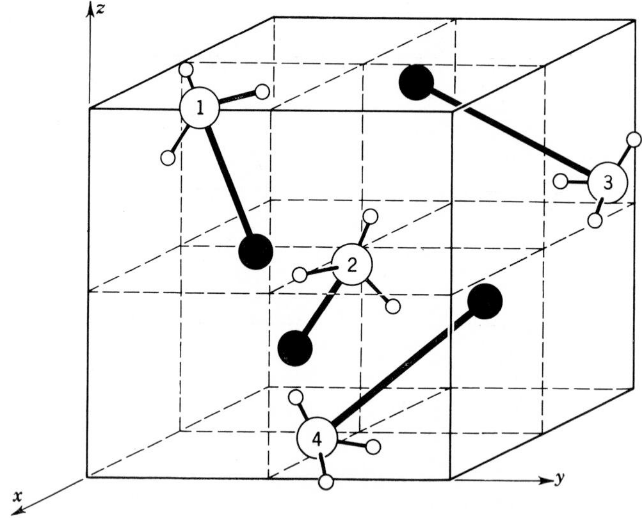

FIG. 7. Disposition of the metal ions and carbonate ions in the aragonite crystal.

operation C_2 is applied to the carbonate ions, and transposition of ion 1 and ion 3 and of ion 2 and ion 4 takes place. In operation C_2^z, operation C_2 is applied to the carbonate ions, and transposition of ion 1 and ion 2 and of ion 3 and ion 4 takes place. In operation i, the C_2^z crystal operation is applied, with subsequent application of operations σ_h to the carbonate ions. In operations σ^x and σ^y, transposition of ion 1 and ion 4 and of ion 2 and ion 3 takes place, followed by the transposition of ion 1 and ion 3 and of ion 2 and ion 4, respectively, with the subsequent application of operation σ_v to the ions.

By using these rules for applying the operations of a crystal, as well as the table of characters of the irreducible representations of the molecule (D_{3h}) (Table 5) and of the crystal (V_h^{16}) (Table 11), we shall find the irreducible representations according to which the wave functions [(3.36)] for excited states of the crystal transform. The results obtained are shown in Table 12.

TABLE 12. CORRELATION TABLE FOR SYMMETRY SPECIES OF CARBONATE ION VIBRATIONS IN THE MOLECULE (D_{3h}) AND THE CRYSTAL (V_h^{16})

Molecule	Wave function of crystal	Irreducible representation	Infrared
A_1'	$\Phi_1^{A_1'}$	A_{1g}	Forbidden
	$\Phi_2^{A_1'}$	A_{2u}	x
	$\Phi_3^{A_1'}$	B_{2u}	y
	$\Phi_4^{A_1'}$	B_{1g}	Forbidden
A_2''	$\Phi_1^{A_2''}$	B_{1u}	z
	$\Phi_2^{A_2''}$	B_{2g}	Forbidden
	$\Phi_3^{A_2''}$	A_{2g}	Forbidden
	$\Phi_4^{A_2''}$	A_{1u}	Forbidden
E'	$\Phi_1^{E''}$	$A_{2u} + B_{2u}$	x, y
	$\Phi_2^{E'}$	$A_{1g} + B_{1g}$	Forbidden
	$\Phi_3^{E'}$	$A_{1g} + B_{1g}$	Forbidden
	$\Phi_4^{E'}$	$A_{2u} + B_{2u}$	x, y .

The intramolecular vibrations of the ion CO_3^{--}, which belong to the symmetry group A_2'', are split in the crystal into four quasi-continuous bands of vibrations. From Table 12, it is apparent that in this connection there must appear in the infrared spectrum only one extreme frequency corresponding to the first band (with a wave function $\Phi_1^{A_2''}$) and that the vibrations will take place parallel to the z axis of the crystal. Each pair of degenerate molecular vibrations of the ion CO_3^{--}, which belong to the irreducible representation E', splits in the crystal (by virtue of the resonance interaction of vibrations) into four quasi-continuous bands of vibrations. Only the extreme vibrations from two of these bands will appear in the infrared spectrum.

In view of the fact that the degeneracy of these vibrations is removed while still in the crystal, the extreme vibrations themselves must be doubly degenerate.

Thus, according to the above, four absorption bands (possibly in the form of two narrow doublets), which correspond to a degenerate vibration in the molecular ion CO_3^{--}, must be observed in the absorption spectrum. Two of the bands (one for each component of the doublets) must be observed with the electric vector oriented along the x axis of the crystal and another two with the electric vector oriented along the y axis. The vibrations occurring in the absorption spectrum when the electric vector is directed along the z axis of the crystal must be single.

As previously indicated, the investigations of infrared spectra of carbonates were carried out at temperatures not lower than 0°C. In this case, the absorption bands are wide and the structural details are lost. Table 13 shows the results of the measurements for certain carbonates (Ref. 47, p. 276) possessing the structure of the aragonite crystal. In accord with theory, Table 13 shows that, for vibrations parallel to the z axis of the crystal, there are no split components for all these crystals. For the vibrations lying in the plane perpendicular to the z axis, instead of the four absorption bands expected according to theory we observe in aragonite three absorption bands in the 1500-cm^{-1} region and two in the 700-cm^{-1} region. In cerussite there are two bands in the 1400-cm^{-1} region and in witherite only one absorption band. However, even in this last case, the twofold splitting of the bands is clearly observed in the majority of overtones; therefore, Schaeffer and Matossi[47] conclude that "there cannot be any doubt that the frequencies really split in two."

TABLE 13. OBSERVED INFRARED FREQUENCIES IN NATURAL CARBONATES

Crystal	Frequencies, cm^{-1} (in parentheses, λ in μ)		
	Vibrations $\perp z$		Vibrations $\parallel z$
Aragonite	1550, 1490 (6.46), (6.70) 707 (14.17)	1500 (6.65) 712 (14.06)	866 (11.55)
Cerussite	1420 (7.04)	1370 (7.28)	833
Witherite	1460 (6.85)	1460 (6.85)	861 (11.61)

A hypothesis on the deformation of the carbonate ions in the lattice, which in our opinion is very artificial and has little basis, was proposed to explain this splitting in two of the frequencies. It was assumed that the atoms of oxygen form a nonequilateral, isosceles triangle.[49] Then a certain orientation (corresponding to the symmetry of the crystal) for these deformed radicals, relative to the axes of the crystal, was suggested.

According to the investigation conducted here, this splitting in two at low temperatures must result in the appearance of four absorption bands and is explained by the removal of the degeneracy in the field of the crystal and by the resonance interaction of the vibrations.

Furthermore, according to theory, in the 10,000- to 11,000-cm^{-1} region of the spectrum of the crystal, one must expect an absorption band corresponding to a vibration in the free radical that is inactive in the infrared spectrum.

c. Benzene Crystal. Crystalline benzene, with four molecules per unit cell, belongs to the V_h^{15} symmetry group. Figure 8 shows the projection of the arrangement of molecules into a plane perpendicular to the b axis. The plane of the molecular ring is approximately perpendicular to the b axis and forms an angle of 40° with the c axis. The crosshatched molecules lie in a plane situated at distances of $b/2$ from the plane in which the noncrosshatched molecules lie.

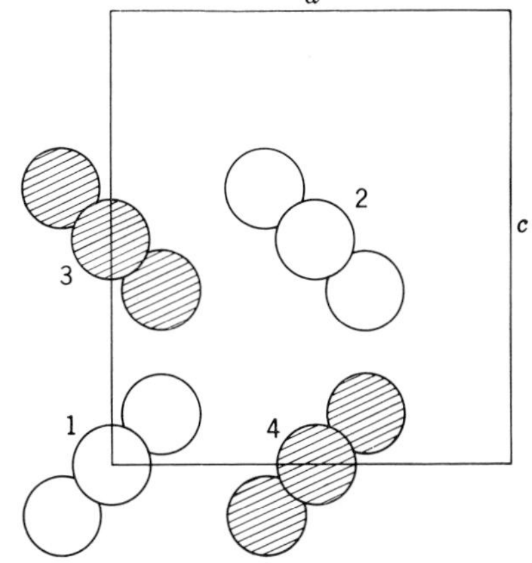

FIG. 8. Disposition of the projection of the four benzene molecules onto the plane perpendicular to the b axis of the crystal.

The wave function for the normal state of the crystal, as well as the wave function for the normal state of the molecule, belong to the totally symmetrical representation A_{1g}.

Knowing the symmetry of wave functions for the excited states of the molecule, we can, by means of group theory, determine the symmetry properties of the corresponding wave functions of the crystal. Consequently, we can determine the selection rules and the polarizations of electronic transitions in the crystal.

The characters of the irreducible representation for the space symmetry group V_h^{15} of the crystal coincide with the characters of group D_{2h} (Table 2). The characters of the irreducible representations for the point symmetry group D_{6h} of the benzene molecule appear in Table 14.

Let us take into consideration the fact that identity operation E and inversion i coincide in the molecule and in the crystal. To the symmetry operations of the crystal C_2^a, C_2^c, σ^a, and σ^c there correspond transpositions of molecules 1 and 2 and of 3 and 4; the symmetry operations for the molecules C_2, C_2'', iC_2, and iC_2'', respectively, are subsequently applied to the molecule. The application to the molecules of the symmetry operation C_2' corresponds to the symmetry operation for the crystal C_2^b. Now, by using the table of characters of the irreducible represen-

TABLE 14. CHARACTER TABLE FOR THE D_{6h} POINT GROUP

D_{6h}	E	C_2	$2C_3$	$2C_6$	$3C_2'$	$3C_2''$	iE	iC_2	$2iC_3$	$2iC_6$	$3iC_2'$	$3iC_2''$
A_{1g}	1	1	1	1	1	1	1	1	1	1	1	1
A_{1u}	1	1	1	1	1	1	−1	−1	−1	−1	−1	−1
A_{2g}	1	1	1	1	−1	−1	1	1	1	1	−1	−1
z, A_{2u}	1	1	1	1	−1	−1	−1	−1	−1	−1	1	1
B_{1g}	1	−1	1	−1	1	−1	1	−1	1	−1	1	−1
B_{1u}	1	−1	1	−1	1	−1	−1	1	−1	1	−1	1
B_{2g}	1	−1	1	−1	−1	1	1	−1	1	−1	−1	1
B_{2u}	1	−1	1	−1	−1	1	−1	1	−1	1	1	−1
E_{2g}	2	2	−1	−1	0	0	2	2	−1	−1	0	0
E_{2u}	2	2	−1	−1	0	0	−2	−2	1	1	0	0
E_{1g}	2	−2	−1	1	0	0	2	−2	−1	1	0	0
(x, y), E_{1u}	2	−2	−1	1	0	0	−2	2	1	−1	0	0

tations for the symmetry group of the benzene molecule, we can determine the irreducible representations for the corresponding wave functions of the crystal. The results, which pertain to the three possible types of wave functions for the excited states of a molecule, are shown in Table 15.

TABLE 15. CORRELATION TABLE FOR SYMMETRY SPECIES FOR ELECTRONIC STATES OF BENZENE IN THE MOLECULE (D_{6h}) AND THE CRYSTAL (V_h^{15})

Irreducible representation of excited state of molecule	Wave function of crystal	Irreducible representations of group V_h^{15}	Selection rules and polarization
B_{1u}	$\Phi_1^{B_{1u}}$ and $\Phi_4^{B_{1u}}$	B_{2u}	Vibration of electric vector parallel to b axis
	$\Phi_2^{B_{1u}}$ and $\Phi_3^{B_{1u}}$	A_{1u}	Forbidden
B_{2u}	$\Phi_1^{B_{2u}}$ and $\Phi_4^{B_{2u}}$	B_{1u}	Vibration of electric vector parallel to c axis
	$\Phi_2^{B_{2u}}$ and $\Phi_3^{B_{2u}}$	A_{2u}	Same, parallel to a axis
E_{1u}	$\Phi_1^{E_{1u}}$ and $\Phi_4^{E_{1u}}$	$B_{2u} + B_{1u}$	Same, parallel to b and c axes
	$\Phi_2^{E_{1u}}$ and $\Phi_3^{E_{1u}}$	$A_{2u} + A_{1u}$	Same, parallel to a axis

Thus, from Table 15, we find that:

1. The forbidden molecular transition to the level B_{1u} in the crystal becomes permitted and must occur when the electric vector of the light wave is directed along the b axis of the crystal.

2. To the forbidden molecular transition to the level B_{2u} in the crystal there corresponds a doublet; the electric vector of one of the components

of the latter is directed along the *c* axis, and that of the other along the *b* axis, of the crystal.

3. The permitted doubly degenerate molecular term E_{1u} in the crystal is split and must appear as a triplet with components *a*, *b*, and *c*.

According to studies by A. F. Prikhotko, V. L. Broude, and V. S. Medvedev[53] on the absorption spectrum of the benzene monocrystal in polarized light, there is a doublet of 37,811 and 37,786 cm^{-1} with sharply polarized components. This doublet is subsequently repeated in the spectrum with a period of 920 cm^{-1}, corresponding to the frequency of the totally symmetrical vibrations in the benzene molecule. A comparison of these data with theory enables us to draw the following conclusions:

1. Monocrystalline laminae of benzene, as used in the experiments, possess a surface which coincides with the plane *ac* of the crystal lattice.

2. To the electronic spectrum in the near ultraviolet there corresponds the molecular term B_{2u}.

CHAPTER IV

GENERAL EQUATIONS DETERMINING THE ENERGY STATES OF MOLECULAR CRYSTALS

15. Introduction. Statement of the Problem

In molecular crystals the molecules preserve their individuality. It is therefore convenient to study the energy states of such crystals by starting from the energy states of isolated molecules.

When investigating the optical behavior of a crystal in the visible and ultraviolet regions of the spectrum, the excited state of a molecule will imply both electronic and electronic-vibrational excitation. This excited state of the molecule will be described by the wave function

$$\varphi^f, \tag{4.1}$$

where the index f indicates the number of the excited state.

When investigating the optical behavior of a crystal in the infrared region of the spectrum, the index f will define the state of intramolecular vibration in the crystal. The wave function [(4.1)] must depend on the coordinates of the optical electrons and of the nuclei of the molecules, and is a solution of the wave equation

$$H\varphi^f = E^f\varphi^f, \tag{4.2}$$

where H is the operator of the internal energy of the molecule.

We shall assume that the molecular problem [(4.2)] is resolved, i.e., that the eigenfunctions φ^f and the eigenvalues for the energy E^f are known. We shall then investigate the energy states of the entire crystal when it is made up of identical molecules.

At present there are no sufficiently satisfactory methods for solving the molecular problem [(4.2)]. All existing methods for calculating the electronic states of complicated molecules (valence-bond method,[54] molecular-orbital method,[55,56,46] antisymmetrized-molecular-orbital method,[57,58] and others) have little foundation and yield very crude results. M. V. Volkenstein, M. A. Elyashevich, and B. I. Stepanov[59] and L. S. Mayants[60] achieved substantial results in the calculation of molecular vibrational states. The methods of investigating molecular vibrations applied by these workers are extremely simple and convenient. These authors succeeded in calculating the vibrational spectra of numerous molecules; however, it has not yet been possible to extend the same methods to aromatic molecules.

The difficulties that arise when calculating the intramolecular states will not be discussed here. We shall study the changes of energy states for a large number of molecules disposed at the points of a crystal lattice, in comparison with the energy states of infinitely separated (free) molecules. The energy states of free molecules are here assumed to be known (albeit from experimental data).

When studying light absorption, it is necessary to consider (1) which electromagnetic frequencies are absorbed by the crystal and how they depend on the direction of the propagation and of the polarization of impinging waves and (2) what happens subsequently to the absorbed energy—does it again appear in the form of electromagnetic radiation (luminescence), or is it absorbed by the crystal and transformed into heat, i.e., distributed over all degrees of freedom of the crystal?

The processes for the transformation of the electronic excitation energy of molecular crystals into heat may take place in two ways: (1) intramolecularly and (2) intermolecularly. The intramolecular deactivation of the molecules in a crystal, i.e., the transformation of electronic excitation energy into vibrational energy of a molecule (if such transformation takes place), will be assumed known. We shall be interested only in the intermolecular deactivation of molecules, i.e., in the transformation of excitation energy of molecules into lattice vibration energy.

16. Quasi-stationary Excited States of a Crystal

Let us consider a molecular crystal, the unit cell of which is determined by the three noncoplanar vectors $\mathbf{a}_1$, $\mathbf{a}_2$, and $\mathbf{a}_3$. Let us assume that in a unit cell there are σ molecules; the positions of their centers of gravity relative to the unit cell corner nearest the coordinate origin are determined by the vectors $\mathbf{r}_\alpha$ ($\alpha = 1, 2, \ldots, \sigma$). The index α characterizes the number of the molecule in the cell and the spatial orientation relative to the vectors $\mathbf{a}_1$, $\mathbf{a}_2$, and $\mathbf{a}_3$.

The position of a desired molecule in the crystal relative to the coordinate origin will then be determined by the radius vector

$$\mathbf{r}_{n\alpha} = \sum_{i=1}^{3} \mathbf{a}_i n_i + \mathbf{r}_\alpha, \tag{4.3}$$

where $n = n_1, n_2, n_3$; the n_i are whole numbers.

Let the crystal have the form of an oblique-angled parallelepiped with axes $N_1\mathbf{a}_1$, $N_2\mathbf{a}_2$, and $N_3\mathbf{a}_3$, so that the total number of unit cells in the crystal is equal to $N = N_1 N_2 N_3$ (here and henceforth the number N will be assumed to be very large), and the over-all number of molecules is equal to σN.

We shall consider all molecules of the crystal to be identical and each one to contain ρ atomic nuclei, as well as S optical electrons determining the optical behavior of the molecule.

The state of the crystal will be characterized by the wave function

$$\Psi(r, R, t), \tag{4.4}$$

which depends on the internal r coordinates of the molecules (coordinates of all optical electrons and relative coordinates of the atomic nuclei in the molecules), on the coordinates and spatial orientations R of all molecules in the crystal, and on the time t. This function must satisfy the time-dependent equation of quantum mechanics:

$$ih \frac{\partial \Psi(r, R, t)}{\partial t} = (T_R + H_0)\Psi(r, R, t) \tag{4.5}$$

where T_R is the kinetic energy operator for the rotational and displacement motion of all molecules.

$$T_R = -\frac{h^2}{2} \sum_{i=1}^{6\sigma N} \frac{\Delta_{R_i}}{M_i}, \tag{4.6}$$

and $H_0 = H_0[r, \partial/(\partial r), R]$ is the energy operator for the crystal of fixed molecules. This operator may be written in the following form:

$$H_0 = \sum_{n\alpha} H_{n\alpha}\left(r, \frac{\partial}{\partial r}\right) + \frac{1}{2} \sum_{n\alpha, m\beta} V_{n\alpha, m\beta}(r, R), \tag{4.6a}$$

where $H_{n\alpha}[r, \partial/(\partial r)]$ is the energy operator for the internal state of the molecule α, which is located in the nth unit cell of the crystal, and $V_{n\alpha, m\beta}$ is the interaction operator of the two molecules.

In solving equation (4.5) we shall proceed from the zeroth approximation, which was analyzed in Chapter III and in which the molecules were assumed to be rigidly fixed ($M \to \infty$) at the lattice points. This permits us to indicate the limits of applicability for the zeroth approximation and to take into consideration in the first approximation the motion (vibrations and rotations) of the molecules in the lattice.

Thus we shall assume that the solution of the equation for fixed molecules in the crystal is known:

$$H_0 \Phi_\nu^f(r, R) = E_\nu^f(R) \Phi_\nu^f(r, R), \tag{4.7}$$

where $\Phi_\nu^f(r, R)$ is the wave function for the electrons of the crystal when the molecules are fixed. This wave function forms such a crystal state when ν_1 molecules are in the f_1th excited state, when ν_2 molecules are in the f_2th excited state, etc., and the other molecules are in a normal state.

In particular, for crystal states which do not contain excited molecules ($\nu = 0, f = 0$), as we have seen in Chapter III, the wave functions are

$$\Phi_0^\circ = \Phi_0^\circ(r, R) \tag{4.8}$$

and the energy of the crystal

$$E_0(R) = \int \Phi_0^{\circ *} H_0 \Phi_0^\circ \, d\tau = \sum_{n\alpha} E_{n\alpha}^\circ + V(R) \tag{4.8a}$$

is determined by formulas (3.2) and (3.4).

The wave function for the state of a crystal containing one molecule in the fth excited state depends on the number μ of the zone of the excited states of the crystal, as well as on the value of the wave number of excitons in the zone [(3.22)].

$$\Phi_\mu^f(k, r, R) = (\sigma N)^{-\frac{1}{2}} \sum_{n\alpha} B_\alpha^\mu \chi_{n\alpha}^f e^{i\mathbf{kn}}, \tag{4.9}$$

and the energy is

$$\begin{aligned} E_\mu^f(k, R) &= \int \Phi_\mu^{f*}(k, r, R) H_0 \Phi_\mu^f(k, r, R) \, d\tau \\ &= \sum_{n\alpha} E_{n\alpha}^\circ + \Delta E_{m\beta}^f + V(R) + D_{m\beta}^f(R) + \sum_\alpha \frac{B_\alpha^\mu}{B_\beta^\mu} \sum_n M_{n\alpha,m\beta}^f(R) e^{i\mathbf{k}(\mathbf{n}-\mathbf{m})}. \end{aligned} \tag{4.9a}$$

If there were (simultaneously) two excited molecules in the crystal, the wave function of this state would have the form

$$\Phi_{\mu\mu'}^{ff'}(k, k', r, R).$$

We shall seek the solution of (4.5) in the following form:

$$\begin{aligned} \Psi(r, R, t) &= \Phi_0^\circ \sum_x b_{0x}^\circ(t) A_{0x}^\circ \exp(-i\omega_{0x} t) \\ &+ \sum_{x,f,k,\mu} b_{1x}^{f\mu}(k, t) A_{1x}^{f\mu}(k, R) \Phi_\mu^f(k, r, R) \exp(-i\omega_{1n}^{fk\mu} t) + \cdots . \end{aligned} \tag{4.10}$$

In (4.10) we did not extract the terms corresponding to the excited states of a crystal with two, three, etc., excited molecules. These terms play a small role if the energy lifting the crystal to an excited state is small.

The squares of the moduli of the coefficients $b_{0x}^\circ(t)$ will characterize the probability that at the moment of time t there are no excited molecules in the crystal. The state of the crystal is determined by the wave function

$$A_{0x}(R)\Phi_0^\circ(r, R)$$

and the total energy of the crystal is equal to

$$U_{0x} = h\omega_{0x}.$$

The function $A_{0x}(R)$ characterizes the vibrational state of the molecules in the lattice and satisfies the equation

$$[T_R + E_0^\circ(R)]A_{0x}(R) = U_{0x}A_{0x}(R). \tag{4.11}$$

The squares of the moduli of the coefficients $b_x^{f\mu}(k, t)$ determine the probability that at the moment of time t there is in the crystal an exciton (corresponding to the excitation of one molecule) in the μth zone with a wave number $\mathbf{k}$, and the lattice vibrations are characterized by the wave function $A_{1x}^{f\mu}(k, R)$, which satisfies the equation

$$[T_R + E_\mu^f(k, R)]A_x^{f\mu}(k, R) = U_x^{fk\mu}A_x^{f\mu}(k, R), \tag{4.12}$$

where

$$U_x^{fk\mu} = h\omega_{1x}^{fk\mu}.$$

If we substitute (4.10) in (4.5), multiply by $A_{0x'}\Phi_0^{\circ *} \exp(i\omega_{0x'}t)$ and by $A_{x'}^{f'k'\mu'}\Phi_{\mu'}^{f'*}(k', r, R) \exp(i\omega_{1x'}^{f'k'\mu'}t)$, and then integrate over r and R, taking into consideration (4.11) and (4.12), we obtain the system of equations

$$ih\frac{db_{0x}(t)}{dt} = \sum_{xfk\mu} b_x^{f\mu}(kt)[0x'|{}_{1x}^{fk\mu}] \exp[-i(\omega_{1x}^{fk\mu} - \omega_{0x'})t], \tag{4.13}$$

where

$$[0x'|{}_{1x}^{fk\mu}] = \int A_{0x'}(R)\gamma_{01}^{fk\mu}A_{1x}^{f\mu}(k, R)\,dR + \sum_i \int A_{0x'}(R)\Gamma_{01}^{fk\mu}(i)\frac{\partial A_{1x}^{f\mu}(k, R)}{\partial R_i}\,dR, \tag{4.14}$$

$$\gamma_{01}^{fk\mu}(R) = \int \Phi_0^{\circ *}(r, R)T_R\Phi_\mu^f(k, r, R)\,d\tau, \tag{4.14a}$$

$$\Gamma_{01}^{fk\mu}(i) = -\frac{h^2}{M_i}\int \Phi_0^{\circ *}(r, R)\frac{\partial \Phi_\mu^f(k, r, R)}{\partial R_i}\,d\tau, \tag{4.14b}$$

and

$$ih\frac{db_{1x'}^{f'\mu'}(k', t)}{dt} = \sum_x b_{0x}(t)[0x|{}_{1x'}^{f'k'\mu'}]^* \exp[-i(\omega_{0x} - \omega_{1x'}^{f'k'\mu'})t] + \sum_{xfk\mu} b_{1x}^{f\mu}(k, t)[{}_{1x'}^{f'k'\mu'}|{}_{1x}^{fk\mu}] \exp[-i(\omega_{1x}^{fk\mu} - \omega_{1x'}^{f'k'\mu'})t], \tag{4.15}$$

where

$$\left[{}^{f'k'\mu'}_{1x'}\middle|{}^{fk\mu}_{1x}\right] = \int A^{f'\mu'}_{1x'}(k')\gamma^{f'k'\mu',fk\mu}_{1,1}A^{f\mu}_{1x}(k)\,dR + \sum_i \int A^{f'\mu'}_{1x'}(k')\Gamma^{f'k'\mu',fk\mu}_{1,1}(i)\,\frac{\partial A^{f\mu}_{1x}(k)}{\partial R_i}\,dR, \quad (4.16)$$

$$\gamma^{f'k'\mu',fk\mu}_{1,1} = \int \Phi^{f'}_{\mu'}(k', r, R)T_R\Phi^{f}_{\mu}(k, r, R)\,d\tau, \quad (4.16a)$$

$$\Gamma^{f'k'\mu',fk\mu}_{1,1}(i) = -\frac{h^2}{M_i}\int \Phi^{f'}_{\mu'}(k', r, R)\,\frac{\partial\Phi^{f}_{\mu}(k, r, R)}{\partial R_i}\,d\tau. \quad (4.16b)$$

From equations (4.13) and (4.15), it follows that if, at the moment of time $t = 0$, the system was in one of the excited states $A^{fk\mu}_{1x}(k)\Phi^{f}_{\mu}(k, r, R)$ with the energy $U^{fk\mu}_{1x}$, then it can spontaneously go over into the state $A_{0x'}\Phi^{\circ}_{0}$, corresponding to the absence of excited molecules in the crystal, with a probability calculated per second of

$$\left(0x'\middle|P\middle|{}^{fk\mu}_{1x}\right) = \frac{2\pi}{h}\left|\left[0x'\middle|{}^{fk\mu}_{1x}\right]\right|^2\delta(U^{fk\mu}_{1x} - U_{0x'}), \quad (4.17)$$

or into the state $A^{f'\mu'}_{1x'}(k')\Phi^{f'}_{\mu'}(k')$ with a probability (per second) of

$$\left({}^{f'k'\mu'}_{1x'}\middle|P\middle|{}^{fk\mu}_{1x}\right) = \frac{2\pi}{h}\left|\left[{}^{f'k'\mu'}_{1x'}\middle|{}^{fk\mu}_{1x}\right]\right|^2\delta(U^{fk\mu}_{1x} - U^{f'k'\mu'}_{1x'}). \quad (4.18)$$

Naturally, the probabilities of the converse transitions will be determined by the same formulas. Thus, in the crystal, molecular excitation energy may be spontaneously transformed into lattice vibration energy without a change in the total energy of the system ($U^{fk\mu}_{1x} = U^{f'k'\mu'}_{1x'}$) or into excitation energy with other values of μ and of the wave number $\mathbf{k}$ of the exciton, also with the conservation of the total energy of the system

$$(U^{fk\mu}_{1x} = U^{f'k'\mu'}_{1x'}).$$

The results obtained above are correct only when the probabilities of the transitions [(4.17) and (4.18)] are sufficiently small. Only under these conditions is it possible to solve equation (4.5) by proceeding from the zeroth approximation for fixed molecules.

If, during lattice vibrations (and upon excitation of the molecules), the translational symmetry of the crystal is not disturbed, the matrix element [(4.16)] and, consequently, also the probability [(4.18)] will be equal to zero when $k \neq k'$. When, however, $k \approx k'$, the transitions from one zone μ of excited states to another zone μ', or from one excited molecular state f to another state f', will be but little probable if, during the vibrations of molecules, the mean displacement, which is

$$\Delta R = \bar{R}(t + \tau) - \bar{R}(t)$$

during the time

$$\tau = \frac{h}{E_{\mu}^{fk} - E_{\mu'}^{f'k'}},$$

satisfies the condition

$$\left| \frac{\partial E_{\mu}^{fk}}{\partial R} \Delta R \right| \ll |E_{\mu}^{fk} - E_{\mu'}^{f'k'}|. \tag{4.19}$$

Similarly, a condition for the small probability of (4.17) is the inequality

$$\left| \frac{\partial E_{\mu}^{fk}}{\partial R} \Delta R \right| \ll |E_{\mu}^{fk} - E_{0}^{\circ}|, \tag{4.20}$$

where $\Delta R = \bar{R}(t + \tau) - \bar{R}(t), \qquad \tau = \dfrac{h}{E_{\mu}^{fk} - E_{0}^{\circ}}.$

This condition [(4.20)] is especially important and significant, since it determines the smallness of the probability for the transition of molecular excitation energy to lattice vibrational energy (and for converse transitions).

The probability for transitions of molecular excitation energy to lattice vibrational energy (to heat) may also be evaluated in the following manner.

In molecular crystals the quantum of lattice vibrational energy $h\omega_r$ is considerably smaller than the molecular excitation energy $h\omega_M$. If, now, the excitation energy of the molecule includes an electronic excitation,

$$\frac{\omega_r}{\omega_M} \sim 10^{-3} - 10^{-4};$$

if there is only an excitation of intramolecular vibrations,

$$\frac{\omega_r}{\omega_M} \sim 10^{-1} - 10^{-2}.$$

When $T = 0$, the excitation of the molecule at the expense of lattice vibrational energy is generally impossible. At higher temperatures, such transitions are also only slightly probable, since they assume a simultaneous transfer to one molecule of the energy of thousands of phonons (or of 100 to 10 phonons in the case of a solely vibrational excitation of the molecule). However, if the temperature is small, then the displacements of molecules from the equilibrium positions are also small.

The matrix elements [(4.14a) and (4.14b)] entering into (4.14) depend on the change of wave functions for the stationary molecular states, when the coordinates of the molecules change. These expressions will be slowly changing functions of the displacements of molecules from equilibrium positions.

The matrix elements given by (4.14) depend on the matrix elements given by (4.14*a*) and (4.14*b*) and on the wave functions $A(R)$. If, upon excitation of the molecules, the molecular equilibrium positions in the crystal and the potential energy as a function of molecular displacement from the equilibrium position do not change, the wave functions $A(R)$ will be orthogonal for the various vibrational states of the crystal. By resolving (4.14*a*) and (4.14*b*) into a power series of displacements, and by substituting the series obtained in the integrals which determine (4.14), we shall see that, for the molecule to be able to absorb the energy, for instance, of 10^3 phonons, it is necessary either to take the thousandth term of the decomposition by powers of displacements or to consider the thousandth order of disturbance if we limit ourselves merely to the terms proportional to the displacements.

If the displacements are small relative to the distances between molecules in the equilibrium position, these probabilities will be small.† In order for large displacements to take place, a fluctuating accumulation of lattice vibrational energy in a small region of the crystal is necessary. At low temperatures, such fluctuations are extremely improbable.

Thus, at low temperatures, the transformation of lattice vibrational energy to molecular excitation energy is practically eliminated. In other words, the molecular motion in a lattice that does not contain excited molecules may be considered adiabatic; i.e., one can set expression (4.17) equal to zero and consider equation (4.11) as the equation of the stationary states of the system.

The situation changes essentially for transitions of the reverse type—transformations of molecular excitation energy to lattice vibrational energy. The state preceding the transition is thermodynamically one of nonequilibrium. We are here dealing with a large energy fluctuation in the region of the excited molecule.

However, this alone is insufficient to transfer molecular excitation energy to lattice vibrational energy. Because of resonance interaction, the excitation energy will migrate from one molecule to another. Therefore, the displacement of molecules from equilibrium positions (corresponding to the nonexcited crystal) to new equilibrium positions may

† L. D. Landau[61] took the general case of a system consisting of a quantum part and of a part whose state may be quasi-classically described as being in a potential field determined by the energy of the quantum part of the system. Landau showed that in this general case the integral, like the integral given by (4.14), is exponentially small if, when the coordinates for the system's quasi-classical part change, one does not obtain intersection points for the polydimensional potential curves, which determine the motion for this part of the system in the corresponding states.

attain large magnitudes only if the excitation is capable of being delayed on one molecule for a time sufficient for the molecular displacement (this time is of the order of a half period of molecular vibrations).

In this last case, even at low temperatures, the displacements may attain significant magnitudes.

As a result, the probability of multiquantum transitions increases, even when we limit ourselves to the harmonic lattice vibrational model, which, for large molecular displacements, is incorrect.

An exact quantitative evaluation of the probability for such transitions is extremely difficult, since one cannot use perturbation theory and since one must allow for the anharmonicity of lattice vibrations.

Thus the conditions for the applicability of the adiabatic approximation to the problem of energy states in molecular crystals differ essentially from the conditions for the applicability of this approximation to other problems (with a small number of degrees of freedom).

The major work of Born and Oppenheimer[62] gives the quantum-mechanical basis for the applicability of electronic potential-energy curves to determining nuclear movement in molecules. In this work, it was shown that the adiabatic approximation is accurate when the square root for the ratio of the mass of the electron to the average mass of the atoms making up the molecule is small. Approximately the same criterion is indicated by Pauli (Ref. 63, p. 143): "The nuclear vibrational frequencies are small in comparison to electronic frequencies."

In the case of molecular crystals (and certain other systems with a large number of degrees of freedom), these conditions governing the accuracy of the adiabatic approximation—i.e., the possibility of determining (1) intramolecular (electronic excitation together with intramolecular vibrations) states for fixed molecular positions and (2) the motion of molecules in a potential field, which constitutes intramolecular energy as depending on the positions of molecules in the lattice—are only necessary but by no means sufficient.

In molecular crystals, the ratio of lattice vibrational frequencies to the frequencies corresponding to the change in intramolecular state is very small. In spite of this, the adiabatic approximation may be utilized only when the temperature† of the crystal is low enough so that the average thermal energy is less than the intramolecular excitation energy.

When analyzing the states of a crystal with excited molecules, even at a temperature of absolute zero, the adiabatic approximation cannot be applied.

† When the temperature rises, there is an exponential increase in the probability of obtaining displacements, corresponding to the intersection points of polydimensional potential curves, determining the motion of molecules in a crystal for two corresponding states.

Such excited crystal states are not rigorously stationary ones, since a spontaneous redistribution of the crystal's energy takes place; the energy of the intramolecular excitation either fully or partially transforms into lattice vibrational energy.

Only in the case in which the time for the transfer of excitation to the neighboring molecule is small by comparison with the time for molecular displacement to new equilibrium positions will the connection between the intramolecular excitation and the lattice vibrations be small, and the probabilities given by expressions (4.17) and (4.18) will be near zero. The corresponding excited states will be almost stationary (quasi-stationary).

However, it must be kept in mind that this stationary condition is disturbed above all for energy transfers, which are linked with a change in the wave number of the exciton (within the zone of excited states).

This nonstationary condition leads to two manifestations: (1) the broadening of levels, which is connected with the shortening of their lifetime, and (2) the change of velocity for the transfer of excitation through the crystal. If the velocity of the movement of excitation decreases, there is a significant increase in the probability for a non-radiative transfer of excitation energy to lattice vibrational energy; i.e., the nonstationary condition increases in proportion to the transformation of excitation energy to heat.

17. Free and "Localized" Excitons

As was indicated in the preceding section, two limiting cases must be distinguished when analyzing the energy states of molecular crystals.

1. The excitation transfers from one molecule to another so quickly that, under a change in the forces of interaction between neighboring molecules upon excitation of one molecule in a crystal, displacement of molecules to new equilibrium positions does not have time to occur.

2. The excitation transfers from one molecule to another so slowly that the molecules do have time to occupy new equilibrium positions. A local deformation, which travels through the crystal together with the excitation, arises in the crystal.

In case 1, at low temperatures, the "adiabatic" approximation may be used with certain reservations; in case 2, this, generally speaking, cannot be done.

The excitation transfer time τ_t, as we shall see later, is determined by the matrix element $M^f_{n\alpha,m\beta}$ [(3.10)], by the band of excited states, by the wave vector of excitation waves, and by the geometry of the unit cell. Thus it depends on the character of the molecular excitation, on the distance between molecules, and on their mutual orientations.

The displacement time τ_d of molecules from the old equilibrium positions depends on the change in the forces of interaction of a molecule with neighboring ones upon excitation of the molecule, this magnitude being characterized by a matrix element $D^f_{m\beta}$ [(3.13)]; on the mass of the molecule; and on the latter's moment of inertia. For large molecules, the time τ_d may be less than τ_t, even if $D^f_{m\beta} \sim M^f_{n\alpha,m\beta}$.

In molecular crystals, apparently, the fulfillment of the inequality

$$\tau_d > \tau_t \tag{4.21}$$

corresponding to case 1 above, as well as the fulfillment of the inequality

$$\tau_d < \tau_t \tag{4.22}$$

corresponding to case 2, are both possible.

If the inequality given by (4.21) is fulfilled, the excitation will be transferred to the neighboring molecule of the crystal with local lattice deformation. This case will correspond to a nonequilibrium state of the lattice. The motion of excitons which is not accompanied by a local lattice deformation will be called free-exciton motion.

If the inequality given by (4.22) is fulfilled, the lattice passes by means of a local deformation into a new equilibrium state. The local deformation will accompany the movement of the exciton. This crystal state will be called a "localized" exciton. One must, of course, keep in mind that this exciton is not localized in the full sense of the word. However, the excitation waves corresponding to the "localized" exciton possess a velocity which is small compared with the velocity of free excitons.

In molecular crystals and under certain conditions, the changeover of free excitons to "localized" ones (and vice versa) is possible.

In the following sections we shall consider the case in which free excitons appear in a crystal (when $T \approx 0$). Here, as we have seen, the corresponding states may be approximately considered quasi-stationary.

18. Equations Determining the Motion of Molecules in a Crystal

If, in expression (4.11), we substitute the value E°_0, where

$$E^\circ_0 = \int \Phi^{\circ *}_0 H_0 \Phi^\circ_0 \, d\tau = \sum_{n\alpha} E^\circ_{n\alpha} + V(R),$$

we obtain an equation determining the wave functions for molecular motions in a crystal when all molecules are not excited.

$$[T_R + V(R)]A_{0x} = \varepsilon^\circ_x A_{0x} \tag{4.23}$$

where

$$\varepsilon^\circ_x = U_{0x} - \sum_{n\alpha} E^\circ_{n\alpha} \tag{4.23a}$$

is the energy of rotational and translational molecular vibrations in a crystal which does not possess any excited molecules.

$$V(R) = \tfrac{1}{2} \sum_{n\alpha, m\beta}' \Big[\int |\varphi^{\circ}_{n\alpha}(\mathrm{I})|^2 V_{n\alpha,m\beta} |\varphi^{\circ}(\mathrm{II})|^2 \, d\tau - \sum_{\mu} \int \varphi^{\circ *}_{n\alpha}(\mathrm{I}) \varphi^{\circ}_{n\alpha}(\mathrm{II}) V_{n\alpha,m\beta} \varphi^{\circ *}_{m\beta}(\mathrm{II}) \varphi^{\circ}_{m\beta}(\mathrm{I}) \, d\tau \Big]; \quad (4.24)$$

here $\varphi_{n\alpha}(\mathrm{I})$ and $\varphi_{m\beta}(\mathrm{II})$ are the wave functions of the molecules $n\alpha$ and $m\beta$ for a certain disposition of the electrons in the molecules, $\varphi_{n\alpha}(\mathrm{II})$ and $\varphi_{m\beta}(\mathrm{I})$ are the same functions upon permutation between the molecules $n\alpha$ and $m\beta$ of any pair of electrons, and the sum over μ extends over all possible permutations of electron pairs between molecules $n\alpha$ and $m\beta$.

Equation (4.23) represents an equation of translational and rotational molecular vibrations in the crystal lattice, with potential energy $V(R)$. The coordinates R (displacements and rotations of molecules) are measured from the equilibrium values corresponding to the minimum potential energy $V(R)$ in a nonexcited crystal. Decomposing the potential energy $V(R)$ into powers of displacements from the equilibrium positions and limiting ourselves to the terms which are quadratic relative to these deviations, we can, by introducing normal coordinates, go over to a system of independent equations. Each one of the latter will represent an equation of a harmonic oscillator. Consequently, the solution of equation (4.23), corresponding to the energy

$$\mathcal{E}^{\circ}_{x} = \sum_{qj} h\omega_{qj}(N_{qj} + \tfrac{1}{2}), \quad (4.25)$$

may be written in the form

$$A_{0x} = \prod_{qj} \Psi^{\circ}_{N_{qi}} \quad (4.26)$$

where $\Psi^{\circ}_{N_{qi}}$ is the wave function of the harmonic oscillator. The vibrational state x of a crystal in this case will be determined by the assignment of numbers N_{qj} characterizing the number of phonons which possess a wave number q and a polarization $j (j = 1, 2, \ldots, 6\sigma)$. In Chapter III, we determined the wave function [(3.7)] for the excited state of a crystal in which one molecule is in the fth excited state and all others are in a normal state for a certain disposition (characterized by the coordinates R) of the molecules in the crystal:

$$\Phi^{f} = (\sigma N)^{-\frac{1}{2}} \sum_{n\alpha} a_{n\alpha} \chi^{f}_{n\alpha}, \quad (4.27)$$

and the energy for the corresponding state of the crystal is

$$E^f(R) = \sum_{n\alpha} E^\circ_{n\alpha} + \Delta E^f_{m\beta} + V(R) + D^f_{m\beta}(R) + \frac{\sum'_{n\alpha} a_{n\alpha} M^f_{n\alpha,m\beta}(R)}{a_{m\beta}}. \tag{4.28}$$

After substituting (4.28) in equation (4.12), we find the equation which determines the motion of molecules in a crystal possessing one molecule excited to the fth state:

$$\left[T_R + V(R) + D^f_{m\beta}(R) + \frac{\sum'_{n\alpha} M^f_{n\alpha,m\beta}(R) a_{n\alpha}}{a_{m\beta}}\right] A^f_x = \mathcal{E}^f_x A^f_x \tag{4.29}$$

where

$$\mathcal{E}^f_x = U^f_x - \sum_{n\alpha} E^\circ_{n\alpha} - \Delta E^f_{m\beta} \tag{4.30}$$

is the energy of molecular vibration in a crystal possessing one excited molecule, $\Delta E^f_{m\beta} = E^f_{m\beta} - E^\circ_{m\beta}$ is the energy for the excitation of one molecule, $D^f_{m\alpha}(R)$ has the same meaning as (3.13), and the matrix element $M^f_{n\alpha,m\beta}$ coincides with (3.10).

The matrix elements $D^f_{m\beta}(R)$ and $M^f_{n\alpha,m\beta}$ in equation (4.29) of the excited crystal play the role of supplementary energy to the potential energy $V(R)$. As a result of the appearance of these terms, the equations for molecular motion in an excited crystal differ from the equations for motion in a normal crystal. The frequencies of normal vibrations change, and the equilibrium positions are displaced in relation to the frequencies and to the equilibrium positions in a nonexcited crystal.

CHAPTER V

FREE EXCITONS IN A MOLECULAR LATTICE

19. Zeroth Approximation

Let us assume that the inequality (4.21) for a given excited state of a crystal is fulfilled and that the crystal is at absolute zero.

The motion of molecules in the excited state of a crystal will be determined by equation (4.29). In a nonexcited crystal, the molecules execute zero-point vibrations near the equilibrium positions ($R = 0$), determined from the minimum of the potential energy $V(R)$.

The matrix elements $D^f_{m\beta}$ and $M^f_{n\alpha,m\beta}$, which enter into equation (4.29) and are functions of the molecular positions in the crystal, may be decomposed into power series of the displacements R relative to the equilibrium positions of the molecules (in a nonexcited crystal):

$$\begin{aligned} D^f_{m\beta}(R) &= D^f_{m\beta}(0) + D^f_{m\beta}(1) + \cdots, \\ M^f_{n\alpha,m\beta}(R) &= M^f_{n\alpha,m\beta}(0) + M^f_{n\alpha,m\beta}(1) + \cdots, \end{aligned} \tag{5.1}$$

where

$$\begin{aligned} D^f_{m\beta}(1) &= -\sum_{xn'\alpha'} R^{x\alpha'}_{n'} \left(\frac{\partial D^f_{m\beta}}{\partial R^{x\alpha'}_{n'}}\right)_0, \\ M^f_{n\alpha,m\beta}(1) &= -\sum_{xn'\alpha'} R^{x\alpha'}_{n'} \left(\frac{\partial M^f_{n\alpha,m\beta}}{\partial R^{x\alpha'}_{n'}}\right)_0, \end{aligned} \tag{5.2}$$

and $D^f_{m\beta}(0)$ and $M^f_{n\alpha,m\beta}(0)$ are the values of the matrix elements $D^f_{m\beta}$ and $M^f_{n\alpha,m\beta}$ for the equilibrium configurations corresponding to the nonexcited crystal; x runs through six values corresponding to the six degrees of freedom of the molecule.

At low temperatures, which are of principal interest here, the displacements of molecules from equilibrium positions are small in comparison with the distances between molecules. Actually, at a temperature of absolute zero, the average quadratic deviation from the equilibrium position will be equal to

$$x^2_{0i} = \frac{h}{2M_i\omega_i}$$

for the ith vibrations; ω_i is the circular frequency of the corresponding vibrations. Thus, for the magnitude of the molecular displacement from the equilibrium positions in a naphthalene crystal ($M = 128$, $\omega \sim 6 \cdot 10^{12}$), we obtain

$$x_0 \sim 6 \cdot 10^{-12} \text{ cm}.$$

Therefore, in the zeroth approximation, only the first terms may be left in (5.1); thus equation (4.29) assumes the form

$$\left[T_R + V(R) + D^f_{m\beta}(0) + \frac{\sum'_{n\alpha} M^f_{n\alpha,m\beta}(0) a_{n\alpha}}{a_{m\beta}} \right] A^{f\circ}_x = \mathcal{E}^f_x A^{f\circ}_x. \quad (5.3)$$

Then, in (5.3), the expression

$$\frac{\sum'_{n\alpha} M^f_{n\alpha,m\beta}(0) a_{n\alpha}}{a_{m\beta}}$$

will have the dimensions of energy and will not depend on R. If we equate this expression to ϵ, we obtain the equation for determining this energy:

$$-\epsilon^f a_{m\beta} + \sum'_{n\alpha} M^f_{n\alpha,m\beta}(0) a_{n\alpha} = 0. \quad (5.4)$$

Equation (5.3) may now be written

$$[T_R + V(R)] A^{f\circ}_x = (\mathcal{E}^f_\nu - D^f_{m\beta}(0) - \epsilon) A^{f\circ}_x. \quad (5.5)$$

Comparing this equation with equation (4.23) for the translational-rotational vibrations of a crystal, we are satisfied that

$$A^{f\circ}_x = A^\circ_{0x}, \quad (5.6)$$

$$\mathcal{E}^\circ_x = \mathcal{E}^f_x - D^f_{m\beta}(0) - \epsilon. \quad (5.7)$$

Thus in the zeroth approximation, as was to be expected, the excitation of the crystal is not accompanied by a change in the vibrational state of the crystal.

At the same time, the excitation energy of the crystal,

$$\Delta E^f = U^f_x - U_{0x},$$

may be calculated with the aid of expressions (4.23a), (4.30), and (5.7), and is equal to

$$\Delta E^f = \Delta E^f_{m\beta} + D^f_{m\beta}(0) + \epsilon^f, \quad (5.8)$$

where $\Delta E^f_{m\beta}$ is the excitation energy of a separate molecule; ϵ^f is determined by a system of homogeneous equations (5.4) coinciding with the system of equations (3.9), which were studied in Chapter III. Consequently, in the zeroth approximation the excitation energy of the crystal already differs from the excitation energy of one molecule by two terms $D^f_{m\beta}(0)$ and $\epsilon^f_\mu(k)$.

Thus the crystal excitation energy obtained here in the zeroth approximation coincides with the excitation energy of the crystal in the case of rigidly fixed molecules in the lattice points. Consequently, the results of Chapter III are correct if, upon excitation, free excitons appear [the inequality given by (4.21) is fulfilled] and if we can limit ourselves to the zeroth terms in the decompositions [(5.1)]. In Chapter III, we analyzed, with the aid of group theory, the properties of the solutions obtained. Here we shall again analyze some of the previous results, without, however, resorting to group theory. The results we shall obtain here are in some respects clearer, and may in principle yield not only qualitative, but also quantitative, data on the spectrum.

Thus the excitation energy of a crystal,

$$\Delta E^f_\mu(\mathbf{k}) = \Delta E^f_{m\beta} + D^f_{m\beta}(0) + \epsilon^f_\mu(\mathbf{k}), \tag{5.9}$$

will depend on the wave number $\mathbf{k}$ of the excitation waves (excitons). Furthermore, to one excitation of a molecule in a crystal, there will correspond σ quasi-continuous bands of excited states, which, generally speaking, may overlap. To each one of these bands of excited states in a crystal there will correspond its own wave function, which depends on the wave number $\mathbf{k}$.

$$\Psi^{f\mu}_x(k, r, R) = A^{f\circ}_x \Phi^f_1 = \frac{1}{\sqrt{\sigma N}} A^\circ_{0x}(R) \sum_{n\alpha} e^{i\mathbf{kn}} B^\mu_\alpha \chi^f_{n\alpha}, \tag{5.10}$$

where B^μ_α are the solutions of the system of equations (3.15) for the corresponding value $\epsilon_\mu(\mathbf{k})$.

The normal state of a crystal, from which we measure off the energy terms, is described by the wave function

$$\Psi^\circ_x(r, R) = A^\circ_{0x}\Phi^\circ, \tag{5.11}$$

where Φ° is determined by (3.2).

20. Energy Terms of Several Molecular Crystals

Let us consider the solution of equations (3.15) and (3.17) for the particular case of crystals of the monoclinic-prismatic system in the spatial symmetry group C^5_{2h} with two molecules in the unit cell ($\sigma = 2$). In crystals of this type, the molecules are at the centers of symmetry of the crystal; therefore, the matrix $L_{\alpha\beta}(\mathbf{k})$ will be real and symmetrical.

Equation (3.17) will assume the form

$$\begin{vmatrix} L_{11}(\mathbf{k}) - \epsilon & L_{12}(\mathbf{k}) \\ L_{21}(\mathbf{k}) & L_{22}(\mathbf{k}) - \epsilon \end{vmatrix} = 0.$$

Since $L_{11}(\mathbf{k}) = L_{22}(\mathbf{k})$ and $L_{12} = L_{21}$, we obtain two solutions:

$$\begin{aligned} \epsilon_1(\mathbf{k}) &= L_{11}(\mathbf{k}) + L_{12}(\mathbf{k}), \\ \epsilon_2(\mathbf{k}) &= L_{11}(\mathbf{k}) - L_{12}(\mathbf{k}). \end{aligned} \tag{5.12}$$

Substituting the values $L_{\alpha\beta}$ from (3.16), we obtain

$$\epsilon_\mu(\mathbf{k}) = \sum_{[n\neq 0} M_{n1,01}e^{i\mathbf{kn}} \pm \sum_n M_{n2,01}e^{i\mathbf{kn}}. \tag{5.13}$$

If $\mu = 1$, the plus sign must be taken, and if $\mu = 2$, the minus sign. Substituting (5.12) in equations (3.15), we obtain

$$\frac{B_1^\mu}{B_2^\mu} = \begin{cases} 1 & \text{if } \mu = 1 \\ -1 & \text{if } \mu = 2. \end{cases}$$

Therefore, to the two energy zones of the excited states [(5.13)], there will correspond two systems of wave functions:

$$\Psi_x^{f\mu}(k, r, R) = (2N)^{-\frac{1}{2}} A_{0x}^{\circ}(R) \sum_n (\chi_{n1}^f \pm \chi_{n2}^f)e^{i\mathbf{kn}}. \tag{5.14}$$

The matrix elements $M_{n\alpha,m\beta}$ for the transfer of excitation from one molecule to another diminish with the distance not more slowly than $R_{n\alpha,m\beta}^{-3}$. However, when calculating (5.13), one cannot limit consideration to interaction with the nearest molecules, which surround the excited molecules, since, with the increase of the distance, the number of molecules interacting with a given molecule also increases (as R^2). At the same time, we must keep in mind that the matrix elements essentially depend on the mutual orientation of induced molecular dipole moments. Therefore, interaction with a more remote molecule will occasionally be greater than with a close one. The signs of the matrix elements are also determined by the orientation of the molecules.

For a rough estimate of the magnitude of (5.13), one may use the approximate expression

$$\begin{aligned} \epsilon_\mu(\mathbf{k}) \approx 2\{M_a \cos \mathbf{ka} + M_b \cos \mathbf{kb} \pm 2M_{ab} \\ + [M_c \pm 2(M_{abc} + M_{abc'})] \cos \mathbf{kc} + \cdots\}. \end{aligned} \tag{5.15}$$

Here M_a is the matrix element for the transfer of excitation to the nearest (first) molecule situated on the a axis of the crystal (see Figure 9). Figure 9 shows the disposition of the molecular centers of gravity in a monoclinic crystal with two molecules in a unit cell. The molecules having an orientation identical with that of the first molecule are designated by shaded circles. The molecules (second) having an orientation which is different from the orientation of the first are designated by white circles.

The matrix element M_b in (5.15) determines the transfer of excitation to the nearest (first) molecule, located on the b axis. The matrix element M_c is for the transfer of excitation to the nearest (first) molecule, situated on the c axis. The matrix element M_{ab} is for the transfer of excitation to the nearest second molecule located in the center of the unit cell face ab. The matrix elements M_{abc} and M'_{abc} are for the transfer of excitation to the nearest second molecules, located at the centers of the faces ab, which do not coincide with the plane, where the primary molecule is.

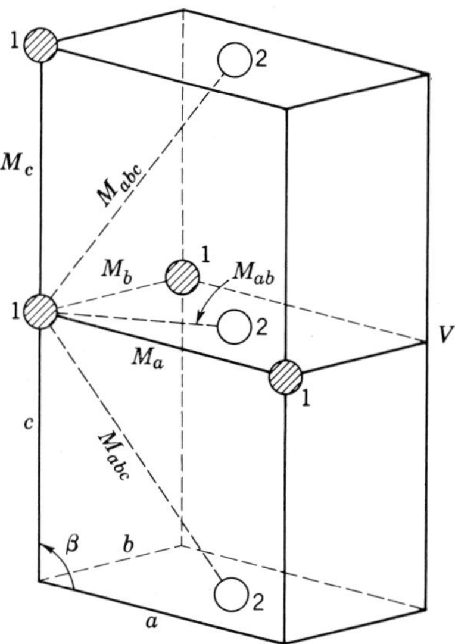

FIG. 9. Disposition of the molecular centers in a monoclinic crystal with two molecules per unit cell.

If in the unit cell there are more than two molecules, a direct solution of the system of σ equations (3.15) and (3.17) is difficult to achieve. For crystals in which the molecules occupy the centers of symmetry, the unknowns B^{μ}_{α} will be real and equal to unity in absolute magnitude. It is then easy to write directly σ independent and orthogonal solutions for this system of equations. Thus, for crystals of this type containing four molecules per unit cell, the values B^{μ}_{α} may be written in tabular form:

$$B^{\mu}_{\alpha} = \begin{pmatrix} 1 & 1 & 1 & 1 \\ 1 & -1 & 1 & -1 \\ 1 & -1 & -1 & 1 \\ 1 & 1 & -1 & -1 \end{pmatrix}. \tag{5.16}$$

Here the number of a row corresponds to the index μ and the number of a column to the index α.

Using the values of B^{μ}_{α} obtained, and utilizing (3.15), we can write the solutions for $\epsilon_{\mu}(\mathbf{k})$:

$$\epsilon^{f}_{\mu}(\mathbf{k}) = \sum_{n\neq 0} M_{n1,01}e^{i\mathbf{kn}} + \sum_{n} \begin{pmatrix} + & & + & & + & \\ - & M_{n2,01} & + & M_{n3,01} & - & M_{n4,01} \\ - & & - & & + & \\ + & & - & & - & \end{pmatrix} e^{i\mathbf{kn}}, \tag{5.17}$$

where $\mu = 1, 2, 3, 4$.

To each energy zone μ, there will correspond its own wave function:

$$\Psi_x^{f\mu}(k, r, R) = \frac{1}{2\sqrt{N}} A_{0x}^{\circ}(R) \sum_n \left(\chi_{n1}^f \begin{matrix} + \\ - \\ - \\ + \end{matrix} \chi_{n2}^f \begin{matrix} + \\ + \\ - \\ - \end{matrix} \chi_{n3}^f \begin{matrix} + \\ - \\ + \\ - \end{matrix} \chi_{n4}^f \right) e^{i\mathbf{kn}}. \quad (5.18)$$

The deduced system of terms of a molecular crystal does not determine the absorption spectrum. We still must determine the selection rules, i.e., the rules indicating those energy-zone sublevels to which the transitions under the action of a light wave are possible. We shall do this in the following section.

21. Transitions under the Action of Light

The electric field intensity (in a crystal) of a plane electromagnetic wave falling on the crystal is

$$\mathbf{E} = \mathbf{E}_0 e^{i(\mathbf{Qr}-\omega t)}. \quad (5.19)$$

Here $\mathbf{E}_0$ is the amplitude, ω is the vibration frequency multiplied by 2π, and $\mathbf{Q}$ is the wave vector. Under the action of this wave, the crystal will pass into an excited state.

To calculate the probability of the transition under the action of the electric field [(5.19)], we must add the operator for the perturbation to the time-dependent equation of quantum mechanics; this yields

$$we^{-i\omega t} = -\frac{eh}{\mu\omega} \mathbf{E}_0 e^{i(\mathbf{Qr}-\omega t)} \text{ grad}. \quad (5.20)$$

Here e is the electronic charge, μ is the electronic mass, and h is Planck's constant divided by 2π.

Then the probability (P_μ^f) for the transition in one second from a normal state of the crystal Ψ° to an excited one $\Psi^{f\mu}$ will be proportional to the square of the matrix element for the operator w from (5.20):

$$P_\mu^f = \frac{2\pi}{h} |(\mu f|w|0)|^2 \, \delta(\Delta E_\mu^f - h\omega), \quad (5.21)$$

where

$$(\mu f|w|0) = \int \Psi_{x'}^{f\mu *} w \Psi_x^\circ \, d\tau \, dR. \quad (5.22)$$

In the matrix element [(5.20)], the integration is carried out over all internal coordinates of the molecules $d\tau$ and the coordinates determining the spatial distribution of molecules dR.

Substituting in (5.22) the value w from (5.20), and taking into consideration that

$$\int \Psi^{f\mu *} \text{ grad } \Psi^\circ \, d\tau = -\frac{\mu\omega}{h} \int \Psi^{f\mu *} \mathbf{r} \Psi^\circ \, d\tau,$$

we obtain

$$(\mu f|w|0) = e\mathbf{E}_0 \int \Psi_{x'}^{f\mu *} e^{i\mathbf{Q}\mathbf{r}}(\mathbf{r}) \Psi_x^\circ \, d\tau \, dR. \tag{5.23}$$

We shall be concerned with light absorption in the infrared, visible, and ultraviolet parts of the spectrum, where the wavelength is significantly greater than the dimensions of the unit cell of the crystal. Therefore, we shall disregard the phase difference between different molecules in one unit cell. In other words, we shall substitute for $e^{i\mathbf{Q}\mathbf{r}}$ at the point where the electron is, the corresponding value $e^{i\mathbf{Q}\mathbf{n}}$ at a certain point of the elemental cell of number n, in which one of the molecules becomes excited.

Let us now substitute into (5.23) the values for the wave functions and $\Psi_x^{f\mu}$ from (5.10) and (5.11). If we consider also that in the zeroth approximation there is no coupling between the molecular vibrations in the lattice and their optical excitation (consequently, the integration over the external molecular coordinates may be carried out independently), we obtain

$$(\mu f|w|0) = (\sigma N)^{-1/2} \sum_n e^{i(\mathbf{Q}-\mathbf{k})\mathbf{n}} e\mathbf{E}_0 \sum_\alpha B_\alpha^\mu \int \chi_{n\alpha}^{f*} \mathbf{r} \Phi^\circ \, d\tau. \tag{5.24}$$

If we take into account the phase difference of the light wave within the limits of the unit crystal cell, the matrix element [(5.24)] becomes somewhat complicated:

$$(\mu f|w|0) = (\sigma N)^{-1/2} \sum_n e^{i(\mathbf{Q}-\mathbf{k})\mathbf{n}} e\mathbf{E}_0 \sum_\alpha B_\alpha^\mu e^{i\mathbf{Q}\mathbf{r}} \int \chi_{n\alpha}^{f*} \mathbf{r} \Phi^\circ \, d\tau. \tag{5.25}$$

In our case $\mathbf{Q}\mathbf{r}_\alpha \ll 1$; therefore, we shall utilize the simpler expression [(5.24)].

In the integral entering into (5.24), the integration is carried out over all internal coordinates of the molecules. By virtue of the translational symmetry of the crystal, which in our case (free excitons) is not disturbed upon light absorption, these integrals will not depend on n. Furthermore, substituting the values $\chi_{n\alpha}^f$ and Φ°, we obtain

$$\int \chi_{n\alpha}^{f*} \mathbf{r} \Phi^\circ \, d\tau = \int \varphi_{n\alpha}^{f*} \mathbf{r} \varphi_{n\alpha}^\circ \, d\tau = \int \varphi_\alpha^{f*} \mathbf{r} \varphi_\alpha^\circ \, d\tau.$$

Now, (5.24) may be written

$$(\mu f|w|0) = (\sigma N)^{-1/2} e\mathbf{E}_0 \sum_\alpha \left(B_\alpha^\mu \int \varphi_\alpha^{f*} \mathbf{r} \varphi_\alpha^\circ \, d\tau \right) \sum_n e^{i(\mathbf{Q}-\mathbf{k})\mathbf{n}}. \tag{5.26}$$

The summation over n always yields zero if the following conditions are not fulfilled:

$$\mathbf{Q} - \mathbf{k} = \begin{cases} 0, & (a) \\ \pm 2\pi \mathbf{a}_l^{-1}, \quad l = 1, 2, 3. & (b) \end{cases} \tag{5.27}$$

The $\mathbf{a}_l^{-1}$ are the vectors of the reciprocal lattice.

The selection rules [(5.27)] express the law for the impulse conservation of the light wave and of the excitation waves produced, as well as the possibility for transmitting this impulse to the lattice as a whole (case b).

For infrared, visible, and ultraviolet light, we can neglect the wave vector for the light wave ($\mathbf{Q} \approx 0$); then the selection rules [(5.27)] will assume the form

$$\mathbf{k} = \begin{cases} 0, \\ \pm 2\pi \mathbf{a}_l^{-1}. \end{cases} \tag{5.28}$$

If conditions (5.27) are fulfilled, then

$$(\mu f|w|0) = \sqrt{\frac{N}{\sigma}}\, e\mathbf{E}_0 \sum_{\alpha=1}^{\sigma} B_\alpha^\mu \int \varphi_\alpha^{f*} \mathbf{r} \varphi_\alpha^\circ \, d\tau. \tag{5.29}$$

Expression (5.29) determines the matrix element for the transition to an excited μf state of the crystal and shows that in the first approximation such a transition takes place only when the matrix element for the dipole operator of a separate molecule is not equal to zero, i.e., when the corresponding transition is permitted in the molecule. If the dipole transition in the molecule is forbidden, then in the dipole approximation the transitions to all μ excited-state zones are also forbidden. In this case, it becomes necessary to use (5.25) and to take into account the change in light wave phases within the limits of the unit cell (we formerly disregarded this change) in order to obtain the probabilities for the transitions of a higher multipole type. These probabilities will be less than for dipole transitions by an order of magnitude

$$x = \left(\frac{\text{dimension of the molecule}}{\text{light wavelength}}\right)^{2l} \tag{5.30}$$

The order of multipole character is l for the corresponding transition in a molecule.

We must, however, keep in mind that the distances between separate μ zones are also proportional to (5.30). These distances are determined by the matrix elements for the resonance interaction of translationally nonequivalent molecules in a crystal. In other words, for forbidden molecular transitions, the crystalline structure is less significant.

If the dipole transition in a molecule is permitted, the transition in a crystal, generally speaking, will also be permitted. However, depending on the mutual orientation of electric moments for intramolecular transitions in molecules in a unit cell, and depending on the polarization and direction of light propagation relative to the crystallographic axes of the crystal, transitions will take place to various zones obtained by the splitting of molecular transitions in the crystal.

Thus, upon light absorption (zeroth approximation of the theory), an excitation does not occur to any arbitrary level of the quasi-continuous excitation zones of energy:

$$\epsilon_{\mu}^{f}(\mathbf{k}) = \sum_{\alpha=1}^{\sigma} \frac{B_{\alpha}^{\mu}}{B_{\beta}^{\mu}} \left(\sum_{n}{}' M_{n\alpha,m\beta}^{f} e^{i\mathbf{kn}} \right). \tag{5.31}$$

On the contrary, transitions occur only to those levels that correspond to the value of the wave number $\mathbf{k}$, satisfying the conditions given by (5.27) or the approximate conditions given by (5.28). Simultaneously, we note that the energy values turn out to be identical, not only when the conditions for case a in (5.27) are fulfilled, but also when conditions for case b are fulfilled.

The results obtained here pertain to a case in which, at the moment of light absorption, free excitons arise in a crystal. For this to occur, it is necessary for the group velocities (proportional to $\mathbf{k}$, for small $\mathbf{k}$) of the excitation waves to be sufficiently large.

Upon excitation of excitons by light ($\mathbf{k} = \mathbf{Q}$), this condition may be violated for certain values of the coefficients B_{α}^{μ}. The corresponding bands of excited states in a crystal will not be realized.

22. Transitions under the Action of Light in Crystals Containing Two Molecules per Unit Cell†

Among the molecular crystals of this group are the naphthalene and anthracene crystals (the structures of which have been thoroughly studied[64,65]), as well as a series of other crystals. It is the custom in this case to designate the vectors ($\mathbf{a}_1$, $\mathbf{a}_2$, and $\mathbf{a}_3$) of a unit cell of a crystal by the letters **a**, **b**, **c**, respectively. The vector determining the position of two molecules in a unit cell of a crystal is given by

$$\mathbf{r}_{\alpha} = \begin{cases} \mathbf{r}_1 = 0, \\ \mathbf{r}_2 = \dfrac{\mathbf{a}}{2} + \dfrac{\mathbf{b}}{2}. \end{cases} \tag{5.32}$$

If we use the functions given by (5.14) for the excited states of the crystal, we obtain two matrix elements for the transitions to an excited state:

$$\begin{aligned} (1f|w|0) &= \sqrt{\frac{N}{2}}\, e\mathbf{E}_0 \left(\int \varphi_1^{f*} \mathbf{r} \varphi_1^{\circ}\, d\tau + \int \varphi_2^{f*} \mathbf{r} \varphi_2^{\circ}\, d\tau \right), \\ (2f|w|0) &= \sqrt{\frac{N}{2}}\, e\mathbf{E}_0 \left(\int \varphi_1^{f*} \mathbf{r} \varphi_1^{\circ}\, d\tau - \int \varphi_2^{f*} \mathbf{r} \varphi_2^{\circ}\, d\tau \right). \end{aligned} \tag{5.33}$$

† The contents of Sections 22 to 24 have been published in part previously.[66]

Each of them will have its own corresponding excitation energy:

$$\begin{aligned} \Delta E_1^f &= \Delta E_{m\beta}^f + D_{m\beta}^f(0) + \sum_n{}' (M_{n1,01}^f + M_{n2,01}^f)e^{i\mathbf{Qn}}, \\ \Delta E_2^f &= \Delta E_{m\beta}^f + D_{m\beta}^f(0) + \sum_n{}' (M_{n1,01}^f - M_{n2.01}^f)e^{i\mathbf{Qn}}. \end{aligned} \tag{5.34}$$

Here $M_{n1,01}$ is the matrix element for the transfer of excitation from the first molecule of the zeroth unit cell of the crystal to all first molecules located in other unit cells; $M_{n2,01}$ is the matrix element for the transfer of excitation from this same molecule to all second molecules.

If both molecules in one unit cell have an identical orientation, only one of the matrix elements [(5.33)], corresponding to the plus sign, will be different from zero for the corresponding direction of $\mathbf{E}_0$. Therefore, in such a case, to each transition in an isolated molecule there will correspond one transition in a crystal; this latter transition will merely be displaced relative to the molecular transition by the magnitude

$$h\,\Delta\omega = D_{m\beta}^f(0) + \sum_n{}' (M_{n1,01}^f + M_{n2,01}^f)e^{i\mathbf{Qn}}.$$

If, however, both molecules possess different orientations, both matrix elements [(5.33)] may be different from zero. In this case, to each transition in a molecule there will correspond in a crystal two absorption bands determined by (5.34). The positions of these bands will, in general, depend on the direction of light propagation in the crystal (direction of vector $\mathbf{Q}$). The emergence of one or another of these bands, or simultaneously of both, will depend on the polarization of the light wave vector $\mathbf{E}_0$.

Crystals of the type studied are usually produced in the form of fine, thin plates whose planes coincide with the cleavage plane of the crystal. This plane contains the monoclinic axis b of the crystal and the a axis perpendicular to it. When this experiment is conducted, the light ray is usually directed perpendicular to this plane of the crystal.

Let us assume that the light falls perpendicularly onto the face ab of the crystal and that the projection onto this face of the electric vector for the transition moment of a molecule forms the angles α and $-\alpha$ ($\alpha < 45°$) with the b axis for the two molecules. This case is realized, for example, for the electronic transition in a naphthalene and an anthracene molecule when the vector for the transition moment is parallel to the intermediate molecular axis. Then, with the aid of (5.33), we see that the frequency corresponding to the energy ΔE_1^f given by (5.34) will be absorbed if the electric vector for the light wave is parallel to the b axis of the crystal. The frequency corresponding to ΔE_2^f of (5.34) will be absorbed also if the light wave vector is parallel to the a axis of the crystal. The intensity ratio of both of these absorption bands is given by

$$\frac{I(1)}{I(2)} = \cot^2 \alpha. \tag{5.35}$$

The distance between these absorption bands, measured in reciprocal centimeters, is

$$\Delta\nu = \frac{2}{hc} \sum_n{}' M^f_{n2,01} e^{i\mathbf{Qn}}. \tag{5.36}$$

Here c is the velocity of light.

When the projection onto the face ab of the transition moment vector in the molecule forms angles γ and $-\gamma$ ($\gamma < 45°$) with the a axis for two molecules, respectively, the frequency $\Delta E^f_1/h$ will be absorbed if the electric vector of the light wave is parallel to the a axis. The frequency $\Delta E^f_2/h$ will be absorbed also if the electric vector of the light wave is parallel to the b axis of the crystal. The intensity ratio of both bands is

$$\frac{I(1)}{I(2)} = \cot^2 \gamma.$$

This case applies to an electronic transition in the naphthalene and anthracene molecule when the vector for the transition moment is parallel to the long axis of the molecule.

Knowing the dependence of the crystal excitation energy [(5.13)] on the wave number $\mathbf{k}$ for excitation waves produced, we can determine the group velocity for the propagation of these waves in the crystal:

$$\mathbf{U}_\mu(\mathbf{k}) = \frac{1}{h} \operatorname{grad}_k \epsilon_\mu(\mathbf{k}). \tag{5.37}$$

Of course, for zones possessing different values of μ and belonging to one excited state of the molecule, the group velocities will be nonidentical.

If the light falls perpendicular to the face ab of the crystal, then for excitons appearing under the action of a light wave and by virtue of the selection rules [(5.27)],

$$\mathbf{ka} = \mathbf{kb} = 0, \qquad \mathbf{kc} = Qc \sin \beta,$$

where β is the angle between vectors $\mathbf{a}$ and $\mathbf{c}$ of the crystal unit cell. The group velocity of free exciton motion will be ($Qc \sin \beta \ll 1$)

$$\begin{aligned} U_1(Q) &\approx -\frac{2Qc^2 \sin^2 \beta}{h} [M_c + 2(M_{abc} + M_{abc'}) + \cdots], \\ U_2(Q) &\approx -\frac{2Qc^2 \sin^2 \beta}{h} [M_c - 2(M_{abc} + M_{abc'}) + \cdots]. \end{aligned} \tag{5.38}$$

These two expressions correspond to the two values for the excitation energy [(5.34)].

The ratio of these velocities is

$$\frac{U_1}{U_2} \approx \frac{M_c + 2(M_{abc} + M_{abc'}) + \cdots}{M_c - 2(M_{abc} + M_{abc'}) + \cdots}. \tag{5.39}$$

Depending on the sign and on the relative magnitude of the matrix elements entering into (5.39), this ratio may assume different values and may be at times substantially different from unity.

Excitons moving with a lower velocity will interact with the lattice more strongly; such states will be less stationary. In certain crystals the velocity of travel for excitons, corresponding to one of the excitation energies [(5.34)], may be so small that the inequality given by (4.22) will be realized; this leads to the formation of "localized" excitons.

We see from (5.38) that the group velocity essentially depends on the dimensions and form of the unit cell and, in particular, on the monoclinic angle β. In lattices with angle β close to 90°, other conditions being equal, the group velocities are extremely high. Therefore, the light absorption bands in such lattices must be narrow. The narrowness of the absorption bands for the phenanthrene crystal[16] is possibly explained by the fact that, in this crystal, angle β is close to 90°.

If the light falls perpendicular to the face *ac* of the crystal, and if the projection onto this face of the electric moment vector for the molecular transition forms an angle δ for both molecules with the direction of the crystal's *a* axis, only the frequency corresponding to the excitation energy ΔE_1^f from (5.34) will be absorbed. This case must apply to the naphthalene crystal. It would be very desirable to conduct a special experiment to investigate the absorption spectrum when the light impinges on a monocrystal in the foregoing manner.

If the molecular transition projections onto the face *ac* of the first and second molecule in the unit cell form various angles with the *a* axis, we can again observe two absorption frequencies corresponding to one transition in the molecule.

23. Transitions under the Action of Light in Crystals Containing Four Molecules per Unit Cell

Among the crystals of this type are phenanthrene, azobenzene, and others. In crystals of the monoclinic system, four molecules usually occupy sites determined by the radius vectors

$$\mathbf{r}_\alpha = \left(\mathbf{r}_1 = 0,\ \mathbf{r}_2 = \frac{\mathbf{a}}{2} + \frac{\mathbf{b}}{2},\ \mathbf{r}_3 = \frac{\mathbf{c}}{2},\ \mathbf{r}_4 = \frac{\mathbf{a}}{2} + \frac{\mathbf{b}}{2} + \frac{\mathbf{c}}{2}\right).$$

If we use the coefficients given by (5.16), we obtain, with the aid of (5.29), the following matrix elements for electronic transitions under the action of light:

$$(\mu f|w|0) = \frac{\sqrt{N}}{2}\, e\mathbf{E}_0 \left(\int \varphi_1^{f*}\mathbf{r}\varphi_1^{\circ}\, d\tau \substack{+\\-\\-\\+} \int \varphi_2^{f*}\mathbf{r}\varphi_2^{\circ}\, d\tau \substack{+\\+\\-\\-} \int \varphi_3^{f*}\mathbf{r}\varphi_3^{\circ}\, d\tau \substack{+\\-\\+\\-} \int \varphi_4^{f*}\mathbf{r}\varphi_4^{\circ}\, d\tau \right). \tag{5.40}$$

For each of these transitions, the corresponding energy for the excitation of the crystal is

$$\Delta E_\mu^f = \Delta E_{m\beta}^f + D_{m\beta}^f(0) + \sum_n{}' \left(M_{n1,01}^f \substack{+\\-\\-\\+} M_{n2,01}^f \substack{+\\+\\-\\-} M_{n3,01}^f \substack{+\\-\\+\\-} M_{n4,01}^f \right) e^{i\mathbf{Qn}}. \tag{5.41}$$

Depending on the orientation of molecules in a unit cell and on the direction and polarization of light, one will observe one or another of the four absorption bands corresponding to the excitation energies [(5.41)]. Knowing the arrangement of molecules in a unit cell as well as the direction of the electric moments for the transitions in these molecules, we can obtain from (5.40) qualitative and quantitative data on the number of split components, on the magnitude of the splitting, and on the displacement of the absorption bands in a crystal for various polarizations and directions of light propagation in the crystal.

24. Molecular Theory of Pleochroism

In white light, certain crystals of both organic and inorganic compounds appear colored, with the color depending on the direction of propagation and polarization of the impinging light waves. This phenomenon is called pleochroism or polychromism. To a larger or lesser degree, it characterizes all double-refracting crystals; however, for many crystals, the phenomenon is observed in the spectral regions not perceived by the eye.

In phenomenological theory, pleochroism is described by introducing the tensor for dielectric constants and the tensor for electric conductivity for each light frequency. As far as we know, a molecular (nonphenomenological) theory of pleochroism does not exist at the present time.

The results of the theory for light absorption by molecular crystals set forth in this chapter, and in Chapter III as well, may be considered as a first attempt toward forming such a theory for molecular crystals. As we know, precisely for molecular crystals, the phenomenon of strong pleochroism is little understood, even when the molecules of the crystal possess high anisotropy so that the light absorption of a given frequency may take place only if the projection of the light wave electric vector onto a given molecular axis differs from zero. Actually, in molecular crystals containing more than one molecule per unit cell, the molecules are found to have a diverse orientation. It is therefore often impossible to find such directions for the light wave electric vector as would produce a zero value projection onto the corresponding directions for all molecules in a unit cell. This may be easily seen, for instance, in Figure 10, which schematically depicts a typical disposition of molecular projections onto one of the crystallographic planes. If a molecule absorbs light of frequency ν when the light wave electric vector is parallel to the long (or short) molecular axis, the intensity for the absorption of light of frequency ν, although changing with polarization of the impinging light, apparently will not be equal to zero.

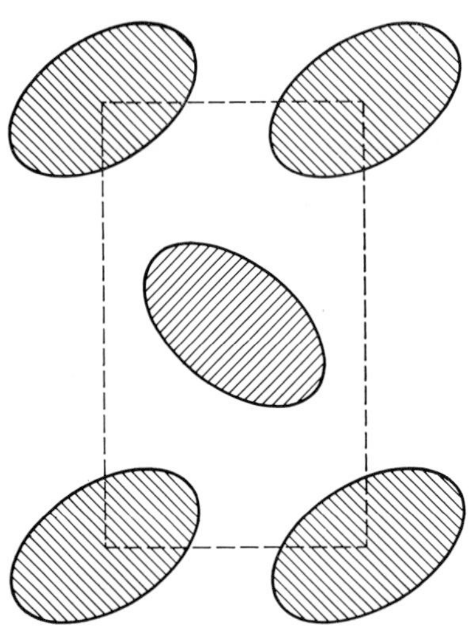

FIG. 10. Typical disposition of molecular projections onto a crystallographic plane.

In his monograph, "Structure of Molecules" (Ref. 67, p. 161), M. V. Volkenstein states: "The question always arises as to whether the difference observed in absorption spectra along and across the crystal axis is a characteristic of the crystal as a whole, occurring upon interaction of molecules in a lattice, rather than a characteristic of separate molecules." In this work, we have taken into account the resonance interaction between molecules, which occurs at the moment of light absorption. This in turn provides an answer to the above question and leads to qualitative results; with the aid of these results, we can, in a uniquely defined way, solve the problem concerning the number of split components in a crystal for each molecular transition, as well as their polarizations, if the number and disposition of molecules in the crystal unit cell is known. In addition, if the wave functions for the normal and excited states of the molecules are known, we can also determine the magnitude of the splitting, i.e., quantitatively calculate the pleochroism, of such a crystal.

CHAPTER VI

EXCITATION OF FREE EXCITONS SIMULTANEOUSLY WITH THE EXCITATION OF LATTICE VIBRATIONS

25. Solution of Equations Determining the Vibrations of Molecules in the Lattice in the First Approximation

We previously disregarded the connection between excitation waves (excitons) and lattice vibrations. Thus, in the decompositions [(5.1)] of matrix elements D and M into powers of displacements from the equilibrium positions, we utilized only the first terms and found the solutions of equation (4.29) for free excitons in the zeroth approximation.

Let us now consider the terms of first order [(5.2)] relative to displacements from the equilibrium positions. Then, taking (5.4) and (5.10) into account, equation (4.29) may be written in the following form:

$$[T_R + V(R) - \mathcal{E}_1^f - D^f_{m\beta}(0) - \epsilon^f_\mu(\mathbf{k})]A^f_x = -K^f_{\mu k}(1)A^f_x. \qquad (6.1)$$

In this,

$$K^f_{\mu k}(1) = D^f_{m\beta}(1) + \sum_{n\alpha}{}' M^f_{n\alpha,m\beta}(1)\,\frac{B^\mu_\alpha}{B^\mu_\beta}\,e^{i\mathbf{k}(\mathbf{n}-\mathbf{m})}. \qquad (6.2)$$

The μth root of equation (3.17) is $\epsilon_\mu(\mathbf{k})$.

The ratios of unknown coefficients B^μ_α/B^μ_β are determined by equations (3.15) for the corresponding values $\epsilon_\mu(\mathbf{k})$.

If we take into account (5.2), as well as the fact that the xth (x runs over six values corresponding to the six degrees of freedom of the molecule) displacement of molecule α' in the n'th cell may be expressed through coordinates a_{qj} (see Section 4) as

$$R^{x\alpha'}_{n'} = (\sigma N)^{-1/2} \sum_{qj} \mathbf{e}^{x\alpha'}_{qj}(a_{qj}e^{i\mathbf{q}\mathbf{n}'} + a^*_{qj}e^{-i\mathbf{q}\mathbf{n}'}) \qquad (6.3)$$

where $j = 1, 2, \ldots, 6\sigma$ and $q_x > 0$, we obtain

$$K^f_{\mu k}(1) = -\sum_{qjn'} W^f_{\mu k}(qjn')(a_{qj}e^{i\mathbf{q}\mathbf{n}'} + a^*_{qj}e^{-i\mathbf{q}\mathbf{n}'}). \qquad (6.4)$$

In the above,

$$W^f_{\mu k}(qjn') = (\sigma N)^{-1/2} \sum_{x\alpha'} \mathbf{e}^{x\alpha'}_{qj} \left[\frac{\partial}{\partial R^{x\alpha'}_{n'}} K^f_{\mu k}(0) \right], \tag{6.5}$$

$$K^f_{\mu k}(0) = D^f_{m\beta}(0) + \sum_{n\alpha}{}' M^f_{n\alpha,m\beta}(0) \frac{B^\mu_\alpha}{B^\mu_\beta} e^{i\mathbf{k}(\mathbf{n}-\mathbf{m})}. \tag{6.6}$$

Equation (6.1) may be written in the following form:

$$[H + K^f_{\mu k}(1)]A^f_x = \mathcal{E}_x A^f_x, \tag{6.7}$$

where

$$H = T_R + V(R) \tag{6.7a}$$

and

$$\mathcal{E}_x = \bar{\mathcal{E}}^f_x - D^f_{m\beta}(0) - \epsilon_\mu(\mathbf{k}). \tag{6.7b}$$

When $K^f_k(1) = 0$, equation (6.7) becomes

$$HA^{f\circ}_x = \mathcal{E}^\circ_x A^{f\circ}_x. \tag{6.8}$$

Here

$$\mathcal{E}^\circ_x = \mathcal{E}^f_x - D^f_{m\beta}(0) - \epsilon_\mu(\mathbf{k}). \tag{6.8a}$$

Equation (6.8) was studied in Chapter V [cf. (5.5)]. Its solution determines the translational-rotational vibrations of molecules in a nonexcited crystal, since by virtue of (5.6) we have $A^{f\circ}_x = A^\circ_{0x}$. The vibrational state of the molecules in a crystal may be described by indicating the number $N_{q'j'}$ of phonons for each value of the wave number q' and of the polarization j'. Then

$$A^{f\circ}_x = A^\circ_{0x} = \prod_{q'j'} \Psi^\circ_{N_{q'j'}}(a_{q'j'}). \tag{6.9}$$

The lattice vibration energy is

$$\mathcal{E}^\circ_x = \sum_{\{N_{qj}} E_{N_{qj}}. \tag{6.10}$$

Here

$$E_{N_{qj}} = h\omega_{qj}(N_{qj} + 1/2). \tag{6.10a}$$

The operator $K^f_{\mu k}(1)$ in equation (6.7) will be considered as a small perturbation. Then, knowing the solution [(6.9)] of the simplified equation (6.8), we can obtain the approximate solution, which allows for the influence of $K^f_{\mu k}(1)$.

The energy of the system in the first approximation does not change:

$$\mathcal{E}_x = \mathcal{E}^\circ_x, \tag{6.11}$$

since the average values (i.e., the diagonal matrix elements), relative to the wave functions for the simplified equation (6.8), of the perturbation operator $K^f_k(1)$ are equal to zero. Besides, by virtue of (6.7b) and (6.8a), we have

$$\bar{\mathcal{E}}^f_x = \mathcal{E}^f_x,$$

where $\mathcal{E}^f_x$ is determined by (5.3).

The change in energy could occur [for operator $K^f_{\mu k}(1)$] only in the second approximation, or in the first if we consider the higher-order terms in the displacements from the equilibrium positions in the decompositions [(5.1)]. Inasmuch as the magnitude of displacements from equilibrium positions depends on the temperature, in this case, owing to the energy change of the system, a displacement of the absorption band, which depended on the temperature, would occur. In this section we shall concern ourselves with low temperatures ($T \approx 0$). We can then limit ourselves to considering only $K^f_{\mu k}(1)$ and the first-order perturbation theory. In this approximation, as we indicated above, a displacement of the absorption band does not take place; however, the wave functions change.

In the first approximation, the wave functions will be:

$$A^f_{x1} = \prod_{qj} \Psi^{\circ}_{N_{qj}}(a_{qj}) + \sum_{N'_{qj}} \prod_{qj} \Psi^{\circ}_{N'_{qj}} \frac{\int \left(\prod_{q'j'} \Psi^{\circ}_{N'_{q'j'}}\right) K^f_{\mu k}(1) \left(\prod_{q'j'} \Psi^{\circ}_{N_{q'j'}}\, da_{q'j'}\right)}{\sum_{q'j'} (E^{\circ}_{N_{q'j'}} - E^{\circ}_{N'_{q'j'}})}. \tag{6.12}$$

In (6.12) the summation $\sum_{N'_{qj}}$ must be taken as follows:

$$\sum_{N'_{qj}} \equiv \sum_{N'_{q_1j_1}} \sum_{N'_{q_2j_2}} \sum_{N'_{q_3j_3}} \cdots .$$

Each N'_{qj} runs over whole numbers $0, 1, \ldots, \infty$.

Using (6.4), we shall introduce the following designations:

$$\int \left(\prod_{q'j'} \Psi^{\circ}_{N'_{q'j'}}\right) K^f_{\mu k}(1) \left(\prod_{q'j'} \Psi^{\circ}_{N_{q'j'}}\, da_{q'j'}\right) = \Lambda^f_{\mu k}(+) + \Lambda^f_{\mu k}(-). \tag{6.13}$$

In the above,

$$\Lambda^f_{\mu k}(-) = -\sum_{qjn'} W^f_{\mu k}(qjn') e^{-i\mathbf{qn}'} \int \left(\prod_{q'j'} \Psi^{\circ}_{N'_{q'j'}}\right) a^*_{qj} \left(\prod_{q'j'} \Psi^{\circ}_{N_{q'j'}}\, da_{q'j'}\right),$$

$$\Lambda^f_{\mu k}(+) = -\sum_{qjn'} W^f_{\mu k}(qjn') e^{i\mathbf{qn}'} \int \left(\prod_{q'j'} \Psi^{\circ}_{N'_{q'j'}}\right) a_{qj} \left(\prod_{q'j'} \Psi^{\circ}_{N_{q'j'}}\, da_{q'j'}\right).$$

Because of the orthogonality and normalization of wave functions $\Psi_{N_{qj}}$ in the integrals, only the integral over the normal coordinates a_{qj} remains from the products of these functions. Thus we obtain

$$\Lambda^f_{\mu k}(+) = -\sum_{qjn'} W^f_{\mu k}(qjn') e^{i\mathbf{qn}'} \int \Psi^{\circ}_{N'_{qj}} a_{qj} \Psi^{\circ}_{N_{qj}}\, da_{qj}, \tag{6.14}$$

$$\Lambda^f_{\mu k}(-) = -\sum_{qjn'} W^f_{\mu k}(qjn') e^{-i\mathbf{qn}'} \int \Psi^{\circ}_{N'_{qj}} a^*_{qj} \Psi^{\circ}_{N_{qj}}\, da_{qj}. \tag{6.15}$$

The integral $\Lambda^f_{\mu k}(+)$ differs from zero only if

$$N'_{qj} = N_{qj} - 1;$$

then

$$\Lambda^f_{\mu k}(+) = -\sum_{qjn'} W^f_{\mu k}(qjn')e^{i\mathbf{qn}'}\sqrt{\frac{hN_{qj}}{2M_{qj}\omega_{qj}}}. \tag{6.16}$$

If $N'_{qj} = N'_{qj} + 1$, then

$$\Lambda^f_{\mu k}(-) = -\sum_{qjn'} W^f_{\mu k}(qjn')e^{-i\mathbf{qn}'}\sqrt{\frac{h(N_{qj}+1)}{2M_{qj}\omega_{qj}}}. \tag{6.17}$$

If, while taking into account (6.16) and (6.17), we substitute (6.13) in equation (6.12), and if we consider that

$$\sum_{q'j'}(E^{\circ}_{N_{q'j'}} - E^{\circ}_{N'_{q'j'}}) = \begin{cases} -h\omega_{qj}, & \text{if } N'_{qj} = N_{qj} + 1, \\ +h\omega_{qj}, & \text{if } N'_{qj} = N_{qj} - 1, \end{cases}$$

we obtain the wave function of equation (6.7) in the first approximation:

$$A^f_1 = \prod_{qj}\Psi^{\circ}_{N_{qj}} + \sum_{qjn'}\frac{W^f_{\mu k}(qjn')}{\sqrt{2hM_{qj}\omega^3_{qj}}}\left(e^{i\mathbf{qn}}\sqrt{N_{qj}}\prod_{qj}\Psi^{\circ}_{N_{qj-1}} - e^{-i\mathbf{qn}'}\sqrt{N_{qj}+1}\prod_{qj}\Psi^{\circ}_{N_{qj+1}}\right). \tag{6.18}$$

If we acknowledge that the distribution of phonons according to possible lattice vibrations qj is, in the case of thermal equilibrium, determined by the Bose-Einstein statistics, then

$$(N_{qj})_{\text{avg}} = \left[\exp\left(\frac{h\omega_{qj}}{kT}\right) - 1\right]^{-1}. \tag{6.19}$$

For absolute zero $(N_{qj})_{\text{avg}} = 0$, and the wave function [(6.18)] adopts a simpler form:

$$\underset{T\simeq 0}{A^f_x} = \prod_{qj}\Psi^{\circ}_{0_{qj}} - \sum_{qjn'}\frac{W^f_{\mu k}(qjn')}{\sqrt{2hM_{qj}\omega^3_{qj}}}e^{-i\mathbf{qn}'}\prod_{qj}\Psi^{\circ}_{1_{qj}}. \tag{6.20}$$

26. Absorption of Light at Low Temperatures. Distribution of Intensity within an Absorption Band

The wave function for an excited state of a crystal (for $T = 0$) may be obtained by multiplying (6.20) by the wave function Φ^f_1:

$$\Psi^{f\mu}_x(k, r, R) = A^f_x\Phi^f_1 = \frac{A^f_x}{\sqrt{\sigma N}}\sum_{n\alpha} e^{i\mathbf{kn}}\frac{B^\mu_\alpha}{B^\mu_\beta}\chi^f_{n\alpha}. \tag{6.21}$$

Here A_x^f is determined by (6.20); $\chi_{n\alpha}^f$ is determined by (3.5); and B_α^μ are the solutions for the system of equations (3.15) for the corresponding value of μ, the latter being the numbers of the zone of excited states.

The wave function for the normal state of a crystal (for $T = 0$) will have the form [Φ° is determined by (3.2)]:

$$\Psi_x^\circ(r, R) = \Phi^\circ \prod_{qj} \Psi_{0_{qj}}^\circ. \tag{6.22}$$

The probability of the transition under the action of a light wave [(5.19)] from the normal state of the crystal [(6.22)] to the excited state [(6.21)] will be proportional to the square of the matrix element for the perturbation operator of [(5.20)]. Let us designate this matrix element as

$$(\mu f|w|0)^1 = \int \Psi_{x'}^{f\mu *}(k, r, R) w \Psi_x^\circ(r, R)\, d\tau\, dR. \tag{6.23}$$

Substituting w from (5.20) as well as the wave functions given by (6.21) and (6.22), we obtain

$$(\mu f|w|0)^1 = (\mu f|w|0)^\circ + \sum_{qj} \frac{e\mathbf{E}_0}{\sqrt{\sigma N}} \sum_\alpha \frac{B_\alpha^\mu}{B_\beta^\mu} \int \varphi_\alpha^{f*}(\mathbf{r})\varphi_\alpha^\circ\, d\tau \cdot Y_{\mu k}^f(qj) \sum_n e^{i(\mathbf{Q}-\mathbf{k}-\mathbf{q})\mathbf{n}}. \tag{6.24}$$

Here

$$Y_{\mu k}^f(qj) = \int \prod_{qj} \Psi_{1_{qj}}^\circ \frac{W_{\mu k}^f(qjn')}{\sqrt{2hM_{qj}\omega_{qj}^3}} \prod_{qj} \Psi_{0_{qj}}^\circ\, dR, \tag{6.25}$$

$$(\mu f|w|0)^\circ = \frac{e\mathbf{E}_0}{\sqrt{\sigma N}} \sum_\alpha \frac{B_\alpha^\mu}{B_\beta^\mu} \int \varphi_\alpha^{f*}(\mathbf{r})\varphi_\alpha^\circ\, d\tau \cdot \sum_n e^{i(\mathbf{Q}-\mathbf{k})\mathbf{n}}. \tag{6.26}$$

The matrix element given by (6.26) exactly coincides with the previously studied matrix element [(5.26)] for the transition without excitation of the lattice vibrations (without production of phonons).

The second matrix element in (6.24) indicates the possibility of molecular excitation with simultaneous lattice vibrational excitation (production of one phonon). This matrix element differs from zero only if the following conditions are fulfilled:

$$\mathbf{Q} - \mathbf{k} - \mathbf{q} = \begin{cases} 0, \\ \pm 2\pi \mathbf{a}_l^{-1}, & l = 1, 2, 3. \end{cases} \tag{6.27}$$

For the spectral region which we are considering, the wave vector of the light wave ($\mathbf{Q} = 0$) may be disregarded. We then obtain the conditions for the possibility of excitation of an exciton simultaneously with phonon excitation in the following form:

$$\mathbf{k} = \begin{cases} -\mathbf{q}, \\ -\mathbf{q} \pm 2\pi \mathbf{a}_l^{-1}, & l = 1, 2, 3. \end{cases} \tag{6.28}$$

If conditions (6.27) are realized, the matrix element responsible for the exciton excitation simultaneously with the phonon excitation will be equal to

$$(\mu f|w|0)^1_{qj} = \sqrt{\frac{N}{\sigma}}\, e\mathbf{E}_0 \left(\sum_\alpha \frac{B^\mu_\alpha}{B^\mu_\beta} \int \varphi^{f*}_\alpha(\mathbf{r})\varphi^\circ_\alpha \, d\tau \right) \cdot Y^f_{\mu k}(qj). \tag{6.29}$$

The excitation energy for the crystal will here be equal to

$$\Delta E^f_\mu(\mathbf{q}j) = \Delta E^f_{m\beta} + D^f_{m\beta}(0) + \epsilon^f_\mu(-\mathbf{q}) + h\omega_{qj}, \tag{6.30}$$

where $\Delta E^f_{m\beta}$ is the excitation energy for one molecule and $D^f_{m\beta}(0)$ is the difference in interaction energy between the excited and normal molecule on the one hand and all other molecules on the other hand. This energy is calculated for an equilibrium disposition of molecules in a nonexcited crystal; $h\omega_{qj}$ is the energy of the excited phonon:

$$\epsilon^f_\mu(-\mathbf{q}) = \sum_{\alpha=1}^{\sigma} \frac{B^\mu_\alpha}{B^\mu_\beta} \sum_n{}' M^f_{n\alpha,m\beta}(0) e^{-i\mathbf{q}\mathbf{n}}. \tag{6.31}$$

For crystals of the monoclinic system, each containing two molecules per unit cell, expression (6.31) can be written in the following form, if we limit ourselves to considering the resonance interaction with only the nearest molecules surrounding the excited molecule:

$$\epsilon^f_\mu(-\mathbf{q}) \cong 2\{M_a \cos \mathbf{qa} + M_b \cos \mathbf{qb} \pm 2M_{ab} + [M_c \pm 2(M_{abc} + M_{abc'})] \cos \mathbf{qc} + \cdots\}. \tag{6.32}$$

The values of all magnitudes entering into (6.32) are determined in (5.13).

From formula (6.30), it can be seen directly that two inequalities may be realized:

$$\begin{aligned} \Delta E^f_\mu(qj) &> \Delta E^f_\mu(0) \qquad (a), \\ \Delta E^f_\mu(qj) &< \Delta E^f_\mu(0) \qquad (b). \end{aligned} \tag{6.33}$$

In these,

$$\Delta E^f_\mu(0) = \Delta E^f_{m\beta} + D^f_{m\beta}(0) + \epsilon^f_\mu(0).$$

The above expression gives the excitation energy for a crystal without lattice vibrational excitation.

Which of the inequalities given by (6.33) is realized, a or b, depends on the zone number μ, on the sign of the matrix elements entering into (6.31), on their relative magnitude and direction, and on the magnitude of the wave vector $\mathbf{q}$ for the phonon. Thus

$$\Delta E^f_\mu(qj) - \Delta E^f_\mu(0) \neq h\omega_{qj}. \tag{6.34}$$

The result obtained is nontrivial. The frequency difference for two absorption lines (excitation with lattice vibration and without lattice vibration) is not equal to the vibrational frequency. Moreover, the frequency of the light absorbed with simultaneous excitation of a phonon may in certain cases be less than the frequency of light absorption without phonon excitation. In other words, even at absolute zero, the frequencies of the light absorbed upon simultaneous excitation of an intramolecular state and of lattice vibrations may be situated on the long-wave side of the frequency that corresponds only to an intramolecular excitation of the crystal.

Furthermore, in contrast to the case in which excitation of the crystal occurs without excitation of phonons, and owing to the impulse conservation law [(5.27)] that the transition take place only at a determined point of each energy zone, with a simultaneous excitation of excitons and phonons, the impulse conservation law leads only to the following requirement: The sum of impulses for the exciton $h\mathbf{k}$ and for the phonon $h\mathbf{q}$ must be equal to the light-quantum impulse $h\mathbf{Q}$. Since $\mathbf{q}$ possesses all possible values (compatible with a cyclic condition), there exists a series of possibilities for light-quantum absorption, which are caused by a diverse distribution of the light-quantum impulse between the impulse of the exciton and that of the phonon. Owing to this, there appear, not absorption lines, but absorption bands, even when thermal motion is absent.

These absorption bands must be continuous. However, since the matrix elements $Y^f_{\mu k}(\mathbf{q}_1, j)$ entering into the transition matrix element [(6.29)] depend essentially on the wave number $\mathbf{q}$, and since the density of states for the various values of $\mathbf{q}$ are not identical, the continuous background will have a complicated distribution of intensity. This effect is apparently the main factor determining the width of molecular monocrystal absorption bands at a temperature near absolute zero.

To determine the form of the absorption band (the distribution of absorption intensity inside the band), it is necessary to calculate the probability of a transition from the initial state (with energy E°) to a state with a given energy E corresponding to light absorption of frequency ω; the latter is determined from the condition

$$E = E^\circ + h\omega. \tag{6.35}$$

The probability of a transition in the unit of time P to a final state with given energy will be determined by the transition matrix element [(6.29)], upon fulfillment of the selection rules [(6.27)] with the help of the well-known formula (Ref. 68, p. 269):

$$P = \frac{2\pi}{h} \sum_j \int [(\mu f|w|0)^1_{qj}]^2 \rho(E)\, d\Omega. \tag{6.36}$$

The differential $d\Omega = \sin\vartheta\, d\vartheta\, d\varphi$ is the element of the solid angle characterizing the direction of the phonon's wave vector; the integration is carried out over all possible directions $\mathbf{q}$; the summation is over various polarizations of the phonon:

$$\rho(E) = h^2 q^2 \frac{\partial \mathbf{q}}{\partial \omega}. \tag{6.37}$$

The derivative $\partial \mathbf{q}/\partial \omega$ and $\mathbf{q}$ are calculated as functions of ω, ϑ, and φ from the equation

$$h\omega = \Delta E^f_{m\beta} + D^f_{m\beta}(0) + \epsilon^f_\mu(-\mathbf{q}) + h\omega_{qj} \tag{6.38}$$

where $\epsilon^f_\mu(-\mathbf{q})$ is determined by (6.31).

With the aid of (6.36), we can calculate the probability for the absorption per volume unit (absorption coefficient) of one light quantum per second.

The number of quanta of light of frequency ω impinging in one second on 1 cm² of crystal surface, perpendicular to the direction of light propagation, is equal to $E_0^2 c/4\pi h\omega$, where c is the velocity of light. Therefore, the absorption coefficient upon excitation of a crystal to the μth zone of the fth excited state will be equal to

$$I_{\mu f}(\omega) = \frac{8\pi^2\omega}{VcE_0^2} \int_\Omega [(\mu f|w|0)^1_{qj}]^2 \rho(E)\, d\Omega.$$

Here V is the volume of the crystal absorbing the light. Substituting the value for the transition matrix element from (6.29) and (6.37), we obtain

$$I_{\mu f}(\omega) = \frac{4\pi^2 N\omega h e^2}{V\sigma c E_0^2} \left(\mathbf{E}_0 \sum_{\alpha=1}^{\sigma} \frac{B^\mu_\alpha}{B^\mu_\beta} \int \varphi^{f*}_\alpha(\mathbf{r}) \varphi^\circ_\alpha \, d\tau\right)^2 \int_\Omega [Y^f_{\mu k}(\mathbf{q}j)]^2 q^2 \frac{\partial \mathbf{q}}{\partial \omega}\, d\Omega. \tag{6.39}$$

Here N is the number of molecules in a molecular crystal of volume V, σ is the number of molecules per unit cell of the crystal, ω is the frequency of the light absorbed, e is the electronic charge, c is the velocity of light, $\mathbf{E}_0$ is the electric field amplitude of the light wave, $Y^f_\mu k(\mathbf{q}j)$ is determined by (6.25), and $\mathbf{q}$ is the wave number of the phonon.

The wave number $\mathbf{q}$ for each polarization j of the phonon is determined from the frequency of absorbed light with the aid of the relation given by (6.38).

Thus, to calculate the absorption coefficient [(6.39)], it is necessary to know explicitly the dependence of frequency ω_{qj} on the wave number $\mathbf{q}$ and on polarization j of the phonon. One must know also the dependence of the wave vector $\mathbf{q}$ on the frequency of absorbed light ω for each direction determined by the solid angle $d\Omega$. The dependence of the first type $\omega_{qj} = \omega_{qj}(\mathbf{q}j)$ is determined by the lattice dynamics. Unfortunately, for the majority of crystals, this dependence is unknown. Calculations have been made only for a small number of very simple lattices. However, the dependence of $\mathbf{q}$ on ω and $d\Omega$ is determined by (6.38), and in principle it may be calculated if the dispositions of molecules in a crystal, as well as the wave functions for the molecular states (for free molecules), are known.

Although it is at present practically impossible to use formula (6.39) to determine the distribution of intensity in the band, it is possible to make a few general qualitative observations.

The statistical weight of states (for small $\mathbf{q}$'s) is proportional to q^2. Furthermore, the matrix elements $Y^f_{\mu k}$ depend on $\mathbf{q}$ in an obvious and a nonobvious way. At the same time, the matrix element increases with

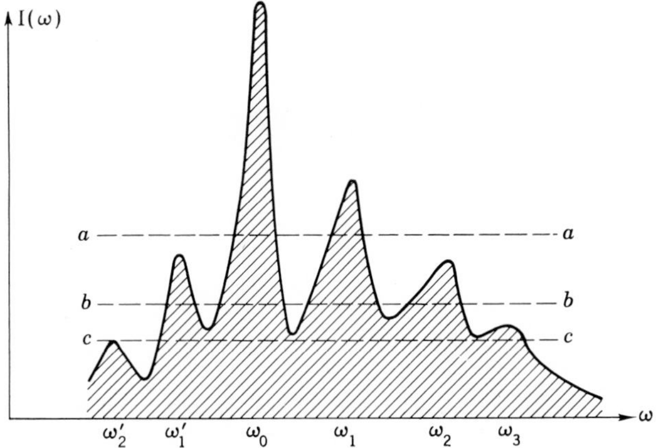

FIG. 11. Schematic representation of absorption of light in the region of an absorption band of a crystal.

the increase of $\mathbf{q}$, since for small $\mathbf{q}$ the phase difference for vibrations of neighboring molecules is small. Therefore, the derivatives $\partial K^f_{\mu k}/\partial R^{x\alpha}_n$, entering into $Y^f_{\mu k}$ through $W^f_{\mu k}(\mathbf{q}jn)$ [cf. (6.5)] and allowing for the changes of matrix elements $D^f_{m\beta}$ and $M^f_{n\alpha,m\beta}$ upon displacement of molecules from equilibrium positions, will also be small. Thus it is to be expected that the absorption coefficients will attain generally different maximum values for different directions and polarizations of the absorbed light.

Figure 11 represents schematically the possible dependence of the absorption coefficient on the frequency of impinging light. This figure enables us to draw the following conclusions, which are apparently confirmed by the experiments of A. F. Prikhotko.[13,32] In the latter experiment the absorption of light by naphthalene monocrystals of thickness varying from 1.5 to 0.05 mm was investigated, at a temperature of 20.4°K. Thick monocrystals absorb in a broad spectral range since even a small absorption coefficient (calculated per unit volume and corresponding to minima of the absorption) is sufficient to totally absorb light. The dashed lines a, b, and c in Figure 11 indicate the absorption coefficients sufficient for total light absorption for the corresponding thickness of a crystal. Line a corresponds to the thin crystal, line c to the thickest one. As the thickness of a crystal decreases, a total absorption will be observed only for frequencies corresponding to the intersection of straight line b, and subsequently of a, with the curve of absorption. Thus, for very thin laminae, the absorption spectrum will represent a series of sharply defined isolated absorption bands.

Figure 12 shows (from A. F. Prikhotko) the portion of an absorption spectrum for naphthalene monocrystal at 20.4°K for two crystalline thicknesses (the direction of the electric vector for the impinging light is parallel to the crystal b axis).

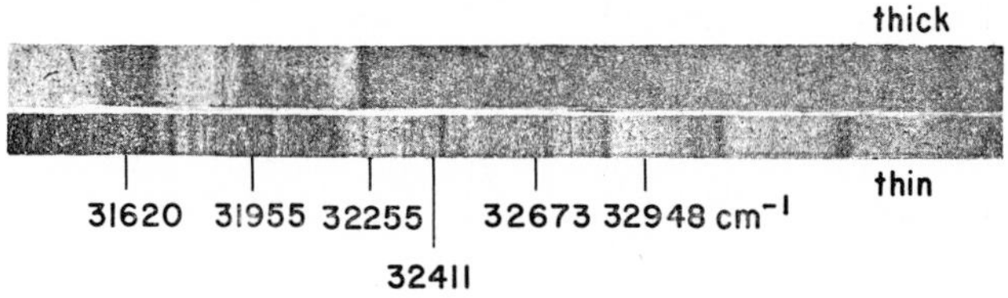

Fig. 12. Absorption spectra of monocrystals of naphthalene at 20.4°K. (*After Prikhotko.*[13,32])

The distances of the subsidiary absorption bands from the basic absorption band depend on $\epsilon_\mu^f(-\mathbf{q})$ and will, generally speaking, be different for the various zones μ and for the various molecular excitations f. In other words, each basic spectral absorption band, corresponding to a given electronic-vibrational excitation of the molecules of the crystal, will be surrounded by its own subsidiary absorption bands. The latter are caused by the interaction of excitons with lattice vibrations. Conversely, in the fluorescence spectra of crystals at low temperature, one can directly observe lattice vibration frequencies, which will appear in the form of satellites near the basic lines.

27. Change in the Structure of an Absorption Spectrum with Temperature Rise. Influence of Translational Symmetry Violations in a Crystal

In the preceding section we studied the structure of a band of light absorption by a molecular crystal at low temperatures ($T \approx 0$). Let us now consider how the appearance of the spectrum will vary when the temperature rises.

In this case we must first of all consider the fact that the average value of the numbers of phonons for each type of lattice vibration wave will not be equal to zero and will increase with the temperature:

$$(N_{qj})_{\text{avg}} = \left[\exp\left(\frac{h\omega_{qj}}{kT}\right) - 1\right]^{-1}.$$

This phenomenon leads to an increase in intensity for the absorption bands caused by the production of phonons and was investigated in the preceding section. The probability of the transition [(6.36)] found for the case $T = 0$ must be multiplied by the factor $(N_{qj})_{\text{avg}} + 1$ to obtain the probability of transition for $T \neq 0$. Moreover, we must keep in mind that the magnitudes entering into the matrix element $(\mu f|w|0)'_{qj}$ also depend in a nonobvious manner on the temperature, since the $Y^f_{\mu k}(\mathfrak{q}j)$ depend on molecular displacements and since the magnitude of the latter varies with temperature rise.

Furthermore, for $T \neq 0$, the matrix elements for the transitions during which the phonons are absorbed, together with the matrix element responsible for the production of phonons, will be different from zero. The probabilities for such transitions depend on the factor $(N_{qj})_{\text{avg}}$ and on the matrix elements, whose magnitudes also increase with temperature rise.

Thus the increase in temperature leads to a general increase in the intensity of absorption bands, which are caused by molecular excitation in a crystal with simultaneous excitation of lattice vibrations. It further leads to the appearance of supplementary absorption bands, which are generated by the excitation of a crystal already having excited lattice vibrational states. The intensity of these supplementary bands will increase with temperature rise.

Upon further temperature rise, the molecular displacements become so great that one must, in the decompositions [(5.1)], take into consideration the terms proportional to the quadratic and higher powers in molecular displacements from equilibrium positions. This leads to the production and absorption simultaneously of two or more phonons. At the same time, the displacement of basic absorption bands may also be observed, for the reason mentioned in Section 25. However, when the processes of the second and higher orders become sufficiently probable, the decomposition into powers of displacements itself loses meaning; it therefore will be impossible to apply perturbation theory.

All results obtained above pertain to an ideal periodic lattice. However, the ideal periodicity of a lattice is violated for a number of reasons: presence of admixtures, presence of isotopes, and finally, presence of thermal density fluctuations. Furthermore, it is also necessary to consider the finiteness of the crystal dimensions, i.e., the influence of the surface.† If monocrystals possess sufficiently large dimensions compared with the lattice constant, the influence of the surface will not be significant. However, the violation of periodicity may lead to significant changes in the absorption spectrum.

Conditions (5.27) and (6.27) were a result of the crystal translational symmetry. These conditions expressed the fact that, in a crystal under the influence of a light wave, only excitons with a wave vector equal to the wave vector of the light wave are excited if the lattice vibrations do not participate. If the lattice vibrations do participate, those excitons are generated that correspond to the differences in the wave vector of the light wave and in the wave vector of the lattice vibration. If the periodicity of the lattice is violated, a change in conditions (5.27) and (6.27) occurs. The excitation of excitons with other wave-number values as well becomes possible. We must expect that, as a result, wide absorption bands appear in a quasi-stationary model. If a crystal does not contain various isotopes or admixtures, the periodicity will even then be violated by fluctuations. This leads us to believe that the violation of periodicity in a crystal with temperature rise is still another reason (in addition to those mentioned in the preceding section) for the widening of absorption bands. In particular, this effect of absorption-band widening must play an important role in the absorption of light by liquids.

Here we shall limit ourselves merely to these qualitative considerations. A quantitative accounting for the influence of factors on absorption spectra causing the violation of crystal translational symmetry must be the subject of a special study. Let us merely observe that a series of very interesting works by I. M. Lifschitz[70] has already been devoted to the problem of the optical behavior of nonideal crystal lattices in the infrared region.

If the molecules possess degenerate energy states, and if the degeneracy is not removed by the field of the crystal lattice (for $T = 0$), then for certain molecular symmetry classes a splitting of degenerate states (upon temperature rise) may occur. This results from the change of symmetry of a crystal unit cell caused by certain types of lattice vibrations. Apparently the effect of the splitting of absorption bands will be significant only for comparatively high temperatures in a crystal.

† The effect of the influence of a molecular crystal surface on the excitation of intramolecular vibrations was investigated in the work of this writer and of V. M. Agranovich of Kiev State University.[69]

CHAPTER VII

"LOCALIZED" EXCITONS IN A MOLECULAR LATTICE

28. Excitation Energy of a Crystal in the Case of "Localized" Exciton Formation

As shown in Chapter IV, upon excitation of a molecule in a crystal there arises a local violation of the equilibrium molecular arrangement, since the excited and the normal molecules act with different forces upon their neighbors. If the excitation remains localized on one molecule, the change in interaction forces between the excited molecule and its neighbors will result in translational and rotational vibrations of molecules relative to a new equilibrium position. If, however, the excitation transfers from one molecule to another with a period shorter than the time necessary for a noticeable displacement of molecules to new equilibrium positions, then the local deformation of the crystal will not have time to take place.

If the excitation transfer time is considerably greater than the time of molecular displacement, i.e., the inequality $\tau_d < \tau_t$ is fulfilled, then the movement of excitons will be accompanied by a local lattice deformation. As a result, the velocity of exciton motion decreases still more, and its effective mass increases. The excitons whose motion is accompanied by the motion of a local crystal deformation we have called "localized" excitons. In this chapter, we shall study the excitation energy of a crystal upon formation of "localized" excitons. When calculating the excitation energy, one must keep in mind that, upon fulfillment of the inequality given by (4.22), the adiabatic approximation is fulfilled only for a nonexcited state ($T \approx 0$). Thus the normal state of a crystal will be described by the function

$$\Psi^{\circ}(r, R) = A_0\Phi_0^{\circ}. \tag{7.1}$$

Here A_0 satisfies equation (4.23) and is given by (4.26), and Φ_0° coincides with (4.8).

For excited states of a crystal, it is impossible to discard the operator [(4.14)] when studying the solutions of equation (4.5). Generally a rigorous solution of this equation is hardly possible for this case. However, approximate solutions of this equation can be obtained.

Owing to nonfulfillment of the adiabatic conditions, it is not possible to seek solutions for equation (4.5) in the form of stationary states for which one or several molecules in the crystal are excited, the remaining molecules not excited, and all molecules in some state of motion. Such a state will not be stationary in the sense that, in the system, transitions will take place (with conservation of the total energy) from excited molecules to lattice vibrations (for $T \approx 0$) until thermodynamic equilibrium is established over the degrees of freedom for the system.

In classical language, when the inequality given by (4.22) is satisfied for the molecular excitation, the system must be considered as one with great anharmonicity in the region of the excited molecule. Because of this anharmonicity, an energy transfer takes place from some normal vibrations to others. We may also formally describe this process of energy transfer in the language of a harmonic model, considering that the vibrations, corresponding to the molecular excitation energy, occur with positive damping and that the lattice vibrations occur with negative damping. Considerable damping of the vibrations of the oscillator, corresponding to the excited molecule, will result in a wide absorption band.

This classical analogy may facilitate finding an approximate solution of equation (4.5). When investigating the problem of light absorption, we shall initially look for quasi-stationary states (stationary during a short time) of equation (4.5); i.e., we shall disregard the terms causing transformation of excitation energy to lattice vibrations. Then we shall consider the influence of these terms as the reason for the widening of excited levels, owing to the short lifetime of such states, and as a mechanism for transforming absorbed energy into heat.

Inasmuch as a state with a given total energy U of a system may be produced by numerous means according to the distribution of energy among the various degrees of freedom, we shall seek the solution of equation (4.5), corresponding to energy U, in the form

$$\Psi(r, R, t) = \left[a(t) A_0^0(R)\Phi_0^0(r, R) + \sum_{n\alpha} b(n\alpha t) A_1^f(n\alpha)\chi_{n\alpha}^f + \cdots \right] e^{-i(U/\hbar)t}, \tag{7.2}$$

where the first term represents the states of a system without excited molecules (the excess of energy over zero-point energy for the system is distributed only among lattice vibrations), and the second sum corresponds to the case in which there is one excited molecule in a system and the remaining ones are in a normal state. Subsequent terms are of little importance if energy U is small. $\chi_{n\alpha}^f$ is the wave function for internal molecular states of a crystal, for which one molecule is excited on site $n\alpha$; $A_1^f(n\alpha)$ determines the vibrational state of molecules in a lattice with local deformation in the region of the lattice point $n\alpha$. By virtue of the equivalence of molecules in a crystal, this state is degenerate. Therefore, we shall seek the solution in the form of a sum of solutions corresponding to the localization of excitation in various molecules of the crystal. Coefficients a and $b(n\alpha)$, the squares of whose moduli are proportional to the probabilities of the corresponding states for the system, will, generally speaking, be slowly changing functions of time.

Let us now substitute (7.2) in (4.5), multiply by $\chi_{m\beta}^{f*}$, and integrate over all internal coordinates of molecules $d\tau$. By virtue of $\chi_{m\beta}^{f}$ being orthogonal to Φ_0° and to all $\chi_{n\alpha}^f$, if $m\beta \neq n\alpha$, we shall obtain

$$b(m\beta, t)[\mathcal{E}^f - V^f(R) - T_R]A_1^f(m\beta, t) = \sum_{n\alpha \neq m\beta} b(n\alpha, t) A_1^f(n\alpha) M_{n\alpha,m\beta}^f + \sum_{n\alpha} b(n\alpha, t)\tau_{n\alpha,m\beta}^1 + a\tau^\circ - A_1^f(m\beta)\frac{\partial b(m\beta, t)}{\partial t}, \quad (7.3)$$

where

$$\mathcal{E}^f = U - \sum_{m\beta} E_{m\beta}^\circ - \Delta E_{m\beta}^f. \quad (7.4)$$

The energy of molecular vibrations in a lattice is $\mathcal{E}^f$. The term $V^f(R)$ is given by

$$V^f(R) = V(R) + D_{m\beta}^f(R). \quad (7.5)$$

Here $V(R)$, $D_{m\beta}^f(R)$, and $M_{n\alpha,m\beta}^f$ have the same values as in (4.24), (3.13), and (3.10), respectively.† Also,

$$\tau_{n\alpha,m\beta}^1 = A_1^f(n\alpha) \int \chi_{m\beta}^{f*} T_R \chi_{n\alpha}^f \, d\tau - h^2 \sum_i \frac{1}{M_i} \frac{\partial A_1^f(n\alpha)}{\partial R_i} \int \chi_{m\beta}^{f*} \frac{\partial \chi_{n\alpha}^f}{\partial R_i} \, d\tau, \quad (7.7)$$

$$\tau^\circ = A_0^\circ \int \chi_{m\beta}^{f*} T_R \Phi_0^\circ \, d\tau - h^2 \sum_i \frac{1}{M_i} \frac{\partial A_0^\circ}{\partial R_i} \int \chi_{m\beta}^{f*} \frac{\partial \Phi^\circ}{\partial R_i} \, d\tau. \quad (7.8)$$

We shall consider as an initial state, after light absorption by a crystal, that for which $|a|^2 = 0$ and $|b(n\alpha)|^2 = 1$. Furthermore, we shall consider the solutions of (7.3) only for time intervals small in comparison with the lifetime of this initial state. Then $a \approx 0$, $[\partial b(m\beta, t)]/\partial t = 0$,

† Here we assume that functions φ° and $\chi_{n\alpha}^f$ may also be written in the form of the product of corresponding wave functions for separate molecules [see (3.2) and (3.5)]. However, the qualitative conclusions obtained by us do not depend on this assumption. If we eliminate this assumption, then instead of (7.5), we must use

$$V^f(R) = \tfrac{1}{2} \sum_{n\alpha,n'\alpha'}' \int \chi_{m\beta}^{f*} V_{n\alpha,n'\alpha'} \chi_{m\beta}^f \, d\tau \quad (7.6a)$$

and

$$M_{n\alpha,m\beta}^f = \int \psi_{m\beta}^{f*} V_{n\alpha,m\beta} \chi_{n\alpha} \, d\tau. \quad (7.6b)$$

and one can disregard the last two terms in (7.3). This consideration does not permit us to take into account the width of the absorption line, because the latter is precisely dependent on the probability decrease of a state for which

$$|b(n\alpha)|^2 = 1 \qquad \text{and} \qquad |a|^2 = 0.$$

We shall subsequently modify the solution of our problem to be able to consider also a time which is comparable with the time of transition to a new state (i.e., with a magnitude the inverse of the transition probability). This allows us to obtain a formula for the width of the absorption line.

Thus, after limiting consideration to only small time intervals and introducing the definitions

$$M^{f\tau}_{n\alpha,m\beta} = M^f_{n\alpha,m\beta} + \frac{\tau^f_{n\alpha,m\beta}}{A^f_1(m\beta)}, \tag{7.9a}$$

$$V^{f\tau}(R) = V^f(R) + \frac{\tau^f_{n\alpha,m\beta}}{A^f_1(m\beta)}, \tag{7.9b}$$

we may reduce equation (7.3) to the form

$$b(m\beta)[\mathcal{E}^f - V^{f\tau}(R) - T_R]A^f_1(m\beta) = \sum_{\substack{n\alpha \\ n\alpha \neq m\beta}} b(n\alpha)A^f_1(n\alpha)^f_{n\alpha,m\beta}. \tag{7.9}$$

Here $A^f_1(m\beta)$ determines the state of lattice vibrations prevailing when one molecule is excited at lattice point $m\beta$ and the remaining ones are in a normal state.

Let us suppose that the localization of the excitation takes place in molecule $m\beta$; then all $b(n\alpha)$ will be small at the first moment, if $n\alpha \neq m\beta$. If, besides, the matrix elements $M^f_{n\alpha,m\beta}$ are sufficiently small, then, discarding in the zeroth approximation all their products by $b(n\alpha)$, we obtain an equation determining the vibrational state of a crystal when the excitation is localized in molecule $m\beta$:

$$[T_R + V^{f\tau}(R)]A^f_1(m\beta) = \mathcal{E}^{f\circ}_{\text{loc}}A^f_1(m\beta). \tag{7.10}$$

In this, $\mathcal{E}^{f\circ}_{\text{loc}}$ is the lattice vibrational energy for localization of the excitation in lattice point $m\beta$.

Equation (7.10) is analogous to the equation for translational and rotational molecular vibrations in a nonexcited crystal [cf. (4.20)], but with a different potential energy:

$$V^{f\tau}(R) = V(R) + D^f_{m\beta}(R) + \frac{\tau^1_{n\alpha,m\beta}}{A^f_1(m\beta)}. \tag{7.11}$$

The minimum for this energy will correspond to the new disposition of molecules in the vicinity of the excited molecule, in comparison with the case of a lattice in which the excitation is not localized or where it is absent altogether.

We shall henceforth designate the deviation of molecules from these new equilibrium positions by means of R^f. It is obvious, then, that $R^f = 0$ may be determined from the variational condition

$$|\delta V^{f\tau}(R)|_{R^f=0} = 0.$$

Let us decompose the potential energy [(7.11)] into a power series of displacements relative to the new equilibrium positions $R^f = 0$ and limit ourselves to quadratic terms of the decomposition. We can thereby obtain eigenfrequencies in a crystal in the harmonic approximation with, generally speaking, new normal frequencies in comparison with the normal frequencies of the nonexcited crystal. At the same time, the wave functions for molecular vibrations in a lattice, upon localization of excitation in the region of molecule $m\beta$, may be written in the form

$$A_1^f(m\beta) = \prod_{qj} \Psi^f_{N_{qj}}(m\beta). \tag{7.12}$$

Here $\Psi^f_{N_{qj}}(m\beta)$ represents the wave functions for harmonic oscillators, corresponding to normal lattice vibrations relative to new equilibrium positions, which arise upon molecular excitation in the $m\beta$th lattice point.

The transition from a system of connected homogeneous equations (7.9) to a system of independent equations (7.10) determining the degenerate (σN-multiple) system of functions $A_1^f(m\beta)$, which belong to one energy $\mathcal{E}^{f\circ}$, is justified if the following inequality is fulfilled:

$$\left[\frac{M^{f\tau}_{n\alpha,m\beta}(R^f)}{V^{f\tau}(R)}\right]_{R^f=0} \ll 1. \tag{7.13}$$

As a rule, the inequality given by (7.13) is fulfilled in (chemical) solutions where, owing to large distances between absorbing molecules separated by a solid or liquid solvent, the excitation energy transfer from one absorbing molecule to another is rendered difficult. However, this inequality may also be fulfilled in molecular crystals for certain excited molecular states. Generally, however, it is not fulfilled, and it is inadmissible to discard the right-hand portions of equations (7.9).

Owing to the presence of the right-hand portion in equations (7.9), the σN-multiple degeneracy of energy $\mathcal{E}^{f\circ}$ is removed.

The system of equations (7.9) is considerably simplified if we take into account the translational symmetry of a crystal and select for the coefficients $b(n\alpha)$ in (7.3) [determining (in a quasi-stationary state) the wave function for the excited state of the crystal

$$\Psi^f(r, R) = \sum_{n\alpha} b(n\alpha) A_1^f(n\alpha)\chi^f_{n\alpha} \tag{7.14}$$

where only one molecule is excited in the fth state] the following expression:

$$b(n\alpha) = B_\alpha e^{i\mathbf{kn}}. \tag{7.15}$$

Here the wave vector $\mathbf{k}$ has the same discrete values as in (3.14).

Substituting (7.15) in (7.9), we obtain a system of σ equations determining the energy for system $\mathcal{E}^f$ as well as the unknown coefficients B_α:

$$B_\beta \,\Delta\epsilon - \sum_{\alpha=1}^{\sigma} B_\alpha L^f_{\alpha\beta}(\mathbf{k}) = 0, \tag{7.16}$$

where

$$\Delta\epsilon = \mathcal{E}^f - \mathcal{E}^{f\circ}, \tag{7.17}$$

$$L^f_{\alpha\beta}(\mathbf{k}) = \sum_n{}' \int A^f_1(0\beta) M^{f\tau}_{n\alpha,0\beta} A^f_1(n\alpha) e^{i\mathbf{kn}}. \tag{7.18}$$

The matrix $L_{\alpha\beta}(\mathbf{k})$ is Hermitian:

$$L_{\alpha\beta}(\mathbf{k}) = L^*_{\beta\alpha}(\mathbf{k}),$$

and for crystals in which each molecule is the center of symmetry, this matrix is real and symmetrical relative to the indices α and β.

The setting equal to zero of the determinant, formed from coefficients with unknowns, is the condition for the solvability of the system of homogeneous equations [(7.16)]. This condition provides an equation of degree σ for determining $\Delta\epsilon$ (as functions of the wave number $\mathbf{k}$).

$$|L^f_{\alpha\beta}(\mathbf{k}) - \Delta\epsilon\,\delta_{\alpha\beta}| = 0. \tag{7.19}$$

The roots of this equation determine σ functions

$$\Delta\epsilon^f_\mu = \Delta\epsilon^f_\mu(\mathbf{k}), \qquad \mu = 1, 2, \ldots, \sigma. \tag{7.20}$$

Using (7.17) we obtain

$$\mathcal{E}^f_\mu = \mathcal{E}^{f\circ} + \Delta\epsilon^f_\mu(\mathbf{k}). \tag{7.21}$$

Taking into consideration (4.23a) and (7.4), we obtain the excitation energy of the crystal in the following form:

$$\Delta E^f_\mu(\mathbf{k})_{\text{loc}} = \Delta E^f_{m\beta} + \mathcal{E}^{f\circ} - \mathcal{E}^\circ + \Delta\epsilon^f_\mu(\mathbf{k}). \tag{7.22}$$

Thus, when "localized" excitons are formed, the crystal excitation energy will be determined by the excitation energy of one molecule $\Delta E^f_{m\beta}$, by the change in lattice energy ($\mathcal{E}^{f\circ} - \mathcal{E}^\circ$) upon formation of localized deformation in a crystal in the vicinity of an excited molecule, and by the energy $\Delta\epsilon^f_\mu(\mathbf{k})$ connected with a movement of excitation together with the local crystal deformation and depending on the index μ, which runs through σ values, as well as on the wave number $\mathbf{k}$ of the excitation waves. Owing to the presence of the last term, the excited state of the crystal corresponding to one molecular excited state will be characterized by μ energy zones, just as in the case of free excitons.

The separation between zones and their width will be determined by the matrix elements

$$\int A_1^f(0\beta) M_{n\alpha,0\beta}^{f\tau} A_1^f(n\alpha)\, dR. \tag{7.23}$$

For example, in the case of crystals containing two molecules per unit cell,

$$\Delta\epsilon_{1,2} = L_{11}(\mathbf{k}) \pm L_{12}(\mathbf{k}), \tag{7.24}$$

where

$$L_{11}(\mathbf{k}) = \sum_n{}' e^{i\mathbf{kn}} \int A_1^f(01) M_{n1,01}^{f\tau} A_1^f(n1)\, dR, \tag{7.25}$$

$$L_{12}(\mathbf{k}) = \int A_1^f(01) M_{02,01}^{f\tau} A_1^f(02)\, dR + \sum_n{}' e^{i\mathbf{kn}} \int A_1^f(01) M_{n2,01}^{f\tau} A_1^f(n2)\, dR. \tag{7.26}$$

Consequently, the separation between zones (for $\mathbf{k} = 0$) is equal to

$$2L_{12}(0) = 2\sum_n \int A_1^f(01) M_{n2,01}^{f\tau} A_1^f(n2)\, dR. \tag{7.27}$$

Thus, in the case of "localized" excitons, both the zones and the distances between them will be considerably smaller than in the case of free excitons, where the corresponding magnitudes are determined only by the matrices $M_{n\alpha,m\beta}^f$. If we consider only the first terms of the decomposition [(5.1)] for matrices $M_{n\alpha,m\beta}^f$ in powers of displacements, then

$$\int A_1^f(0\beta) M_{n\alpha,0\beta}^{f\tau} A_1^f(n\alpha)\, dR \approx M_{n\alpha,0\beta}^{f\tau}(0) S_{n\alpha,0\beta}, \tag{7.28}$$

where

$$S_{n\alpha,0\beta} = \int A_1^f(0\beta) A_1^f(n\alpha)\, dR. \tag{7.29}$$

The integral $S_{n\alpha,0\beta}$ represents an overlap integral for wave functions corresponding to crystal vibrational states for which there is a local deformation in the region of the 0βth lattice point and, correspondingly, in the region of the $n\alpha$th lattice point.

In the zeroth approximation (when the mass of molecules in a crystal is infinitely large), functions $A_1^f(0\beta)$ and $A_1^f(n\alpha)$ may be represented in the form of δ functions:

$$\begin{aligned} A_1^f(0\beta) &= \prod_i \delta[R_{0\beta}(i) - R_{0\beta}^{f\circ}(i)], \\ A_1^f(n\alpha) &= \prod_i \delta[R_{n\alpha}(i) - R_{n\alpha}^{f\circ}(i)], \end{aligned} \tag{7.30}$$

where $R_{0\beta}(i) - R_{0\beta}^{f\circ}(i)$ is the displacement of the ith normal coordinate from among the $6\sigma N$ normal coordinates, determining the position of molecules in a crystal away from the equilibrium value $R_{0\beta}^{f\circ}(i)$, corresponding to a local crystal deformation in the 0βth lattice point; $R_{n\alpha}(i) - R_{\alpha n}^{f\circ}(i)$ is the displacement of the ith normal coordinate away from the equilibrium value $R_{n\alpha}^{f\circ}(i)$, corresponding to a local crystal deformation in the $n\alpha$th lattice point.

If we utilize (7.30), then

$$S_{P\gamma,m\beta} = \delta_{P\gamma,m\beta} = \begin{cases} 1, & \text{if } P\gamma = m\beta \\ 0, & \text{if } P\gamma \neq m\beta. \end{cases} \tag{7.31}$$

If we take into account the finiteness of the molecular mass for a crystal, we obtain, in lieu of δ functions, the harmonic oscillator functions:

$$A^{f\circ}(m\beta) = \prod_i \frac{1}{\sqrt{2x_0(i)}} \left[\exp\left(-\frac{\xi^2}{4x_0^2(i)}\right)\right] H_n(\xi), \tag{7.32}$$

where $x_0^2(i) = h/(2M_i\omega_i)$ is the average quadratic deflection for zero-point vibrations with frequency ω_i, $\xi = [R_{m\beta}(i) - R_{m\beta}^{f\circ}(i)]/[2x_0(i)]$, and $H_n(\xi)$ is the Chebyshev-Hermite polynomial of the nth degree.

In the zeroth approximation, by virtue of (7.28) and (7.31), we obtain

$$\int A_1^f(0\beta) M_{n\alpha,0\beta}^{f\tau} A_1^f(n\alpha)\, dR \approx 0. \tag{7.33}$$

Consequently, the width of zones and the separations between them are equal to zero in this approximation.† In reality, of course, this is too coarse an approximation; however, it is to be supposed that both the splitting of zones and their spread have small value because of the small magnitude of matrix elements [(7.23)].

The physical meaning of the smallness of the integrals [(7.23)] can be described approximately as follows. For an excitation to pass from one molecule to another in the case of a "localized" exciton, it is necessary that the wave functions for vibrational states $A(0\beta)$ and $A(n\alpha)$, corresponding to the localization of excitation in two molecules, overlap each other, i.e., that $S_{0\beta,n\alpha} \neq 0$. If $S_{0\beta,n\alpha} = 0$, the excitation, together with the local deformation, cannot pass and remains "frozen" in one molecule.

To each of the μ bands of the excited states [(7.22)] there will correspond its own wave function

$$\Psi_{1,\mathrm{loc}}^{f\mu}(\mathbf{k}, r, R) = \frac{1}{\sqrt{\sigma N}} \sum_n e^{i\mathbf{kn}} \sum_\alpha A_1^f(n\alpha) B_\alpha^\mu \chi_{n\alpha}^f, \tag{7.34}$$

where coefficients B_α^μ are the solutions of homogeneous equation (7.16) for the μth root $\Delta\epsilon_\mu^f$ of equation (7.19). The wave function [(7.34)] is normalized in such a manner that $|B_\alpha^\mu|^2 = 1$.

† In this approximation the group velocity for excitation waves, corresponding to localized excitons, is also equal to zero, but the effective mass of excitons is equal to infinity.

The functions found by us describe the behavior of a crystal only during a very short time, since the corresponding states are not stationary states.

In order to calculate the width of the absorption band which arises as a result of the corresponding excited-state levels being nonstationary, we can use a method applied by Weisskopf and Wigner[71] for calculating the natural width of a spectral line.

Inasmuch as we shall be concerned with the change of crystal energy levels in time, we must consider the solution of the time-dependent equation (4.5).

According to the preceding investigation for time $t \approx 0$, we may conclude that the velocity of localized exciton travel is very small; therefore, phenomena connected with the propagation of excitation over the crystal (splitting and polarization) do not play any noticeable role. Consequently, in order to study the problem of transformation of molecular excitation energy into heat energy (lattice vibrational energy), it suffices to consider, as a possible solution of equation (4.5), the wave function

$$\Psi(r, Rt) = a(t)A_0^\circ(R)\Phi^\circ(r, R)e^{-i\omega t} + b(n\alpha)\chi_{n\alpha}^f(r, R)A_1^f(R, n\alpha)e^{-i\omega_0 t}, \tag{7.35}$$

where $A_1^f(n\alpha)$ satisfies equation (7.10) and characterizes lattice vibrations for localization of intramolecular excitation on molecule $n\alpha$; $h\omega_0$ is the total energy of this crystal state, which we shall here consider an initial one; $A_0^\circ(R)$ satisfies equation (4.23) and determines lattice vibrations when there is not a single excited molecule in a crystal; and $h\omega$ is the total energy for the corresponding state of the crystal.

Let us substitute (7.35) in (4.5), then multiply the expression obtained by $\Phi_0^{\circ *}A_0^\circ(R)$ and by $\chi_{n\alpha}^{f*}A_1^f(n\alpha)$; let us now integrate over variables r and R. We then obtain a system of equations:

$$\begin{aligned} ih\frac{da(t)}{dt} &= b(t, n\alpha)\mathfrak{M}^{f\circ}e^{i(\omega_0-\omega)t} \\ ih\frac{db(t, n\alpha)}{dt} &= a(t)\mathfrak{M}^{f\circ}e^{i(\omega-\omega_0)t} \end{aligned} \tag{7.36}$$

where

$$\begin{aligned} \mathfrak{M}^{f\circ} &= \sum_i \int A_0^\circ\Gamma^{f\circ}(i)\frac{\partial A^f(n\alpha)}{\partial Ri}\,dR + \int A_0^\circ\gamma^{f\circ}A^f(n\alpha)\,dR, \\ \Gamma^{f\circ}(i) &= -\frac{h^2}{M_i}\int \Phi^{\circ *}\frac{\partial\chi_{n\alpha}^f}{\partial Ri}\,dR, \end{aligned} \tag{7.37}$$

$$\gamma^{f\circ} = -\frac{h^2}{2}\int \Phi^{\circ *}\sum_i \frac{1}{M_i}\frac{\partial^2\chi_{n\alpha}^f}{\partial R_i^2}\,d\tau. \tag{7.37a}$$

Let us suppose that for $t = 0$, $b(0, n\alpha) = 1$ and $a(0) = 0$. Then we can determine the change of $a(t)$ by taking into account for $b(t, n\alpha)$ the value which satisfies the initial conditions

$$b(t, n\alpha) = e^{-t/2\tau}, \tag{7.38}$$

where τ is the average lifetime of the initial state.

Substituting (7.38) in the first equation of (7.36), we obtain

$$a(t) = \frac{\mathfrak{M}^{f0}}{h} \frac{(e^{[i(\omega_0-\omega)-1/(2\tau)]t} - 1)}{\omega_0 - \omega + i/(2\tau)}. \tag{7.39}$$

The value found for $a(t)$ is substituted in the second equation of (7.36); then

$$\frac{1}{\tau} = \frac{2}{ih} |\mathfrak{M}^{f0}|^2 \frac{1 - e^{[i(\omega-\omega_0)+1/(2\tau)]t}}{\omega_0 - \omega + i/(2\tau)} = \frac{2\pi}{h} |\mathfrak{M}^{f0}|^2 \, \delta(\omega_0 - \omega). \tag{7.40}$$

In this manner, the transition is accomplished without energy change ($\omega = \omega_0$). There exist a very large number of states, determining lattice vibrations, with the very same energy $h\omega$; these states are distinguished by a different number of phonons and by the direction of the propagation q and polarization j of these phonons. Furthermore, we are not concerned with the transition to one of these states, but to any of them. In view of all this, the total value of τ may be obtained by integrating (7.40) over all these states in the range of values for $\Delta\omega$. If we designate the density of phonon states with wave vector $\mathbf{q}$ and with polarization j in the frequency range $d\omega$ through $\rho_{qj}(\omega)$, then

$$\frac{1}{\tau} = \frac{2\pi}{h} \sum_j \int_\Omega |\mathfrak{M}^{f0}|^2 \rho_{qj}(\omega_0) \, d\Omega. \tag{7.41}$$

Thus, $1/\tau$ is equal to the total probability for the transformation per unit time of intramolecular vibration energy into heat. If we designate this probability by P_T, we obtain

$$P_T = \frac{1}{\tau}. \tag{7.42}$$

The width of level, which is determined by the finiteness of the lifetime of the state, will be equal, in energy units, to

$$\Delta E \approx \frac{h}{\tau} = hP_T, \tag{7.43}$$

where P_T must be taken from (7.42) and (7.41).

29. Comparison of Crystal Excitation Energy upon Formation of a "Localized" and Free Exciton

Let us now compare the crystal excitation energy upon formation of a "localized" exciton

$$\Delta E_\mu^f(\mathbf{k})_{\rm loc} = \Delta E_{m\beta}^f + \mathcal{E}^{f\circ} - \mathcal{E}^\circ + \Delta\epsilon_{\mu,\rm loc}^f(\mathbf{k}) \approx \Delta E_{m\beta}^f + \mathcal{E}^{f\circ} - \mathcal{E}^\circ \quad (7.22)$$

with the excitation energy upon formation of a free exciton

$$\Delta E_\mu^f(\mathbf{k}) = \Delta E_{m\beta}^f + D_{m\beta}^f(0) + \epsilon_\mu^f(\mathbf{k}). \quad (5.15)$$

The fundamental distinction between excitation energy values amounts to the dependence of excitation energy on the wave number of the exciton. By virtue of (7.28), the following inequality is always fulfilled:

$$0 \approx |\Delta\epsilon_{\mu,\rm loc}^f(\mathbf{k})| \ll |\epsilon_\mu^f(\mathbf{k})|. \quad (7.44)$$

Furthermore, $D_{m\beta}^f(0)$ in (5.15) determines the energy difference for the interaction between either an excited or a normal molecule and its neighbors [usually $D_{m\beta}^f(0) < 0$]. This energy is calculated relative to equilibrium dispositions of molecules in a nonexcited crystal. Now $\mathcal{E}^{f\circ} - \mathcal{E}^\circ$ determines the same difference for a new equilibrium configuration, plus the lattice vibration energy change. In view of all this, and since the transition to a new equilibrium state cannot be accompanied by an energy increase,

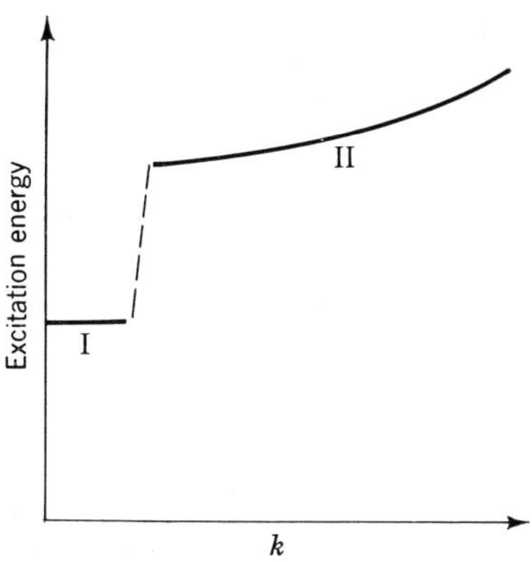

FIG. 13. Dependence of excitation energy of excitons on wave number. Case A: Free exciton (II) greater than localized exciton (I).

$$D_{m\beta}^{f\circ} \gtrless \mathcal{E}^{f\circ} - \mathcal{E}^\circ. \quad (7.45)$$

Let us now determine the energy difference between a free and a "localized" exciton:

$$\Delta E_\mu^f(\mathbf{k}) - \Delta E_\mu^f(\mathbf{k})_{\rm loc} = D_{m\beta}^f(0) - (\mathcal{E}^{f\circ} - \mathcal{E}^\circ) + \epsilon_\mu^f(\mathbf{k}). \quad (7.46)$$

The difference [(7.46)] may be either positive or negative, depending on the type of crystal, on the excited molecular states f, on the number of μ zones for the excited states, and on the wave vectors of free excitons.

CASE A. The excitation energy of the free exciton is larger than the excitation energy of the "localized" exciton. This case is schematically represented in Figure 13. Section I of the curve pertains to the case of "localized" excitons; section II of the curve refers to the case of free excitons. Owing to (7.45), in order to realize case A, it is sufficient that the following inequality be fulfilled:

$$\epsilon_\mu^f(\mathbf{k}) \geqslant 0. \tag{7.47}$$

Thus, if (7.47) is fulfilled, the excitation of free excitons to the μth zone of excited states with wave number $\mathbf{k}$ will require more energy than the excitation of "localized" excitons (small $\mathbf{k}$).

Case B. The excitation energy of the free exciton is smaller than the excitation energy of the "localized" exciton. In order to realize this case, it is necessary that

$$D_{m\beta}^f(0) - (\mathcal{E}^{f\circ} - \mathcal{E}^\circ) < -\epsilon_\mu^f(\mathbf{k}), \tag{7.48}$$

i.e., that

$$\epsilon_\mu^f(\mathbf{k}) < 0$$

and that $\epsilon_\mu^f(\mathbf{k})$ be sufficiently large in absolute magnitude. Figure 14 shows schematically the relative disposition of excitation levels for both types of excitons (I, "localized" excitons; II, free excitons) for this case.

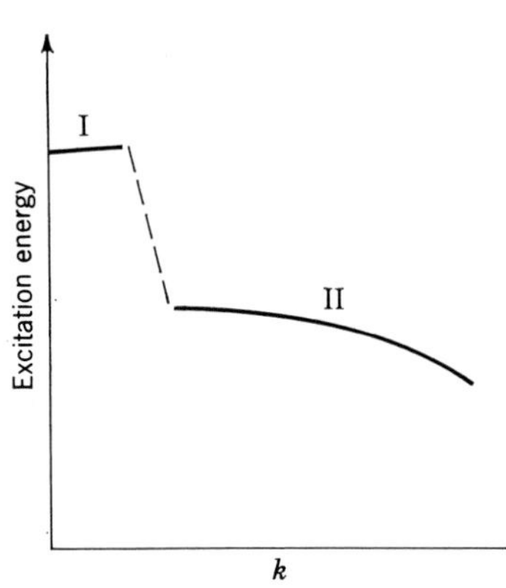

Fig. 14. Dependence of excitation energy of excitons on wave number. Case B: Localized exciton (I) greater than free exciton (II).

We must note that, in all works known to us[21,72,73] in which exciton concepts were utilized, the following was always assumed: Free exciton levels are disposed higher than the level of a "localized" exciton. In this manner, case B, as indicated here, was not analyzed. Yet, as we shall see later, this case may be realized comparatively often and leads to interesting phenomena.

30. Excitation of "Localized" Excitons by Light. Structure of the Absorption Band

In order to determine the probabilities for the transition from a normal state Ψ° [(7.1)] to an excited state $\Psi_{1,\text{loc}}^{f\mu}$ [(7.34)] under the influence of a light wave [(5.19)], one must consider the matrix element

$$(\mu f|w|0)_{\text{loc}} = e\mathbf{E}_0 \int \Psi_{\text{loc}}^{f\mu *} e^{i\mathbf{Q}\mathbf{r}}(\mathbf{r}) \Psi^\circ \, d\tau \, dR. \tag{7.49}$$

Substituting (7.1) and (7.34) in (7.49), we obtain

$$(\mu f|w|0)_{\text{loc}} = \frac{e\mathbf{E}_0}{\sqrt{\sigma N}} \sum_n e^{i(\mathbf{Q}-\mathbf{k})\mathbf{n}}$$
$$\times \left[\sum_{\alpha=1}^{\sigma} B_\alpha^\mu \int \prod_{qj} \Psi_{N'_{qj}}^{f\circ}(n\alpha) \cdot \prod_{qj} \Psi_{N_{qj}}^\circ \, dR \cdot \int \varphi_\alpha^{f*}(\mathbf{r}) \varphi_\alpha^\circ \, d\tau \right]. \tag{7.50}$$

For the excitation of "localized" excitons, the correct selection rules are again

$$\mathbf{Q} - \mathbf{k} = \begin{cases} 0, \\ \pm 2\pi \mathbf{a}_l^{-1}, \qquad l = 1, 2, 3. \end{cases} \tag{7.51}$$

Upon their fulfillment, the matrix element [(7.50)] is equal to

$$(\mu f|w|0)_{\text{loc}} = \sqrt{\frac{N}{\sigma}}\, e\mathbf{E}_0 \sum_{\alpha=1}^{\sigma} B_\alpha^\mu \int \prod_{qj} [\Psi_{N'_{qj}}^{f\circ}(n\alpha)\Psi_{N_{qj}}^{\circ}]\, dR \int \varphi_\alpha^{f*}(\mathbf{r})\varphi_\alpha^\circ\, d\tau. \tag{7.52}$$

Since wave functions $\Psi_{N'_{qj}}^{f\circ}(n\alpha)$ and $\Psi_{N_{qj}}^{\circ}$ belong to diverse potential fields with diverse equilibrium positions, the integral

$$\int \prod_{qj} [\Psi_{N'_{qj}}^{f\circ}(n\alpha)\Psi_{N_{qj}}^{\circ}]\, dR, \tag{7.53}$$

entering as a factor into (7.52), will be different from zero if $N'_{qj} = N_{qj}$. In other words, together with the excitation of molecules, several phonons will be simultaneously excited (or absorbed at high temperatures). It must be emphasized that this result is obtained in the case in which "localized" excitons are already formed in the zeroth approximation, whereas in the case of free excitons, the possibility of multiquantum phonon absorptions and emissions arose only in the highest approximations of the theory.

Thus, upon "localized" exciton excitation, wide absorption bands are to be expected owing to the combination of molecular excitation with lattice vibrations and owing to the fact that excited states are nonstationary. Because of the closeness of excitation energy zones, corresponding to various values of μ, and because of the above-mentioned broadening of absorption bands, separate bands will not be permitted but will occur in the form of one wide absorption band. The distribution of intensity in the band may depend on the direction of light propagation and polarization (there will appear bands corresponding to various values of μ), as well as on the mutual disposition of polydimensional potential-energy surfaces as functions of the disposition of molecules in a lattice.

Since, upon local deformation of a crystal, a change in equilibrium position of molecules takes place, a strong probability arises for considerable changes in vibrational quantum numbers. At the same time, noticeable intensity fluctuations must be expected in the band, since the value of the integral [(7.53)] changes with the change of ΔN_{qj}, not monotonically, but in a rather irregular manner. This is the result of the chance disposition of wave-function nodes and antinodes corresponding to the initial and final vibrational states of molecules in a crystal.

CHAPTER VIII

TRANSFORMATION OF ABSORBED ENERGY INTO HEAT AND RADIATION

31. Introduction

If a crystal has passed into an excited state, and if there is no change in the composition of the solid as a result of a photochemical reaction, then such a crystal state is thermodynamically not in equilibrium. The transition of a crystal to a thermodynamically equilibrated state may take place in two ways:

1. The molecular excitation energy is transformed into heat; i.e., a distribution of excitation energy takes place among degrees of freedom which are connected with the molecular vibrations in the lattice.

2. The crystal excitation energy is re-radiated in the form of electromagnetic waves; luminescence of the crystal takes place. Sometimes energy of the same wavelength is radiated (resonance radiation); however, more often, energy of lower frequencies is radiated, and a portion is transformed into heat.

In this work, we shall concern ourselves only with pure substances which do not contain admixtures of foreign materials. Luminescence of pure substances has been comparatively poorly studied. The opinion already has been expressed[74] that, in a pure state, only those substances can luminesce in whose unit cell there is a noncompensated electron layer screened from surrounding neighbors. To such substances belong the rare-earth-element salts, uranyl salts, and others. However, a series of works has shown that many crystals of inorganic and organic compounds, although not containing foreign admixtures, produce luminescence.

S. I. Vavilov showed[75] that luminescence of solid nitrogen is a typical example of luminescence of a pure substance in a solid crystalline state. In this case, the diatomic nitrogen molecules, forming a molecular-type crystal in the solid state, constitute the emitter.

Especially convincing in this respect are the works of I. V. Obreimov, A. F. Prikhotko, and their collaborators.[15,18] In their work, they showed that there is a bright luminescence even in completely pure monocrystals of naphthalene, anthracene, phenanthrene, and other organic compounds.

The problem of transformation of excitation energy into heat in a solid initially excited as a result of photon absorption was first investigated theoretically by J. I. Frenkel[19–21] for atomic lattices of inert gases. By means of qualitative reasoning, Frenkel pointed out the possibility of transitions in a solid which were not accompanied by radiation and which consisted in the emission or absorption of any number of phonons, or in particular, of a number such as would correspond to the transformation of the total excitation energy into heat. According to Frenkel, the possibility of such transitions arises from the following: The corresponding wave functions for vibrational states of a normal and an excited crystal are unlike owing to the displacement of equilibrium distances between atoms in a crystal at the moment of light absorption. This is especially pronounced for localized ("adherent" as J. I. Frenkel calls them) excitons whose emergence is accompanied by local lattice deformation.† J. I. Frenkel considered that this transformation of excitation energy into heat always takes place when light is absorbed by a solid. According to Peierls,[22] in certain cases a crystal must emit the absorbed energy in the form of "modified resonance" radiation and not transform it into heat, i.e., behave like a "diffuser." Frenkel criticized Peierls' work and showed (Ref. 21, p. 653) that in all probability there are no "diffusers" within the meaning of Peierls' theory. Besides, Frenkel proceeded from the assumption that, at the moment of light absorption, free and "localized" excitons are formed. The former pass into a state of "adherent" ("localized") excitons. "Localized" excitons subsequently transform their energy into heat. The transformation process of a free exciton into a "localized" one is, in Frenkel's opinion, a necessary intermediate stage of the transformation of excitation energy into heat.

Apparently, for some molecular crystals the conclusions of Frenkel are essentially correct. However, one cannot unconditionally apply them to all molecular crystals.

In this chapter, we shall study the problem of the transformation of absorbed energy into heat for the case of molecular crystals consisting of polyatomic molecules. In such crystals, the process of transformation of molecular excitation energy into heat may take place in two different ways:

1. Conversion of excitation energy (including electronic excitation) to lattice vibration energy with the aid of interaction forces between molecules

† The probability of excitation energy (of a "localized" exciton) transforming into heat was calculated incorrectly by Frenkel. When calculating this probability, Frenkel did not consider that the wave function of the electronic states of atoms changes when the interatomic distances change. In this work a more rigorous expression [(7.4)] was found for the probability of this conversion (Section 28).

2. Intramolecular conversion of electronic excitation energy into vibrational energy of the atoms which make up the molecules, and a further conversion of vibrational energy of atoms in a molecule to vibrational energy of molecules in a lattice

The first portion of method 2, i.e., the transformation of electronic excitation energy into atomic vibrational energy, was called *intramolecular deactivation* by A. N. Terenin (Ref. 76, p. 74). A. N. Terenin maintains that "the transformation of all electronic excitation energy into potential energy of atomic nuclear motion is characteristic for polyatomic molecules." Here we shall not study the reason for this phenomenon. We shall merely analyze the influence of the interaction between molecules on the transfer of the vibrational energy of atoms in a molecule to lattice vibrations. We shall also study the direct transition of molecular electronic excitation energy to lattice vibrational energy.

Experiments have demonstrated that, at low temperatures, the vibrational portion of energy for molecular electronic vibrational excitation is extremely rapidly (within a period of less than 10^{-8} sec) transferred to lattice vibrations. Among the most convincing works of this kind are those of I. V. Obreimov, A. F. Prikhotko, and their collaborators[13,17,18] on the study of naphthalene, anthracene, and phenanthrene absorption spectra and luminescence, as well as on the comparison of these spectra. In these works, they showed that at low temperatures the absorption spectrum corresponds to the electronic transition plus the vibrational frequencies of the excited molecule; the luminescence spectrum corresponds to transitions from the lowest vibrational state of an excited molecule. Thus the vibrational energy of nuclei can pass over to the lattice vibrations in a period of time less than the lifetime of a molecule in an excited state. These experiments indicate beyond any doubt that the vibrations of nuclei, in any case those of the totally symmetrical type, i.e., those which combine with electronic transitions, quickly lose their energy to lattice vibrations.

The total intramolecular excitation energy may be represented as the sum of vibrational and electronic excitation energy; i.e., one may assume the absence of interaction between both types of molecular excited states. This assumption is approximately justified in molecules, since intramolecular vibration frequencies are considerably smaller than frequencies corresponding to the energy differences of two electronic states.†

In such an approximation, one may consider the problem of the transmission of intramolecular excitation energy to lattice vibrations sepa-

† To study intramolecular deactivation processes it is, of course, impossible to limit oneself to this first approximation; it is necessary to take into account the possibility of energy transition between both types of excited states in a molecule, i.e., pass over to the next approximation.

rately for the electronic excitation of molecules and for the excitation of intramolecular vibrations in a molecule.

Therefore, we shall henceforth assume that the excited state of a molecule is the state which corresponds either to a vibrational or to a purely electronic excitation.

When we study the question of transfer of intramolecular excitation energy to lattice vibrations, we must distinguish two cases: (1) Upon excitation of a crystal, free excitons are formed. (2) Upon excitation of a crystal, "localized" excitons are formed.

32. Behavior of Free Excitons after Their Formation

As was noted above, according to J. I. Frenkel, free excitons must after their formation turn into "localized" excitons. In F. Seitz's work,[72] these views found the following graphic interpretation. In optical transitions excitons appear with wave vectors equal to the wave vector of light. Their group velocity is generally small but may be sufficient for a free exciton to form. However, the group velocity of an exciton must decrease when the wave number decreases. Therefore, if at the moment of formation the exciton's speed is sufficiently great, then within a certain time, as a result of giving its kinetic energy to the lattice vibrations, the exciton loses its velocity and becomes "localized."

In these observations regarding the necessary transformation of a free exciton into a "localized" one, the above-mentioned authors seemingly overlook the following circumstance: The exciton energy loss is not always linked with a decrease in the wave number and speed of the exciton but, on the contrary, may sometimes lead to an increase of the speed of the exciton (see Figure 14).

A second important circumstance which was not taken into account consists in the following: The energy of the free exciton may be less than the energy of the "localized" exciton (see Section 29). In this case, the free exciton will not be able to pass spontaneously into the state of a "localized" one, unless it obtains the necessary energy from heat fluctuation. At low temperatures, this last process is not very probable.

We must, of course, also keep in mind that a free exciton state is not rigorously stationary, since there is a probability (albeit very small) for the direct transformation of exciton energy into lattice vibrational energy. However, this process plays practically no role at all for free excitons, since usually the free exciton gives up its energy in the form of electromagnetic radiation during a considerably shorter time. Thus the luminescence of states which correspond to free excitons may occur only if the excitation energy of the free exciton is less than that of the "localized" exciton, and if, when wave number $\mathbf{k}$ increases, the energy of the free exciton decreases (the exciton has a negative effective mass). Furthermore, the probability for transformation to a "localized" exciton state (or exciton state of other value μ) is less than the probability for photon radiation.

When an exciton with negative "effective" mass forms, the transfer of energy to lattice vibrations will be accompanied by an increase in the wave number of the exciton. As a result of this, the transformation of excitation energy into radiation will be rendered difficult, since the wave number of the exciton will no longer correspond to the wave number of the light wave. The lifetime (with respect to radiation) of the exciton may increase.

Let us now find the probability for the transformation of a crystal from an excited state having a free exciton to the same excited state with a "localized" exciton. The wave function for the excited crystal with one free exciton is given by (5.10):

$$\Psi_1^{f\mu} = \frac{1}{\sqrt{\sigma N}} A_0^\circ(R) \sum_n e^{i\mathbf{kn}} \left(\sum_{\alpha=1}^{\sigma} B_\alpha^\mu \chi_{n\alpha}^f \right). \tag{8.1}$$

The wave function for the excited state of a crystal with one localized exciton is given by (7.34):

$$\Psi_{1,\mathrm{loc}}^{f\mu} = \frac{1}{\sqrt{\sigma N}} \sum_n e^{i\mathbf{kn}} \left[\sum_\alpha B_\alpha^\mu A_1^f(n\alpha) \chi_{n\alpha}^f \right]. \tag{8.2}$$

If both these functions represented stationary states, i.e., if they were exact solutions of equation

$$(T_R + H_0)\Psi = U\Psi, \tag{8.3}$$

then there would be no spontaneous transitions between them. In reality, neither solution is stationary; therefore, there can take place between them spontaneous transitions whose probability in 1 sec will be determined by

$$P_t = \frac{2\pi}{h} \left| \int \Psi_1^{f'\mu'*} (T_R + H_0) \Psi_{1,\mathrm{loc}}^{f\mu}\, d\tau\, dR \right|^2 \delta(U_{\mathrm{loc}} - U_{\mathrm{free}}). \tag{8.4}$$

It follows from (8.4) that the transition probability differs from zero if the law of conservation of energy for the system as a whole is satisfied:

$$U_{\mathrm{loc}} = U_{\mathrm{free}}. \tag{8.5}$$

If the condition given by (8.5) is fulfilled, the probability for transformation in 1 sec from one excited state corresponding to excitation with a localized exciton into a state corresponding to excitation with a free exciton (or the reverse), will be equal to

$$P_t = \frac{2\pi}{h} |\Omega|^2 \tag{8.6}$$

where

$$\Omega = \int \Psi_1^{f'\mu'*}(T_R + H_0)\Psi_{\text{loc}}^{f\mu} \, d\tau \, dR. \tag{8.7}$$

The probability P_t depends on the degree of overlap of wave functions A° and $A_1^f(m\beta)$ for vibrational lattice states without local crystal deformation and with local deformation in the region of one of the molecules of the crystal. Furthermore, P_t depends on the derivatives of wave functions with respect to molecular displacements from their equilibrium positions.

Besides transformation of free exciton excitation energy into lattice vibrational energy or into "localized" exciton energy (and lattice vibrational energy), transitions of free excitons from one excited-state zone into another are also possible. The probability of this type of transition was determined in Chapter IV [expression (4.18)].

33. Behavior of "Localized" Excitons after Their Formation

As we noted previously, excitons with local lattice deformation may form directly at the moment of light absorption or may result from free excitons if the free exciton energy is equal to, or greater than, the "localized" exciton energy. The probability of this transition is determined by expression (8.6).

The "localized" excitons formed do not correspond to stationary crystal states. Because of the violation of adiabatic conditions, there will take place spontaneous transitions into states, in which all of the excitation energy will be distributed over the lattice vibrations. The probability of this process was determined in Section 28.

$$P_T = \frac{2\pi}{h} \sum_j \int_\Omega \Bigg| \sum_i A_0^\circ \left(-\frac{h^2}{M_i} \int \Phi^{\circ *} \frac{\partial \chi_{n\alpha}^f}{\partial R_i} \, d\tau \right) \frac{\partial A^f(n\alpha)}{\partial R_i} \, dR$$
$$+ \int A^\circ \left(-\frac{h^2}{2} \int \Phi^{\circ *} \sum_i \frac{1}{M_i} \frac{\partial^2 \chi_{n\alpha}^f}{\partial R_i^2} \, d\tau \right) A^f \, dR \Bigg|^2 \rho_{qj}(\omega) \, d\Omega. \tag{8.8}$$

We must keep in mind that the processes of energy transfer from the excited molecule to lattice vibrations are determined not only by a change in wave functions for vibrational states of a crystal, by which multiquantum transitions become possible, but also by the fact that corresponding states of a crystal are not quasi-stationary [by the nonzero value of the expressions in parentheses within the integrals of (8.8)]. If the adiabatic conditions were fulfilled (if there were stationary states), the above-mentioned change in wave functions for molecular vibrations in a lattice would result only in the absorption of light quanta with more energy, and the surplus of energy over that necessary to excite molecules would be transferred to lattice vibrations. The process of total transformation of light into heat must necessarily pass through nonstationary states of a crystal.

Since the lattice vibrational frequency differs less from intramolecular vibrational frequencies than from electronic excitation frequencies, we must assume that the probability of intramolecular vibrational energy transformation into heat is greater than the corresponding probability for electronic excitation energy. This apparently explains the rapid transition (mentioned at the end of Section 31) of the vibrational portion of electronic-vibrational molecular excitation energy to lattice vibrational energy.

Thus, upon formation of "localized" excitons, as a result of such states being nonstationary, an excitation energy transformation to heat, i.e., the disappearance of the "localized" exciton, will take place within a certain time, if, of course, during the localized exciton's lifetime (with respect to the transformation into *heat*),

$$\tau_T = \frac{1}{P_T}, \tag{8.9}$$

the exciton is not subjected to other transformations. Such transformations consist of:

1. Disappearance of the "localized" exciton due to radiation (luminescence)
2. Transformation of a "localized" exciton into a free one
3. Disappearance of a "localized" exciton as a result of intramolecular deactivation

Luminescence from "localized" states is possible if the lifetime of the "localized" state τ_T with respect to the transfer of its energy to lattice vibrations is greater than, or comparable to, the lifetime of the localized state with respect to luminescence τ_L. The latter is determined by the relation

$$\tau_L = \frac{h}{2\pi|(\mu f|w|0)_{\text{loc}}|^2}, \tag{8.10}$$

where $(\mu f|w|0)_{\text{loc}}$ must be taken from (7.45).

It seems that, contrary to the generally accepted opinion, the transformation of a "localized" exciton into a free one is also possible in certain cases. At low temperatures, a necessary condition for this process is the requirement that the excitation energy of the "localized" exciton be greater than, or equal to, the excitation energy of the free exciton. In Section 29 we showed that this may take place (case B).

In this connection, if the lifetime of the "localized" exciton with respect to the transformation into a free exciton state ($\tau_t = 1/P_t$) does not exceed the lifetime with respect to the transformation into heat τ_T of the "localized" exciton energy and the lifetime with respect to luminescence τ_L, then such transitions will occur and may subsequently result in luminescence (see Section 34).

In some cases, apparently, an essential role is also played by the intramolecular deactivation of excitation energy. The probability of these processes may be determined in principle when studying luminescence spectra of greatly rarefied vapors.†

34. Necessary Conditions for the Occurrence of Luminescence of Solid Bodies Not Containing Admixtures

Let us analyze the conditions that could favor the occurrence of luminescence of a solid. As was noted above, both free and "localized" excitons may arise as a result of light absorption in a crystal. The luminescence will arise from the radiative transitions between excited states and the ground state. However, these processes will compete with a series of other processes which lead to the disappearance of both types of excitons.

Let us determine the ratio of the number of excitons emitting their energy in the form of radiation to the total number of excitons formed. This ratio is equal to

$$\eta = \frac{P_L}{P_L + P_T + P_D + P_t}, \tag{8.11}$$

where P_L is the probability that in 1 sec the exciton emits its energy in the form of luminescence

P_T is the probability that in 1 sec the exciton gives up its energy to (thermal) lattice vibrations

P_D is the probability that in 1 sec there takes place an intramolecular deactivation which results in the destruction of the exciton

P_t is the probability that in 1 sec a transition of excitons of a given type (free or "localized") to another type takes place

Among possible processes of exciton disappearance we are not considering molecular ionization processes due to heat fluctuations, which transfer the electron over to a free zone. These processes are essential only at comparatively high temperatures and for sufficiently highly excited molecular states.

† In a molecular crystal, however, the role of intramolecular deactivation may be less than in an isolated molecule, since, as a result of the transmission of excitation along the crystal, the lifetime of the excited state for one isolated molecule will be shortened, although the lifetime for the crystal emission is greater than that for the free molecule.

For luminescence to be observable, it is necessary that

$$P_L \sim (P_T + P_D + P_t). \tag{8.12}$$

In the case of localized exciton formation, usually $P_T \gg P_L$; thus such states, as a rule, do not luminesce. If in some cases such luminescence takes place, it must decrease when the temperature rises, since P_T increases with temperature rise. Actually, P_T [(8.8)] depends on the magnitude of molecular displacements from equilibrium positions (see Section 18). As a result of heat fluctuations, fluctuation-type displacements will be superimposed upon the displacements brought about by the exciton localization. If we designate the fluctuation energy necessary to attain a sufficient magnitude of displacements (corresponding to the intersection of potential surfaces) by E_T, the probability of P_T will increase according to the exponential law

$$P_T \sim e^{-E_T/kT}.$$

In the case of free exciton formation, as has been previously noted, P_T does not play an essential role. Therefore, if the intramolecular deactivation is small, and if the probability of P_t is small, a noticeable luminescence will be observed.

If the excitation energy of free excitons is greater than that of "localized" ones, luminescence is hardly possible. If, however, the excitation energy of free excitons is less than that of "localized" excitons, then a luminescence with a large quantum yield will be observed at low temperatures. In this case, luminescence will be promoted by transitions from "localized" states to free exciton states.

Luminescence must decrease even in this case when the temperature rises, since the number of free excitons will decrease at the expense of thermal transfers to localized states, which will subsequently give off their energy to lattice vibrations.

When an exciton moves through a crystalline lattice, a portion of exciton energy is spent on emitting phonons. At the same time, for excitons with negative effective mass, the exciton wave number increases ($\mathbf{k} \to \mathbf{k}' > \mathbf{Q}$). The effect indicated may be evidenced experimentally in two relations:

1. The lifetime of a crystal excited state may increase, since optical transitions are permitted only when the law of photon- and exciton-impulse conservation is observed. If $\mathbf{k} > \mathbf{Q}$, the transition to radiation will be possible only upon simultaneous emission of a photon and a phonon, whose composite quasi impulse is equal to the exciton quasi impulse, or as a result of the presence of inhomogeneities in the lattice (crystalline surface, fissures, isotopes, heat fluctuations, etc.). The violation of lattice periodicity makes optical transitions possible even

when $\mathbf{k} \neq \mathbf{Q}$; therefore, at temperatures different from zero, an increase in lifetime is scarcely possible.

2. The position of the absorption band corresponding to the origin of a free exciton with wave number $\mathbf{k} = \mathbf{Q}$ will not coincide exactly with the luminescence band corresponding to the disappearance of an exciton with wave number $\mathbf{k} \neq \mathbf{Q}$.

Thus we arrive at the following conclusion: If a solid is composed of molecules which, in a high-f excited state, luminesce (small intramolecular deactivation), one will observe the luminescence of such a solid at low temperatures, provided that the magnitude P_T is small for "localized" excitons, and provided that, free exciton excitation with an excitation energy smaller than the localized exciton excitation energy is possible in the solid.

A weak dependence of wave functions, which determine the optical behavior of a molecule, upon the distances between the molecules of a crystal and the deformation of a molecule is conducive to small values of P_T. Such weak dependence occurs in a series of cases:

1. Solids containing atoms of rare-earth elements, uranyl salts, and others. The optical behavior of such solids is determined by internal electron transitions within $4f$ (or $5f$) levels in atoms. The bonding of these atoms with other atoms depends on external electrons. In other words, in this case optical electrons differ from electrons which participate in interaction forces between atoms. As a result, when distances between atoms and ions change, only the surfaces of external electron distributions are deformed; electron states of (internal) electrons of the $4f$ shell are little affected. Conversely, a change in the state of internal electrons of the $4f$ shell tells but little concerning the change of interaction forces between atoms in a crystal lattice. In this manner, the stationary character of states increases, since the derivatives $\partial\Phi^\circ/\partial R_i$ and $\partial^2\Phi^\circ/\partial R_i^2$ will be small, and since, consequently, the probability P_T will also be small. Absorption spectra of such crystals must not be strongly displaced in relation to the spectra of corresponding gases, inasmuch as the displacement magnitude of the absorption band is determined by the change in interaction forces between molecules upon excitation of one of the molecules. Crystals of this type should display intense luminescence (especially at low temperatures).

2. Solids formed from molecules of organic compounds which contain multiple (double, triple) bonds. To these solids belong molecular crystals of the aromatic series. In molecules of these crystals, the π electrons of double (triple) bonds are involved in the optical properties, while the σ electrons play the essential role of the formation of intramolecular bonds. In addition, molecules of such compounds usually contain a large number of hydrogen atoms (or of other groups of atoms),

which are situated on the periphery of the molecule and which are bonded only by σ electrons; the latter do not take part in the optical excitation of the molecule. In a certain sense, hydrogen atoms (CH_3 groups and others) play the same role as the external electrons of the atoms in rare-earth elements. They accept all influences of the surrounding molecules and protect the π electrons from perturbations. Thus the dependence of molecular wave functions for π electrons on molecular displacements is diminished. This leads to a decrease in matrix elements [(8.8)] and, therefore, to an increase in the lifetime of the corresponding molecular states also. Consequently, the probability of luminescence increases. Actually, all these substances display a strong luminescence, especially at low temperatures. If, upon light absorption, excitons with negative effective mass form, the lifetime of excited crystalline states may exceed that of the corresponding excited states of an isolated molecule. This last effect may be observed only in large monocrystals which do not contain inhomogeneities and which are at low temperature.

Investigations by the Soviet school of luminescence of S. I. Vavilov have established the scientific basis for classifying luminescence according to various characteristics. S. I. Vavilov[75] proposed the division of luminescence into three types—spontaneous, forced, and recombinational—which are distinguished by their mechanism. This division is not linked with the aggregation state of the substance. V. L. Levshin[77] proposed dividing the luminescence of solids into two types, differing completely in their external characteristics and in their radiation mechanism. One fluorescence was named by him *crystalline fluorescence.* This fluorescence was observed only in a crystalline state; it did not have any direct link with the absorption spectrum; it possessed a complicated damping character and was accompanied by photoconductivity. The second fluorescence was called by V. L. Levshin *fluorescence of discrete centers.* It was observed in all states of aggregation; it has a direct connection with the absorption spectrum, possesses an exponential damping character, and is not accompanied by photoconductivity. V. L. Levshin relates fluorescence in crystals of aromatic compounds to fluorescence of discrete centers.

The above-mentioned division is extremely essential and necessary in scientifically establishing the investigation of luminescence in solids. However, it seems that, on the basis of the present work and of certain experimental data relative to luminescence spectra of molecular crystals at low temperatures (works of I. V. Obreimov, A. F. Prikhotko, and their school), the following conclusions may be made: luminescence of molecular crystals may essentially depend on the crystalline structure of the solid. The luminescence of such solids often takes place during transitions to a normal state from excited crystal states, which correspond to the occurrence in a crystal of free excitons. Such excited states may arise only in crystalline solids, and they depend on the lattice structure.

Therefore, luminescence of discrete centers should not always be understood to be a luminescence which takes place completely in localized fluorescence centers. Sometimes excitation energy may execute a considerable path in a crystal, passing from one "center" to another prior to being radiated. It is necessary in this connection that a direct transmission of excitation energy from one center to another occur. This process of energy transmission affects relatively little the character of the luminescence. Therefore, if we do not take into consideration these small changes, we can sometimes identify such a luminescence with the luminescence of the center, as found in a free state.

For crystalline fluorescence, excitation energy is transmitted by the electron over the crystal, and the change from a crystalline state to other states of aggregation may destroy the capacity for luminescence.

CHAPTER IX

COMPARISON OF THEORY WITH EXPERIMENT

In some of the preceding chapters we pointed out the connection between results obtained and experimental data. In this chapter we shall consider supplementary experimental data.

It must be noted here that available experimental material is often only preliminary and incomplete. The reasons for this are, on the one hand, the great experimental difficulties that arise when carrying out experiments of this kind, and on the other hand, the absence of theory, which often causes an insufficiently rational foundation of the experiment. For instance, many measurements were made in nonpolarized light and at relatively high temperature.

We hope this work will serve as a certain stimulus to setting up additional experiments which, on their part, will lead to a fuller development of the theory.

35. Combinational Scattering (Raman) Spectra

Despite the fact that the discovery of combinational scattering (Raman scattering) in 1928 by L. I. Mandelstam and G. S. Landsberg was made on crystalline quartz, combinational scattering (Raman scattering) of solids up to the present time has had considerably less study than the scattering of liquids and gases. This is explained first of all by the great experimental difficulties of investigating combinational scattering (Raman scattering) of monocrystals. One must have transparent monocrystals of sufficient dimensions. The investigations must be conducted in polarized light and at low temperatures. Secondly, it seems to be explained by the prevailing, long-standing opinion that combinational scattering (Raman scattering) of crystals is not different from scattering of liquids and gases.

For many vibrational frequencies, the differences between combinational scattering (Raman) spectra of gases, liquids, and solids are actually very small. However, as follows from the investigation conducted here, significant deviations from this rule may be observed.

As was shown in the preceding chapters, upon transition from a gaseous state to a crystalline one, a displacement of molecular frequencies, a splitting (if, in a unit cell, there is more than one molecule or if, in a molecule, there are degenerate states and the symmetry of the crystal is lower than that of the molecule), and a widening of lines as a result of interaction with lattice vibrations take place.

If the corresponding molecular vibration in an isolated molecule is not accompanied by a change of the dipole moment of the molecule, all changes enumerated above are very small and, except for the widening of lines, may often not be observed under present experimental conditions.

Thus intramolecular vibrational frequencies, observed in combinational scattering (Raman scattering), may be divided into two groups: (1) vibrations noticeably affected by crystalline structure (these vibrations must be active in the infrared spectrum) and (2) vibrations not noticeably affected by crystalline structure. Sometimes, for one and the same molecule, vibrations may belong to both above-mentioned groups. Several researchers have already noted this circumstance. Thus G. Herzberg, in a monograph devoted to infrared and Raman spectra of polyatomic molecules, writes (Ref. 50, p. 534): "Worthy of our attention is the fact that in certain cases various vibrations of one and the same molecule give non-identical relative frequency displacements."

Table 16 shows frequency displacements for certain substances as observed in the combinational scattering (Raman scattering) of gas, liquid, and solid, as well as frequencies observed in the infrared spectrum, if these frequencies coincide with combinational scattering (Raman scattering) frequencies. Although the molecule C_6H_6 possesses a center of symmetry and should not have coinciding vibration frequencies in the infrared spectrum and the combinational scattering (Raman) spectrum, nevertheless, owing to the chance coincidence of certain vibrational frequencies in the combinational scattering (Raman) spectrum, larger frequency displacements occur upon transition from gas to crystal than

TABLE 16. DISPLACEMENT OF C. S. (RAMAN) FREQUENCIES IN CONDENSED PHASES FOR MOLECULAR VIBRATIONS, CORRELATED WITH SIMULTANEOUS INFRARED ACTIVITY

Molecule	Combinational scattering (Raman)			Corresponding infrared frequency	Literature source
	Gas ν, cm^{-1}	Liquid $\Delta\nu = \nu_G - \nu_L$	Solid $\Delta\nu = \nu_G - \nu_S$		
HCl	2886	101	118	2886.7	[78], [79]
CS_2	665	−1.5	.....	......	[80]
C_6H_6	992	0	.....	......	[81]
C_6H_6	3069	7.1	.....	3073	[81]
C_6H_6	3099	9.0	10.0	3099	[81]
C_6H_6	3045	10.0	11.0	3045	[81]

for vibrations that are only present in the combinational scattering (Raman) spectrum.

Other experimental data were mentioned in Section 10.

36. Infrared Spectra

Studies of changes in infrared absorption spectra, with changes in the state of aggregation for a substance, encounter numerous experimental difficulties. There are comparatively few works devoted to these problems.

From all that was stated above, it is clear that, in order to discover the corresponding changes, one must conduct experiments at the lowest possible temperature, with thin absorbing layers, and certainly in polarized light. We do not know of any works where all these conditions were fulfilled.

Of great interest are the investigations undertaken by A. F. Prikhotko, I. V. Rodnikova, and K. Shabaldas to clarify the changes introduced in an infrared spectrum upon transition of certain substances to a crystalline state. Unfortunately, since these authors conducted their investigations in the photographic infrared region, they were only able to observe spectra corresponding to high combinational frequencies. Besides, the investigations were carried out in nonpolarized light. Although these works were interrupted by the war and were not completely finished, the results published by I. V. Rodnikova are still of interest.

The spectra of ethylene were studied at a temperature near the melting point. The molecule of ethylene C_2H_4 belongs to the point symmetry group D_{2h} (the characters of irreducible representations for this group were given in Table 2). This molecule possesses 12 normal vibrations which are distributed among the irreducible representations of the molecule's symmetry group in the following manner:

$$3A_{1g} + 2A_{2g} + B_{1g} + A_{1u} + 2B_{1u} + A_{2u} + 2B_{2u}.$$

The molecule has a center of symmetry; therefore, the vibrations active in the infrared spectrum $(2B_{1u} + A_{2u} + 2B_{2u})$ should not appear in the combinational scattering (Raman) spectrum. Experimental data corroborate the absence of coincidences in both spectra of gases.[50]

As has already been indicated in the preceding section, when there is absence of coincidences of vibrational frequencies in the infrared spectrum and the combinational scattering (Raman) spectrum, one must expect small changes in the combinational scattering (Raman) spectrum when the state of aggregation changes. The combinational scattering (Raman) spectrum of the ethylene molecule well confirms this rule. All combinational scattering (Raman) lines observed in a gas are also observed in a liquid with very small displacements (Ref. 50, p. 326).

Vibrations observed in the infrared spectrum behave quite differently. In her doctoral dissertation, A. F. Prikhotko, on the basis of the analysis of spectra for a crystal, a liquid, and a gas in the photographic infrared region, concludes: "The absorption spectrum of the ethylene crystal is remarkable in that it has a large number of satellites and a series of new absorption lines, which are absent in a gas and which appear in a liquid and mainly in a crystal."

Figure 15 represents schematically (according to data furnished by I. V. Rodnikova's work[82]) absorption spectra of a gas (without rotational structure) and of a crystal. We see in the absorption spectrum of the crystal a large number of new absorption bands in comparison with the gas spectrum. A portion of these absorption bands must be

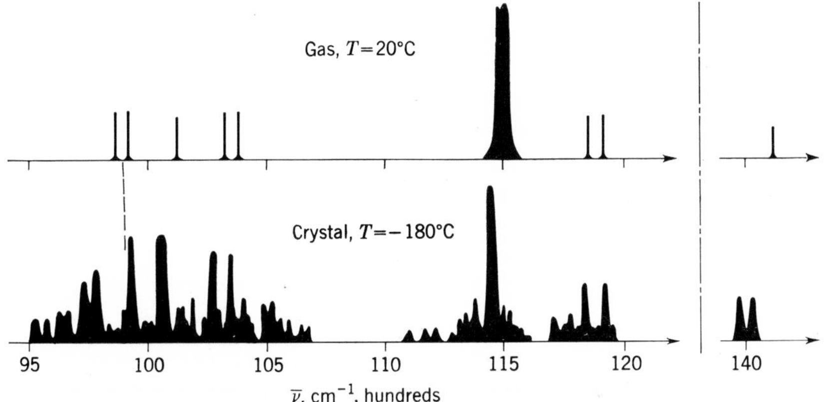

FIG. 15. Schematic representation of the absorption spectrum of the ethylene molecule in the photographic infrared region. (*After Rodnikova.*)

attributed to the combination with small lattice vibrational frequencies. However, the genesis of other absorption bands is apparently linked to the splitting of absorption bands in a crystal; this splitting was analyzed in this work and is caused by intermolecular interaction.

Since ethylene molecules do not have degenerate vibrations, it is quite impossible to explain the observed splitting (as is frequently done) by the removal of degeneracy in the crystalline field.

According to X-ray studies,[83] an ethylene crystal at $-175°$ belongs to the rhombic system with two molecules per unit cell. Therefore, a splitting of absorption bands into two components must be expected. Figure 15 clearly shows the splitting (noted in the previously cited work[82]) of the absorption band at 14,100 cm^{-1} for a gas into two components in a crystal of 13,972 and 14,014 cm^{-1} ($\Delta\nu = 42$ cm^{-1}). These two components should have a different polarization.

The methane spectrum in the photographic infrared region was investigated at 20.4°K in the laboratory for crystals of UFTI [Ukrainian Photo-Technical Institute]. A. F. Prikhotko notes in her dissertation that the spectrum of the crystal is richer in lines than the spectrum of the gas. A. F. Prikhotko points out the removal of degeneracy in the crystalline field of degenerate molecular vibrations as a possible reason for this. In view of the incompleteness of this work (there are no measurements taken in polarized light), it is at this time still difficult to say whether one can explain all new absorption bands merely by the removal of vibrational degeneracy in the isolated molecule. Apparently this is not so, if only because, owing to the neutrality and absence of a static dipole moment in a methane molecule, it is not possible to expect noticeable absorption-band splittings as a result of the removal of degeneracy.

Besides the splitting by a crystalline field of degenerate vibrations in a free molecule, other forms of absorption-band splitting in crystals were not known. Therefore, an attempt was made to explain every splitting by means of this first phenomenon. And, if it was not possible to do this, an attempt was made to explain the splitting by a different kind of polymerization and association of molecules. Without denying the possibility of molecular polymerization and association in some cases, we believe that splitting phenomena may frequently be explained by the theory developed in the present work.

The difference in position and in relative intensity of vibrational bands in a liquid, a solid, and a vapor state is noted by other authors as well. Thus, in a recently published work of Richards and Thompson,[84] the infrared spectra of more than 20 substances (in a solid and liquid state) were investigated. These substances consisted of nonpolar molecules (in order to exclude effects connected with the association of molecules). The authors came to the conclusion that "the bands of a solid are sharper; many wide bands, existing in a liquid, split into two or more components upon transition to a solid state; in many cases, albeit not always, there are more bands in a solid state than in a liquid." Unfortunately, the authors conducted their measurements at relatively high temperatures and in nonpolarized light.

It would be very desirable to conduct a series of experimental investigations of crystalline absorption spectra at low temperatures and in polarized light, especially for crystals consisting of molecules that do not have degenerate vibrations in a free state.

37. Absorption and Luminescence Spectra in the Visible and Ultraviolet Regions

a. Naphthalene Crystal. Henri and de Lazlo[85] and de Lazlo[86] investigated the spectrum of light absorption (in the ultraviolet region) by naphthalene vapor. A fuller investigation, together with an analysis of the vibrational structure of the spectrum, was made by A. F. Prikhotko.[32]

When analyzing the absorption spectrum in a layer of gas 100 cm long, Prikhotko established three electronic transitions and the vibrational frequencies which combine with them. Table 17 lists the results obtained.

TABLE 17. OBSERVED ELECTRONIC TRANSITION FREQUENCIES IN NAPHTHALENE, WITH STATE SYMMETRIES, POLARIZATIONS, AND COMBINING VIBRATIONAL FREQUENCIES

Electronic transition, cm^{-1}	Irreducible representation	Direction of vibration of electric vector	Vibrational frequencies, cm^{-1}
32,455	B_{2u}	y	473, 703, 1002, 1181, 1415, 1449, and 1603
35,905	B_{1u}	z	493 and 1397
About 44,000	B_{1u}	z	

The irreducible representations corresponding to these electronic transitions, as well as the direction of electric-vector vibrations in the molecule, are shown as the basis of a comparison with this author's theoretical calculation.[46] The same results were obtained in a later theoretical work by Coulson[87] for the first two electronic transitions, which are the only ones that interest us further.

The absorption spectra for solutions of naphthalene in hexane, studied by de Lazlo,[86] furnish the same picture as the gas spectrum. The spectrum of the solution is merely displaced in relation to the spectrum of the gas. The displacement of the first transition is unlike that of the second. For each group of lines in a gas, de Lazlo was able to show in the solution the corresponding absorption maximum. Figure 16 juxtaposes the spectrum of naphthalene gas and that of a solution in hexane (according to de Lazlo). Thus the interaction of the solvent molecules with the naphthalene molecules does not result in the emergence of new absorption lines, but merely displaces the spectrum. This was to be expected, since, as a result of the absence of resonance interaction, the excitation energy of a naphthalene molecule in solution ΔE_p will differ from the excitation energy of free molecule ΔE_m only by the energy difference for the interaction of an excited and a normal naphthalene molecule with the surrounding molecules of the solvent:

$$\Delta E_p = \Delta E_m + D.$$

A considerably more complicated picture is observed in a crystal. The absorption spectrum of naphthalene monocrystals at the temperature of liquid hydrogen is now relatively well known, thanks to the works of A. F. Prikhotko.[13,32] Here we shall merely indicate the most fundamental features of the spectrum which are necessary for a comparison with theory.

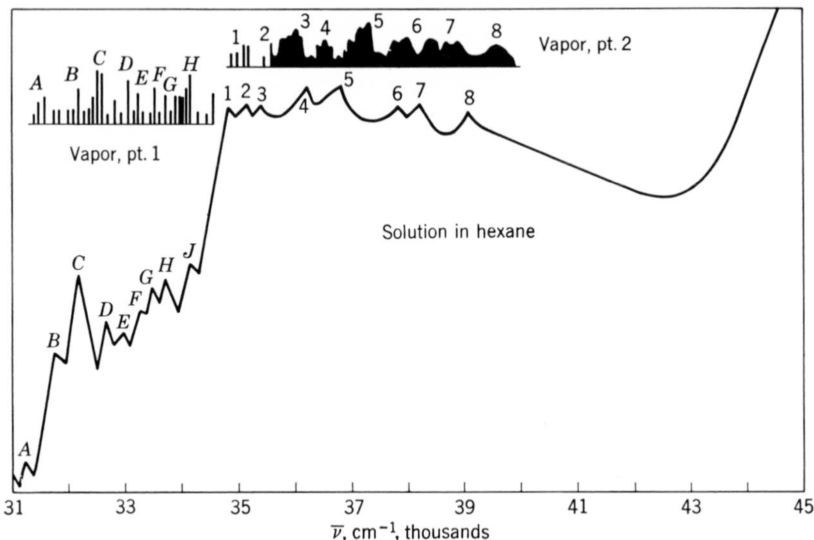

FIG. 16. Schematic representation of the absorption spectrum of naphthalene in the near ultraviolet. (*After de Lazlo.*)

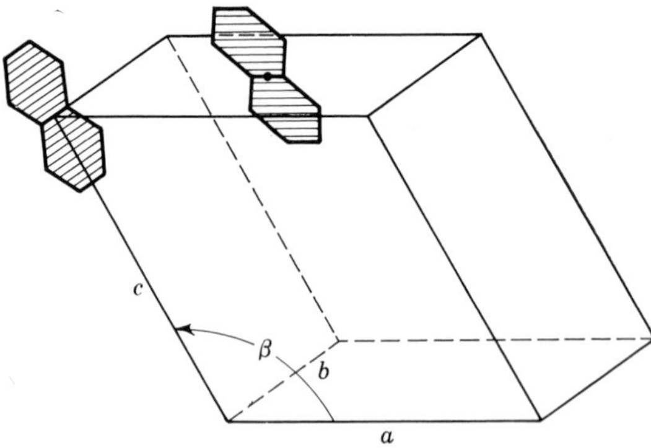

FIG. 17. Disposition of the two molecules of naphthalene in the unit cell of the monoclinic crystal.

Naphthalene crystallizes[64] in a monoclinic-prismatic system C_{2h}^{5}, with $a = 8.29$ A, $b = 5.97$ A, $c = 8.68$ A, and $\beta = 122.7°$. In the unit cell there are two molecules whose disposition is schematically shown in Figure 17. The long molecular axis z forms, with axes a and b of the unit cell and with the perpendicular to planes ab, angles of 115.3°, 102.6°, and

28.7°, respectively. The intermediate axis of the molecule forms, with the same axes of the cell, angles of 71.2°, 28.8°, and 69.1°.

Crystals obtained from vapors represent fine leaves whose plane coincides with the plane *ab* of the crystal. When studying the absorption of light, the latter is usually directed perpendicularly to the plane of the leaf. The vibrations of the electric vector for the light wave are in this case either parallel to axis *a* of the crystal (*a* component) or parallel to axis *b* of the crystal (*b* component).

The absorption spectrum of very fine (fraction of a micron) naphthalene monocrystals at a temperature of 20.4°K represents the sum total of a large number of absorption bands; some of these bands (especially in the *a* component) have a very small width. Between bands of strong absorption, a background of continuous absorption is usually observed. This background becomes stronger in proportion to the increase in the thickness of the crystal, especially in the short-wave portion, and, for thicknesses beginning with 1 mm, turns into a continuous absorption beginning with a frequency of 31,476 cm^{-1}. New absorption bands simultaneously appear in the long-wave portion of the spectrum.

It is to be noted that the study of the naphthalene absorption spectrum was usually limited to the study of absorption bands in the long-wave portion, and that of continuous absorption in the short-wave portion, of the spectrum. It was only work with very fine layers of monocrystals which enabled A. F. Prikhotko to obtain absorption bands in the short-wave portion of the spectrum.

The first electronic transition in the molecule (32,455 cm^{-1}), together with its vibrational structure in the crystal, yields corresponding series in both spectral components (*a* and *b*); in relation to the absorption in a gas, these series are displaced by 500 cm^{-1} toward long waves. These absorption bands must be determined by the excitation in the crystal of "localized" excitons. According to (7.22), the energy of the crystal is in this case equal to

$$\Delta E^1_{\text{loc}} = \Delta E^1_m + \mathcal{E}^{1\circ} - \mathcal{E}^\circ,$$

since $\Delta\epsilon_\mu(\mathbf{k}) \simeq 0$ for "localized" excitons. In this manner, the change in lattice energy upon excitation of a "localized" exciton will be determined from the condition

$$\frac{\mathcal{E}^{1\circ} - \mathcal{E}^\circ}{2\pi hc} \approx 500 \text{ cm}^{-1}.$$

However, to the first electronic transition in the molecule in a crystal, there correspond weak and extremely long wave absorption bands: 29,944 cm^{-1} in a *b* component and 29,931 cm^{-1} in an *a* component. The splitting ($\Delta\nu = 13$ cm^{-1}) and the sharp polarization of these split components indicate that both of them appear as a result of the formation of free excitons in a crystal. In this case, by virtue of (5.34), the crystal excitation energy will be equal to

$$\Delta E_1^1 = \Delta E_m^1 + D^1 + \sum_n{}' (M_{n1,01}^1 + M_{n2,01}^1), \qquad b \text{ component},$$

$$\Delta E_2^1 = \Delta E_m^1 + D^1 + \sum_n{}' (M_{n1,01}^1 - M_{n2,01}^1), \qquad a \text{ component}.$$

If we equate the frequency difference to the experimental magnitude

$$\Delta E_1^1 - \Delta E_2^1 = 2 \sum M_{n2,01}^1 = 13 \cdot 2\pi hc,$$

we obtain

$$\sum_n M_{n2,01}^1 \approx 8 \times 10^{-4} \text{ ev}. \tag{9.1}$$

The displacement of the absorption band in relation to the gas is equal to 2518 cm^{-1}; consequently,

$$D^1 + \sum_n{}' M_{n1,01}^1 = -0.31 \text{ ev}. \tag{9.2}$$

The ratio of the intensities of both components of the splitting, according to (5.35), must be

$$\frac{I(1)}{I(2)} = \cot^2 \alpha \approx 7.2.$$

In A. F. Prikhotko's experiments, the intensities were not measured; however, it is noted that the line in the a component (29,931 cm^{-1}) is very faint; in the b component (29,944 cm^{-1}), it is sharp and more intense.

Utilizing Robertson's data concerning the dimensions of the naphthalene unit cell and the disposition of molecules therein, one can roughly estimate the sum of matrix elements [(9.1)] in theory, if one limits oneself to taking into account the interaction of the nearest molecules and if, for the matrix elements, one uses the approximate expressions (3.20).

$$\sum_n{}' M_{n2,01} \approx 3.6 \times 10^{14} \left| \int \varphi^{1*}(\mathbf{r}) \varphi^\circ \, d\tau \right|^2. \tag{9.3}$$

Inasmuch as (9.3) is positive, it indicates that the disposition of split components is qualitatively in agreement with the experiment.

Equating the calculated value of (9.3) with the experimental one of (9.1), we obtain for the square of the matrix element of the transition in a molecule the value

$$\left| \int \varphi^{1*}(\mathbf{r}) \varphi^\circ \, d\tau \right|^2 \approx 2.2 \times 10^{-18} \text{ cm}^2. \tag{9.4}$$

Using (9.4), one can estimate (by order of magnitude) the oscillator strength for the transition in a molecule

$$f \approx 0.01.$$

To each molecular excitation consisting of the first electronic transition, there must, in a crystal, correspond a split absorption band; one component of the latter will be in the *b* spectrum, the other, considerably less intense, will be in the *a* component. Insofar as the matrix elements of the electronic-vibrational transition and D^1 differ from the corresponding magnitudes of a purely electronic transition, the magnitude of the splitting and the displacement of corresponding absorption bands will also be different. Therefore, the distances of the vibronic bands from the corresponding purely electronic absorption bands will not be rigorously equal to the vibrational frequencies observed in a free molecule. This actually occurs for absorption bands observed in a *b* component.

Vibrational frequencies in a gas, cm⁻¹	*Vibrational frequencies in a crystal, cm⁻¹*
473	400
703	724
1002	1051
1181	1282
1415	1383
1603	1463

In a crystal, all these bands are of very low intensity in the *b* component; in the *a* component, there are very weak absorption traces, the position of which is difficult to measure.

To the second transition in the molecule (35,905 cm^{-1}), a large number of wide absorption bands correspond in a crystal; among them, an absorption band of 33,736 cm^{-1} stands out by its extremely high intensity; it is comparatively easy to establish from the latter band combinational repetitions with frequencies of 518 and 1398 cm^{-1}. On this basis, Prikhotko identifies precisely this absorption band, with the frequency 35,905 cm^{-1}, observed in naphthalene vapor. A characteristic peculiarity of all these absorption bands is their large displacement in comparison with corresponding bands of the gas spectrum:

$$\mathcal{E}^{2°} - \mathcal{E}° \approx -2169 \text{ cm}^{-1} \cdot 2\pi hc.$$

A crystal absorption-band displacement large in comparison with gas absorption bands indicates a significant change in interaction forces upon excitation of molecules in a crystal. Therefore, absorption is always linked to lattice vibrational excitation. The corresponding absorption lines are wide.

To molecular excitations involving the second electronic transition as well as molecular vibrations, there is a corresponding free exciton excitation in a crystal. This results in a corresponding splitting of crystalline absorption bands. Table 18 indicates the split frequencies (in reciprocal centimeters) observed in an absorption spectrum corresponding to the second transition in a molecule.

TABLE 18. FREQUENCIES OF LINES OF THE SECOND ELECTRONIC TRANSITION IN NAPHTHALENE IN THE VAPOR AND THE CRYSTAL

Vapor, cm^{-1}	Crystal, cm^{-1}		
	b component	*a* component	Magnitudes of splitting
35,905	31,063	31,050	13
36,398	31,620	31,474	146
37,302	32,255	32,227	28

Figure 18 represents (according to A. F. Prikhotko's work) a portion of the absorption spectrum (at a temperature of 20.4°K), of a naphthalene monocrystal, of light with two polarizations (*a* is the direction of the electric vector parallel to axis *a* of the crystal, and *b* is the direction of the electric vector parallel to axis *b* of the crystal). The splitting of the two absorption bands and the sharp polarization of split components are

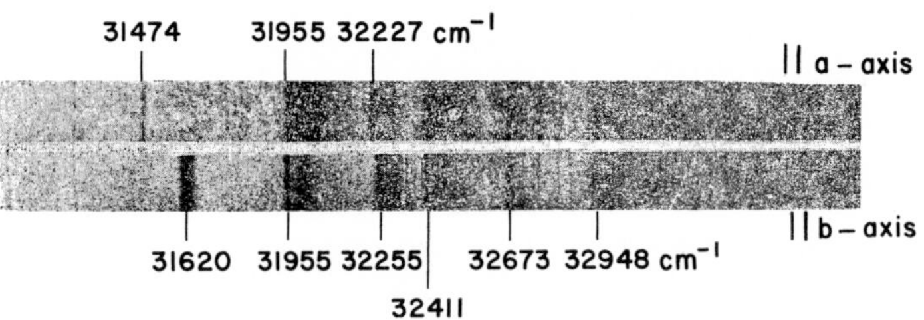

FIG. 18. Polarized light absorption spectra of monocrystals of naphthalene at 20.4°K for two orientations of the elective vector of the light wave. (*After Prikhotko.*[13,32])

clearly visible on the photograph. The bands, whose positions coincide in both components, correspond to the excitation of "localized" excitons in the crystal.

It would be interesting to investigate the absorption spectra of the naphthalene monocrystal with the ray directed along the monoclinic axis and with only one of the two split components present in the spectrum. The intensity of the component should vary from zero to a certain maximum magnitude for a Nicol turn of 90°.

All the most intensive absorption bands in the naphthalene crystal are linked to the second electronic transition in the molecule. For such excitations, the interaction of the molecule with its neighbors in the crystal varies considerably. As a result of this, the molecular equilibrium positions are displaced, and the excitation energy passes over to lattice vibrations. These excited states will possess a short lifetime, shorter than the time necessary for radiation. Luminescence from states which correspond to absorption with formation of "localized" excitons of the second electronic transition in a molecule is therefore not possible.

Since the free exciton states have, in this case, less energy than the "localized" exciton states, a certain portion of "localized" excitons will pass to a free exciton state (see Chapter VIII). The latter free excitons will give off their energy in the form of radiation. This process is apparently responsible for the intense luminescence of naphthalene crystals. The luminescence begins with frequencies of 31,062 and 31,044 cm^{-1} (weaker), and these frequencies correspond to the excitation energy for free excitons of the second transition in the molecule. According to a detailed investigation conducted by I. V. Obreimov and K. G. Shabaldas[15] on the luminescence spectrum for the naphthalene crystal at a temperature of 20.4°K, the most intense luminescence spectrum begins with the above-indicated lines and extends further toward lower frequencies. This is because the transition to a normal state is accompanied by the excitation of intramolecular vibrations and thus lower frequency lines.

Light absorption bands corresponding to the excitation of the first electronic transition in the molecule and to its combinations with molecular vibrations are of low intensity. The frequencies of this band are not much displaced (500 cm^{-1}) in relation to the frequencies of corresponding excitations in a free molecule. This small displacement indicates a small change in interaction forces (this is also corroborated by the comparatively small width of absorption bands); it also bears witness to a lifetime sufficient for luminescence to occur by transition to the ground state.

To an absorption band of 31,960 cm^{-1} (this band is dependent on "localized" exciton excitation), there corresponds in the luminescence spectrum a doublet of 31,960 and 31,965 cm^{-1}. Connected with this doublet is a series of lines located at periodic distances from it. The distances are equal to the periods of progressions starting with the line of 31,062 cm^{-1}. We also observe in the luminescence spectrum a frequency of 29,941 cm^{-1}, which appears upon transition to the ground state from an excited state corresponding to free excitons of the first electronic transition in the molecule.

b. Anthracene Crystal. The anthracene crystal belongs to the monoclinic-prismatic group of symmetry C_{2h}^5 with two molecules per unit cell;

the disposition of these molecules recalls that of the molecules in a naphthalene crystal. The first electronic transition in the molecule has an electric moment direction parallel to the intermediate axis of the molecule.

The absorption spectrum of anthracene crystals at a temperature of 20.4°K was investigated by I. V. Obreimov and A. F. Prikhotko.[17] Figure 19 is a diagram borrowed from the work cited and representing the absorption for components *a* and *b* of the spectrum. From this diagram, one can see immediately that the portion of absorption bands starting with an electronic transition of 25,370 cm^{-1} is simultaneously

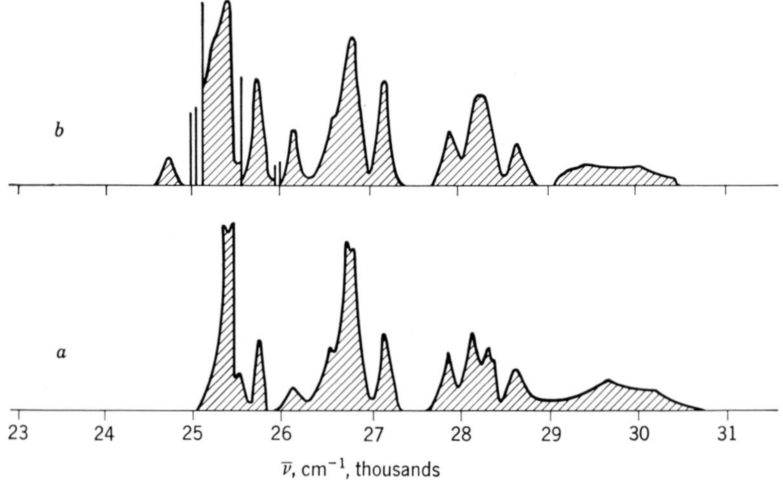

FIG. 19. Schematic representation of *a* and *b* components of the absorption spectrum of anthracene at 20.4°K. (*After Obreimov and Prikhotko.*)

present in both spectral components (absorption bands in component *b* are more intense). All these absorption bands correspond to the excitation of "localized" excitons in the crystal. The general displacement of absorption bands in comparison with the gas spectrum is very great ($\sim$2246 cm^{-1}). This indicates a significant change in interaction forces upon molecular excitation.

Besides absorption bands coinciding in *a* and *b* components, there is in the *b* component a series of absorption bands (as a rule, considerably narrower), which are situated primarily on the short-wavelength side. These are absorption bands of 24,700, 24,962, 25,046, 25,367 cm^{-1}, etc. (Ref. 17, Table 4). These absorption bands are explained by the excitation of free excitons in a crystal.

As was shown in Section 22, in crystals containing two molecules per unit cell, two types of free excitons ($\mu = 1, 2$), with a wave number equal to the wave number of the light wave, may be excited under the action of light. The movement of these excitons is of various velocities. The velocity of movement for excitons of one type may be so small that the formation of free excitons of this type becomes impossible. The fact that, in an anthracene crystal, one observes absorption in one component only indicates that this absorption is dependent on the excitation of free excitons of one type only.

The luminescence spectrum of an anthracene crystal at a temperature of 20.4°K was studied by I. V. Obreimov, A. F. Prikhotko, and K. G. Shabaldas.[18] The entire luminescence spectrum begins with a frequency of 24,909 cm^{-1}; therefore, it corresponds to a transition from the excited state formed by a free exciton to the ground state of the crystal.

c. *Naphthacene Crystal.* The naphthacene molecule belongs to the point symmetry group D_{2h}. The molecule does not possess degenerate energy levels. According to Bethe, it is therefore impossible to expect level splittings in its crystalline state. Scheibe and Kandler[89] investigated the spectrum of crystalline naphthacene and showed that the absorption spectrum differs for two mutually perpendicular polarizations. In one component, an absorption band of 525 mμ is observed; in the other component, bands of 475 and 445 mμ, and others, are observed. In the polycrystal reflection spectrum, absorption bands of 434, 462, 495, and 526 mμ are found.[89] The same absorption bands are observed upon absorption in a fine layer of naphthacene sublimed on glass (see solid curve in Figure 20). The dashed curve in Figure 20 shows the optical absorption spectrum for a solution of naphthacene in α-bromnaphthalene. It is evident from this figure that the spectrum of the solution does not contain two extremely long-wave "crystalline" absorption bands.

The presence of dichroism was also confirmed in Jelley's more recent experiments (Ref. 90, p. 338) with naphthacene crystals obtained upon crystallization from α-bromnaphthalene.

The most detailed studies of naphthacene-monocrystal absorption spectra in polarized light and their comparison with vapor spectra were carried out by A. Y. Eichis in her candidate's dissertation. The results obtained by her are listed in Table 19.

TABLE 19. FREQUENCIES OF LINES OF THE FIRST ELECTRONIC TRANSITION IN NAPHTHACENE IN THE VAPOR AND THE CRYSTAL

Absorption spectrum	Frequency, cm^{-1}		
Naphthacene vapor (15-cm path), 20°C	22,200	23,625	25,000
Monocrystal of thickness of order of tenths of micron, −190°C:			
Vibration of electric vector ∥ *b*	19,235	20,715	22,320
Vibration of electric vector ⊥ *b*	19,810	21,145	22,545
Magnitude of splitting	575	430	225

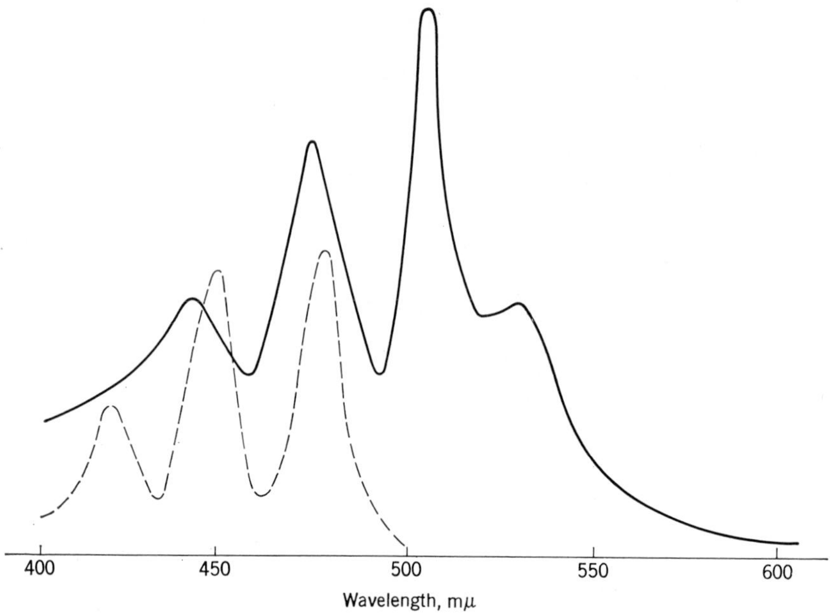

Fig. 20. Schematic representation of the first absorption band of naphthacene. *Continuous curve,* absorption of a solid layer; *Dashed curve,* absorption of a solution in α-bromnaphthalene.

Figure 21 shows a photograph of absorption spectra for vapors and for a monocrystal in polarized light, according to the data of A. Y. Eichis (a is the absorption spectrum for vapors; b is the absorption spectrum of a naphthacene monocrystal for two polarization components). A. Y. Eichis also determined the dispersion curves of monocrystals in polarized light. From these curves, she was able to estimate the oscillator strength of the first electronic transition in a crystal. The oscillator strength proved to be equal to 0.2 for the spectrum with an electric vector of light vibration parallel to axis b, and equal to 0.1 for a vibration perpendicular to axis b.

It follows from Table 19 that, relative to the spectrum of vapors, the crystalline spectrum is displaced by approximately 2600 cm^{-1}. Besides, each band is split into two sharply polarized bands, each of which is found in only one component of the spectrum. The magnitude of the splitting is indicated in Table 19. The sharp polarization of absorption bands in a naphthacene monocrystal indicates that, upon light absorption, free excitons are formed. The formation of free excitons is facilitated by the relatively great oscillator strength for this transition, as well as by the large molecular size, which causes a large time of deformation in the crystal.

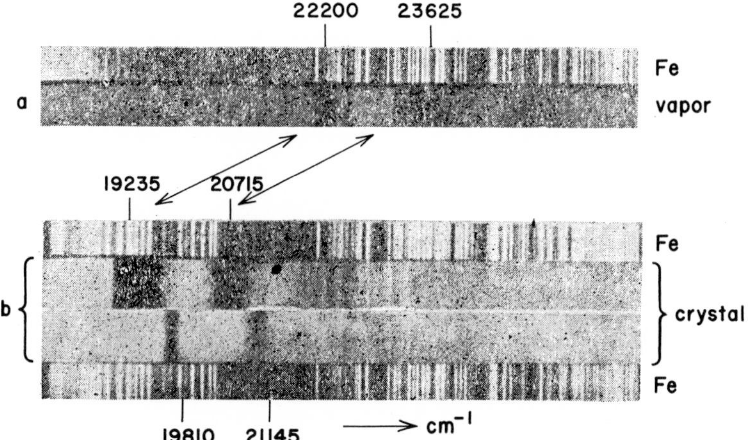

FIG. 21. Absorption spectra of naphthacene in the vapor state and as a monocrystal in polarized light for two polarization components. (*After Eichis.*)

d. Phenanthrene Crystal. The phenanthrene molecule belongs to the point symmetry group C_{2v}. Consequently, it should not have degenerate energy levels.

The spectrum of polarized light absorption at low temperatures by the phenanthrene monocrystal was investigated by I. V. Obreimov and A. F. Prikhotko.[12,16] The most detailed comparisons of phenanthrene spectra in various states of aggregation and the measurement of oscillator strengths for normal electronic transitions in the molecule were carried out in the candidate dissertation of A. Y. Eichis. In this work, it was shown that the first absorption region, which is usually observed in thick crystals and which starts with a frequency of 25,967 cm^{-1}, owes its existence not to phenanthrene itself, but to an admixture of anthracene in the phenanthrene. However, the absorption of phenanthrene itself at a temperature of -253°C begins with a frequency of 28,649 cm^{-1} for the case of light wave electric vector vibrations parallel to the b axis of the crystal and with a frequency of 28,604 cm^{-1} for vibrations perpendicular to the b axis (the monocrystal was several microns thick).

The phenanthrene monocrystal spectrum is displaced by approximately 440 cm^{-1} with respect to the spectrum of the vapor. To each electronic-vibrational absorption band in a vapor, there correspond two bands in a crystal. The distance between the first two bands, which correspond to a purely electronic transition and which are observed in various spectral components (a and b), is equal to 45 cm^{-1}. For electronic-vibrational bands, these distances are still smaller.

The small magnitude of the splitting (smaller by an order of magnitude than in naphthacene) indicates a small oscillator strength for corresponding transitions in the molecule. This deduction is confirmed by the direct measurements carried out by A. Y. Eichis for oscillator strengths of electronic transitions in a phenanthrene molecule. For the first electronic transition, the oscillator strength was approximately equal to 0.01. (For naphthacene, as we previously noted, the oscillator strength of the first electronic transition was greater by an order of magnitude.)

e. Benzene and Its Monoderivatives. The region of 36,000 to 45,000 cm^{-1} is the most thoroughly investigated region of benzene absorption. The absorption spectrum of benzene vapors in this region consists of a complicated system of bands beginning with a frequency of 37,482 cm^{-1}.

The benzene molecule belongs to the point symmetry group D_{6h}. The above-indicated absorption region corresponds to the forbidden transition $A_{1g} \rightarrow B_{2u}$, which becomes permitted owing to an excitation with e_g^f-type vibrations. The frequency of the electronic transition itself is assumed to be equal to 38,089 cm^{-1}.[91]

The absorption spectrum of solid benzene was studied by Pringsheim and Kronenberger at temperatures of 93 and 20.4°K.[92,93] In comparison with the absorption spectrum of vapors, the absorption spectrum of the crystal is displaced by 253 cm^{-1}. There are several differences in the distribution of intensity and in structural details of the crystal spectrum. Low frequencies belonging to lattice vibrations occur. The luminescence spectrum[92,94] is also very similar to the luminescence spectrum of benzene vapors. The displacement relative to the luminescence spectrum of vapors is 240 cm^{-1}.

The small change in the absorption and fluorescence spectra upon transition to a crystalline state is in agreement with the forbidden character of the corresponding electronic transition. Since the transition is forbidden, the resonance interaction is small; as a result, the corresponding changes are also small. A more detailed comparison of theory with new experimental data was conducted in Section 14*d*.

If, for one hydrogen atom in benzene, we substitute an atom of Br, Cl, etc., symmetry D_{6h} becomes symmetry C_{2v}, and forbidden transition in benzene $A_{1g} \rightarrow B_{2u}$ will correspond to transition $A_1 \rightarrow B_1$ in the monoderivative benzene. This transition is permitted in group C_{2v}, and the electric moment for the transition lies in the molecular plane in a direction perpendicular to the bond of the carbon substituent.[91] Therefore, in the case of benzene derivatives, one should expect considerable changes upon transition from a gaseous state to a crystalline one.

Absorption spectra of benzene derivatives (bromobenzene, iodobenzene, and others) at a temperature of 20.4°K were studied in the candidate dissertation of E. M. Bronstein under the direction of A. F. Prikhotko.

The absorption spectrum of gaseous bromobenzene in the ultraviolet consists of two regions:[95,96] (1) absorption bands (36,334 to 40,181 cm^{-1}) and (2) continuous absorption regions starting with 41,781 cm^{-1}.

The absorption spectrum for a solution of bromobenzene in hexane[97] is displaced into the long-wave region by 250 cm^{-1} with respect to the gas spectrum and, as was also to be expected, differs but little from the latter.

In the spectrum of solid bromobenzene at 20.4°K, Bronstein observed absorption in the regions 28,700 to 31,900 cm^{-1} and 34,900 to 42,200 cm^{-1}. Absorption bands contained in the range of 28,700 to 31,900 cm^{-1} do not exist in the spectra of the vapor and of solutions. Figure 22 is a diagram

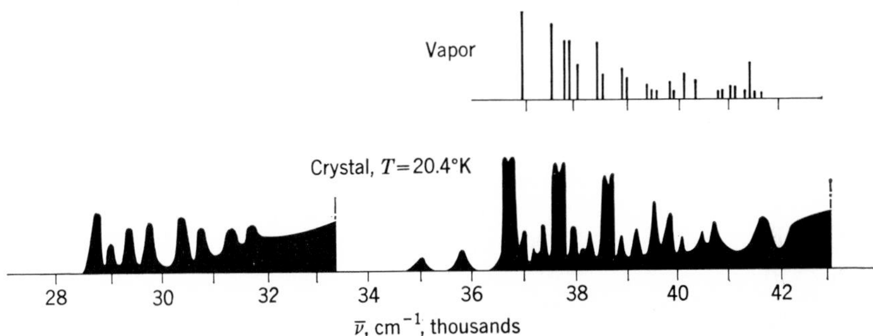

FIG. 22. Schematic representation of the near ultraviolet absorption of bromobenzene. (*After Bronstein.*)

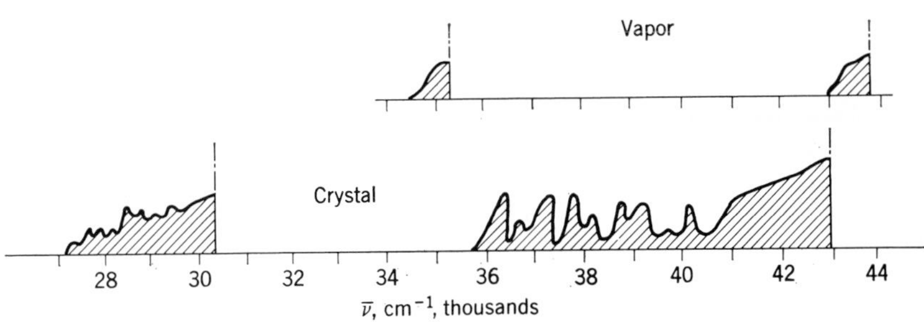

FIG. 23. Schematic representation of the near ultraviolet absorption of iodobenzene. (*After Bronstein.*)

of vapor and crystalline bromobenzene absorption according to Bronstein's work.

The presence of a new absorption band in the crystal in comparison with the vapor was also discovered by Bronstein for iodobenzene, chlorobenzene, and several other benzene monoderivatives. Figure 23 is a diagram of the absorption of iodobenzene vapors and crystal according to Bronstein's work.

The appearance of new absorption bands in all benzene monoderivatives upon transition from a gaseous state to a crystalline one is connected with the action of intermolecular forces in a crystal. The considerable absorption-band displacement, as well as the width of the absorption bands, points to the presence of great interaction forces which, apparently, possess a resonance character.

For a fuller clarification of this problem, additional studies of gases in large paths and of crystals at low temperature in polarized light are needed.

CHAPTER X

APPLICATION OF EXCITON CONCEPTS TO THE CALCULATION OF THE ENERGY STATES OF SEVERAL POLYATOMIC MOLECULES†

38. Dependence of the Frequency of Light Absorption in Para-polyphenyls on the Number of Phenyl Groups

At the present time, the methods of calculating energy states of polyatomic molecules are definitely unsatisfactory. Usually, three approximation methods are applied: (1) the valence bond method, (2) the molecular orbital method, and (3) the antisymmetrized molecular orbital method. In connection with the study of complicated molecules, the first method proves to be so cumbersome as to be practically inapplicable. For example, in the calculation on the naphthalene molecule, one must solve an equation of the 42d degree; on anthracene, a 429th-degree equation, etc. The method of molecular orbitals is significantly simpler and is therefore applied more frequently. However, in this method, when reducing the polyelectronic problem to the problem of the motion of one electron in the coordinated field of the remaining electrons, an essential assumption is made concerning the smallness of the change in interaction magnitude of one electron with all the remaining ones when the state of the given electron changes. Furthermore, in the molecular orbital method, the exchange interaction of electrons is ignored. An effort to eliminate the latter simplification was made in the method of antisymmetrized orbitals, in which antisymmetrized wave functions are utilized. However, it seems to us that one must not believe that the same relationship exists between the molecular orbital methods with antisymmetrized and nonantisymmetrized functions as exists between the methods of self-consistent fields with and without quantal exchange, worked out for atomic systems by Academician V. A. Fock.[100] Antisymmetrization of wave functions in an atomic system always leads to improved results. However, the introduction of antisymmetrized molecular orbitals for calculations on complicated molecules is usually connected with the separate study of large electronic and ionic interactions in lieu

† The results of this chapter have been previously published.[98,99]

of study of small interactions of electrons of a given atom with the remaining neutral atoms. The mistakes introduced thereby are so large (an incorrect use of the perturbation method) that at times they exceed the improvement obtained by virtue of the antisymmetrization of functions. Furthermore, the result of the calculation is expressed in the form of a combination of a large number of integrals, each of which can only be approximately computed (the integrals are extremely complicated, and the functions entering into them are known with insufficient accuracy). This may also lead to large errors and, besides, an extreme complication of the calculations.

The calculation on the relatively simple molecule benzene may serve as an illustration of what we have just said. As A. London has shown (Ref. 58, p. 418), the refinement of the calculation by means of introducing integrals referring to nonneighbor atoms leads not to better but to decisively worse results (the levels rise by 3 ev).

On the basis of this method, M. A. Kovner and L. M. Sverdlov† calculated the energy levels of the fulvene molecule and established the fact that, by applying perturbation theory, the first approximation changes even the sequence of levels of the zeroth approximation of the theory. This clearly shows that the method is mathematically not well founded.

We can apply the calculation methods for energy states, used by us for molecular crystals, to molecules consisting of a certain number of identical groups of atoms if the bonds between these groups are weaker than the bonds between atoms making up the group.

We must note that, when calculating the optical behavior of complicated molecules by means of this method, it is sufficient merely to require that the optical electrons should be little involved in the binding between the atomic groups. In this connection, the length of the bond involving the other electrons, for example, the σ electrons in the case of aromatic compounds, is of no concern whatsoever.

If the energy levels of one such group of atoms are known, then one can show how they change upon formation of a molecule consisting of a certain number of such groups.

As is well known, a large class of organic dyes includes compounds whose absorption spectrum depends upon the presence of several identical groups of atoms (chromophoric groups) occurring in a state of mutual conjugation. In this regard, the length of the conjugation chain is one of the important factors determining the color. Depending upon the type of binding between chromophoric groups, we observe dependence, in one

† This paper was presented at the Sixth Spectroscopy Colloquium, Kiev, 1948. A summary of the paper may be found in the proceedings.[101]

or another way, of the wavelength of the absorbed light on the number of conjugated groups. The study of this dependence is of great interest.

In this section, we shall give the quantum-mechanical deduction of the dependence of the wavelength and intensity of light absorption by para-polyphenyls on the number of phenyl groups in the chain. The molecules of para-polyphenyls represent chainlike linear formations with the phenyl group as a structural element; therefore, they may be treated as small unidimensional crystals of finite length.

Let H_k be the energy operator for the kth phenyl group in the para-polyphenyl formed by N phenyl groups, and let V_{km} be the interaction operator between the kth and the mth groups. Then the energy operator for the molecule may be written in the form

$$H = \sum_{k=1}^{N} H_k + \sum_{k<m} V_{km}. \tag{10.1}$$

Let us further assume that the normal state of the π electrons of the carbon atoms in the kth phenyl group is characterized by the wave function ϕ_k, depending on the coordinates and spins of the π electrons; the energy of the normal state is E_k°; the energy of the lowest excited state is E_k', and the corresponding wave function is φ_k'. The positions of the phenyl groups in the molecules will be considered fixed. The normal state of the whole molecule will be determined by the wave functions

$$\Phi^\circ = [(\sigma N)!]^{-\frac{1}{2}} \sum_\nu (-1)^\nu P_\nu \Psi, \tag{10.2}$$

where $\Psi = \varphi_1 \varphi_2 \cdot \cdot \cdot \varphi_N$. The excited state of the molecule will be determined by the function

$$\Phi = (N)^{-\frac{1}{2}} \sum_n a_n \chi_n, \tag{10.3}$$

where

$$\chi_n = [(\sigma N)!]^{-\frac{1}{2}} \sum_\nu (-1)^\nu P_\nu \Psi_n, \qquad \Psi_n = \varphi_1 \varphi_2 \cdot \cdot \cdot \varphi_n' \cdot \cdot \cdot \varphi_N$$

Using (10.1) and the wave functions [(10.2) and (10.3)], we can calculate the energies of the normal and excited states of the molecule; their difference determines the energy of excitation of the molecule:

$$\Delta E = \Delta E_m + D + \epsilon, \tag{10.4}$$

where ΔE_m is the excitation energy of one phenyl group; the magnitude D characterizes the difference in interaction energy of the excited and normal phenyl group with all remaining $(N - 1)$ groups in the molecule. In this interaction, an essential part will be played only by the interaction between neighboring groups, since the interaction between nonneighbor groups will be significantly less. Therefore, the magnitude D will not in the first approximation depend on the number of phenyl groups in the molecule, and ϵ in (10.4) is determined by the system of linear equations

$$\sum_n{}' a_n M_{n,m} - \epsilon a_m = 0, \qquad m = 1, 2, \ldots, N, \tag{10.5}$$

where $M_{n,m}$ is the matrix element for interaction between the nth and the mth molecules. If we limit consideration only to the interaction between neighboring groups, and if we introduce the designation $M_{n,n+1} = M$, the system of equation (10.5) will attain the following form:

$$\begin{aligned} -a_1\epsilon + a_2M &= 0 \\ a_1M - a_2\epsilon + a_3M &= 0 \\ \cdots\cdots\cdots\cdots\cdots \\ a_{N-1}M - a_N\epsilon &= 0. \end{aligned} \tag{10.6}$$

The system of equations (10.6) possesses nontrivial solutions only in the case where the determinant of the Nth order, Δ_N, composed of the coefficient of these equations, is equal to zero. One can easily see that

$$\Delta_N = \frac{\sin (N+1)\theta}{\sin \theta}, \tag{10.7}$$

where

$$2 \cos \theta = \frac{\epsilon}{M}. \tag{10.8}$$

The equation $\Delta_N = 0$ will have N roots:

$$\theta_l = \frac{\pi l}{N+1}, \qquad l = 1, 2, \ldots, N.$$

Using (10.8), we obtain

$$\epsilon_l = 2M \cos \frac{\pi l}{N+1}. \tag{10.9}$$

For the energy of excitation of the molecule, determined by (10.4), we obtain

$$\Delta E_l = A + 2M \cos \frac{\pi l}{N+1}, \tag{10.10}$$

where

$$A = \Delta E_m + D.$$

From (10.9), it follows that the dependence of the lowest [excited] energy level of the molecule on the number of phenyl groups in the molecule will be expressed by the relation (since $M < 0$)

$$\Delta E_{\min} = A - 2|M| \cos \frac{\pi}{N+1}. \tag{10.11}$$

Consequently, as the number of phenyl groups increases, the red absorption limit is displaced toward longer wavelengths. As the length of the chain increases, the displacement of the absorption band regularly decreases.

Substituting ϵ_l [(10.9)] in the system of equations (10.6), we can determine the nth coefficient of the linear combination [(10.3)] and, consequently, the wave function of the excited state as well. After the corresponding normalization, we obtain

$$\Phi^l = \left[\sum_{n=1}^{N} \sin^2 \frac{\pi ln}{N+1}\right]^{-1/2} \sum_n \chi_n \sin \frac{\pi ln}{N+1}. \tag{10.12}$$

In order to determine the oscillator strength for the transitions to the lth excited level in the molecule, the matrix element of the transition must be calculated:

$$\mathbf{Q}_l^1 = \int \Phi^{l*}(\mathbf{r})\Phi^\circ \, d\tau. \tag{10.13}$$

Using (10.12) and (10.2), we obtain

$$\mathbf{Q}_l^1 = \mathbf{Q}_m \left[\sum_{n=1}^{N} \sin^2 \frac{\pi nl}{N+1}\right]^{-1/2} \sum_{n=1}^{N} \sin \frac{\pi nl}{N+1}$$

$$= \begin{cases} \mathbf{Q}_m \dfrac{\cot\,[\pi l/2(N+1)]}{\sqrt{2/(N+1)}}, & \text{if } l \text{ is odd,} \\ 0, & \text{if } l \text{ is even,} \end{cases}$$

where $\mathbf{Q}_m$ is the matrix element of the transitions in one phenyl group. Consequently, the oscillator strength f_l of transitions to the lth level will be

$$f_l = \begin{cases} \dfrac{2}{(N+1)} |Q_m|^2 \left(\dfrac{4\pi mc}{3h}\right) \nu \cot^2\left[\dfrac{\pi l}{2(N+1)}\right], & \text{if } l \text{ is odd,} \\ 0, & \text{if } l \text{ is even.} \end{cases}$$

In the case of large N, the oscillator strength of the transition to the first excited level will change in direct proportion to N:

$$f_l \approx \text{const } \nu |Qm|^2 N, \tag{10.14}$$

where ν is the frequency of the transitions reciprocal centimeters.

Experimental investigations of the absorption of para-polyphenyls were carried out by Gillam and Hey.[102] They determined the wavelength of the maximum of absorption in solutions of five para-polyphenyls ($N = 2$, 3, 4, 5, 6) in chloroform, and of four para-polyphenyls ($N = 2, 3, 4, 6$) in hexane. Utilizing for biphenyl ($N = 2$) and for hexaphenyl ($N = 6$) the values for the absorption of frequencies found by them, we can obtain A and M (in reciprocal centimeters); for the solution in chloroform, $A = 50{,}060$, $M = 10{,}300$; for the solution in hexane, $A = 50{,}900$, $M = 10{,}200$.

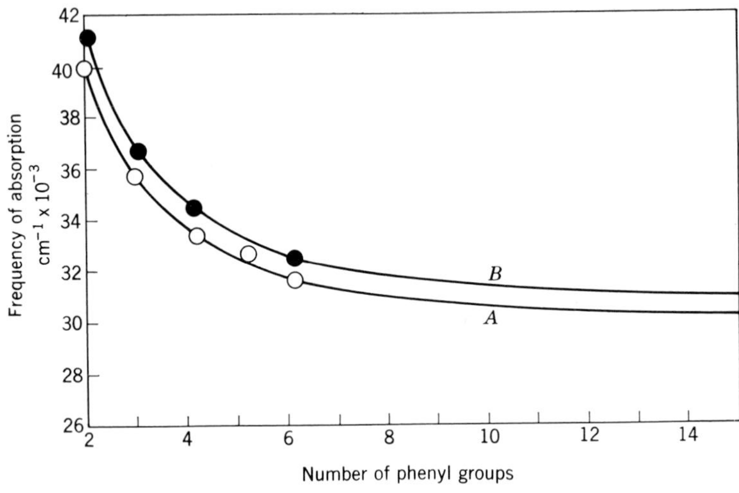

FIG. 24. Dependence of frequency of absorption on number of phenyl groups in linear para-polyphenyls.

Figure 24 shows, according to formula (10.11) for the values of A and M obtained, the curved or nonlinear dependence of the frequency for the absorption of light by para-polyphenyls on the number of phenyl groups. Curve A is for solutions of para-polyphenyls in chloroform; curve B is for solutions in hexane. The open circles correspond to the experimental values obtained by Gillam and Hey for solutions in chloroform and the solid circles to those for solutions in hexane.

The results obtained in this section can be used when studying the optical behavior of large molecular chains that are formed in the polymerization of several molecules.

39. Spectrum of Light Absorption by the Biphenyl Molecule

a. Energy Levels of the Molecule. The energy states of the biphenyl molecule were recently calculated by A. London.[58] London used the method of antisymmetrized molecular orbitals. London's calculation is exceptionally complicated and is not without basic flaws, which we already have mentioned in Section 38. In that section we used (just as London did) Goeppert-Mayer and Sklar's[57] data for calculations on the benzene molecule, and we computed the change of the energy spectrum of two benzene molecules (more precisely, of phenyl groups) when they form a biphenyl molecule.

The lowest energy levels of the aromatic molecules are determined by the π electrons of carbon atoms. Therefore, we shall consider the phenyl-group spectrum to coincide with the benzene spectrum.

According to data from X rays[104] and from geometrical analysis, the biphenyl molecule is planar and belongs to the point symmetry group D_{2h}. Figure 25 shows the schematic location of carbon atoms in the biphenyl molecule.

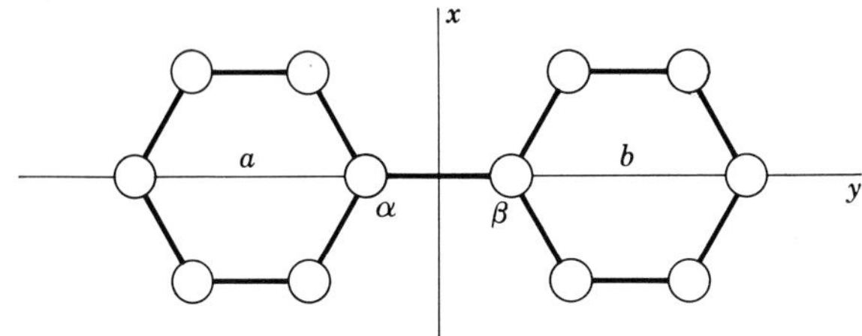

FIG. 25. Coordinate axes for the biphenyl molecule.

Let us designate by H_a the energy operator for the phenyl group a, and by H_b the energy operator for the second group; then

$$\begin{aligned} H_a\Phi_a^l &= E_a^l\Phi_a^l, \\ H_b\Phi_b^l &= E_b^l\Phi_b^l, \end{aligned} \tag{10.15}$$

where the Φ^l are the wave functions of the six π electrons of each phenyl group.

If V is the operator for the interaction between two groups, then the equation for determining the stationary energy states of a biphenyl molecule will have the form

$$(H_a + H_b + V)D = ED, \tag{10.16}$$

where D is the wave function of the biphenyl molecule.

In the zeroth approximation, the product of wave functions of the normal state of the benzene molecule (of the phenyl groups) $\Phi_a^\circ\Phi_b^\circ$ may be taken as the wave function of the normal state of the biphenyl molecule. The spin function for the normal singlet state of the biphenyl molecule may also be represented in the form of the product of the corresponding spin states for the combining molecules a and b:

$$\chi_0 = \chi_a\chi_b.$$

The complete antisymmetrical wave functions of the normal singlet state of the biphenyl molecule may now be written in the form

$$D_0 = (12!)^{-1/2} \sum_\nu (-1)^\nu P_\nu \Phi_a^\circ\Phi_b^\circ\chi_0, \tag{10.17}$$

where the summation is carried out over all possible permutations of 12 electrons, and where P_ν is one of the possible permutations.

The energy of the normal state of the biphenyl molecule in the first approximation will be equal to

$$E = E_a^\circ + E_b^\circ + \int |\Phi_a^\circ(\mathrm{I})|^2 V |\Phi_b^\circ(\mathrm{II})|^2 \, d\tau - \sum_\mu \int \Phi_a^{\circ *}(\mathrm{I}) \Phi_a^\circ(\mathrm{II}) V \Phi_b^{\circ *}(\mathrm{II}) \Phi_b^\circ(\mathrm{I}) \, d\tau. \quad (10.18)$$

Here $\Phi_a^\circ(\mathrm{I})$ and $\Phi_b^\circ(\mathrm{II})$ represent the wave functions of the molecules a and b for a certain position 1, 2, . . . , 6 of the electron in the molecule a and 7, 8, . . . , 12 of the electron in the molecule b; $\Phi_a^\circ(\mathrm{II})$ and $\Phi_b^\circ(\mathrm{I})$ correspond to the states, differing from the preceding ones in the permutation between the molecules a and b of any pair of electrons; the summation $\sum_\mu$ is carried out over all possible permutations of the pairs of electrons between the molecules a and b (the number of terms in this sum is equal to 36).

The lowest lth excited state of the biphenyl molecule will correspond to the excitation of only one of the "benzene" molecules in the lth state. Therefore, the wave function of the zeroth approximations, corresponding to the lth excited state of the molecule, will be written in the form

$$D^l = (2)^{-1/2}[c_a k_a^l + c_b k_b^l], \quad (10.19)$$

where

$$k_a^l = (12!)^{-1/2} \sum_\nu (-1)^\nu P_\nu \Phi_a^l \Phi_b^\circ \chi_a^l \chi_b^\circ,$$
$$k_b^l = (12!)^{-1/2} \sum_\nu (-1)^\nu P_\nu \Phi_a^\circ \Phi_b^l \chi_a^\circ \chi_b^l. \quad (10.20)$$

Using (10.19), we shall, with the aid of (10.16), obtain two homogeneous linear algebraic equations for determining c_a and c_b in (10.19):

$$-\epsilon^l c_a + M^l c_b = 0, \qquad M^l c_a - \epsilon^l c_b = 0, \quad (10.21)$$

where

$$-\epsilon^l = E_a^\circ + E_b^\circ + \int |\Phi_a^l(\mathrm{I})|^2 V |\Phi_b^\circ(\mathrm{II})|^2 \, d\tau - \sum_\mu \int \Phi_a^{l*}(\mathrm{I}) \Phi_a^l(\mathrm{II}) V \Phi_b^{\circ *}(\mathrm{II}) \Phi_b^\circ(\mathrm{I}) \, d\tau - E, \quad (10.22)$$

$$M^l = \int \Phi_a^{l*}(\mathrm{I}) \Phi_a^\circ(\mathrm{I}) V \Phi_b^{\circ *}(\mathrm{II}) \Phi_b^l(\mathrm{II}) \, d\tau - \sum_\mu \int \Phi_a^{l*}(\mathrm{I}) \Phi_a^\circ(\mathrm{II}) V \Phi_b^{\circ *}(\mathrm{II}) \Phi_b^l(\mathrm{I}) \, d\tau. \quad (10.23)$$

In order to obtain the nontrivial solutions of the system of equations (10.21), it is necessary to have

$$\epsilon^l = \pm M^l. \quad (10.24)$$

Thus to each energy term of the phenyl group there will correspond two terms in the biphenyl molecule, depending on whether the plus or minus sign is taken in (10.24).

Henceforth, only the excitation energy of the biphenyl molecule $\Delta E^l = E^l - E^\circ$ will interest us. If we designate the excitation energy of the lth level in the phenyl group by $\Delta E_a^l (= -\Delta E_b^l)$, then we arrive at the following two values for the excitation energy corresponding to ΔE_a^l of the biphenyl molecule:

$$\begin{aligned} \Delta E_1^l &= \Delta E_a^l + B^l + M^l, \\ \Delta E_2^l &= \Delta E_a^l + B^l - M^l, \end{aligned} \tag{10.25}$$

where

$$B^l = \int \Phi_a^{l*}(\mathrm{I})\Phi_a^l(\mathrm{I}) V \Phi_b^{\circ *}(\mathrm{II})\Phi_b^\circ(\mathrm{II})\, d\tau - \int \Phi_a^{\circ *}(\mathrm{I})\Phi_a^\circ(\mathrm{I}) V \Phi_b^{\circ *}(\mathrm{II})\Phi_b^\circ(\mathrm{II})\, d\tau - \text{exchange terms.} \tag{10.26}$$

B^l is characterized by a general displacement of the excitation energy of the biphenyl molecule with respect to the excitation energy of the phenyl group (benzene). For the first excited states of the molecule, this term is small, since the difference in the energy for the interaction of an excited and normal "benzene" molecule with another normal molecule is, in this case, small compared with M^l, which characterizes the resonance interaction between benzene molecules. Henceforth, we shall assume that

$$B^l \approx 0.$$

Substituting (10.24) in (10.21), we obtain two values for the ratio of the coefficients c_a and c_b; accordingly, the wave functions of the excited states [(10.25)] of the biphenyl molecule will have the form:

$$D_1^l = 2^{-\frac{1}{2}}(k_a^l + k_b^l), \qquad D_2^l = 2^{-\frac{1}{2}}(k_a^l - k_b^l). \tag{10.27}$$

In order to determine the magnitude of the splitting of corresponding levels, the matrix elements [(10.23)] must be calculated. The function V entering into these integrals and forming the classical interaction energy between two neutral molecules may be represented in the form of a sum of terms which takes into account the dipole-dipole, dipole-quadrupole, and other types of interaction:

$$V = -\frac{e^2}{R^3}\sum_{i=1}^{6}\sum_{j=7}^{12}(2y_{ai}y_{bj} - x_{ai}x_{bj} - z_{ai}z_{bj}) + \cdots \tag{10.28}$$

where R is the distance between the centers of the molecules; x_{ai}, y_{ai}, . . . , x_{bj}, . . . are the coordinates for the electrons of the "benzene" molecules a and b relative to the systems of coordinates located on the centers of the molecules, with the y axis directed along a line which links the centers of the molecules; and e is the electronic charge.

If we substitute (10.28) in (10.23), we obtain for the dipole-dipole interaction

$$M^l = -\frac{e^2}{R^3}\left|\int \Phi^{l*}(\mathbf{r})\Phi^\circ\, d\tau\right|^2 (2\cos\theta_a^y \cos\theta_b^y - \cos\theta_a^x \cos\theta_b^x$$

$$- \cos\theta_a^z \cos\theta_b^z) - \sum_\mu \int \Phi_a^{l*}(\mathrm{I})\Phi_a^\circ(\mathrm{II}) V \Phi_b^{\circ*}(\mathrm{II})\Phi_b^l(\mathrm{I})\, d\tau, \quad (10.29)$$

where $\mathbf{r} = \sum_{i=1}^{6} \mathbf{r}_{ai}, \qquad \sum y_i = r\cos\theta^y, \qquad$ etc.

For forbidden dipole transitions,

$$\int \Phi^{l*}(\mathbf{r})\Phi^\circ\, d\tau = 0.$$

It is then necessary to take into account in (10.28) the interaction of a higher order. For the first two forbidden transitions in the benzene molecule, transition matrix elements different from zero correspond to the octupole transitions only. Consequently, the terms of the octupole-octupole interaction must be taken into account in the matrix element.

According to Goeppert-Mayer and Sklar,[57] the lowest singlet excited state of the benzene molecule belongs to the irreducible representation B_{2u} of the D_{6h} point group.[105] The transition from the normal state A_{1g} to the level B_{2u} is forbidden. In the biphenyl molecule, two wave functions will correspond to this level:

$$D_1^1 = 2^{-1/2}(k_a^1 + k_b^1), \qquad D_2^1 = 2^{-1/2}(k_a^1 - k_b^1), \quad (10.30)$$

where k_a^1 and k_b^1 are determined through Φ^1 and Φ°, with the aid of (10.20). Accordingly, we obtain for the excitation energy

$$\Delta E_1^1 = \Delta E_a^1 + M^1, \qquad \Delta E_2^1 = \Delta E_a^1 - M^1. \quad (10.31)$$

By utilizing the table of irreducible-representation characters for the symmetry group D_{2h} (Table 2), to which the biphenyl molecule belongs, we can, by comparing the characters, determine the irreducible representations of the functions given by (10.30) if we consider the symmetry properties of benzene wave functions.

We will obtain:

D_1^1 transforms as B_{1u}
D_2^1 transforms as A_{2g}.

Knowing the symmetry of wave functions, one can determine the selection rules and the polarization of the corresponding quantum transitions by using the methods of group theory. Thus we find that the first forbidden transition of the benzene is split into two in the biphenyl molecule. The transition to one of the split levels becomes permitted and will have the polarization of an electric vector along the intermediate axis of the molecule (axis x in Figure 25).

The second forbidden transition (to B_{1u}) in the benzene also splits into two in the biphenyl molecule:

$$\begin{aligned} \Delta E_1^2 &= \Delta E_a^2 + M^2 \qquad (B_{2u}), \\ \Delta E_2^2 &= \Delta E_a^2 - M^2 \qquad (A_{1g}), \end{aligned} \tag{10.32}$$

with wave functions

$$\begin{aligned} D_1^2 &= 2^{-1/2}(k_a^2 + k_b^2) \qquad (B_{2u}), \\ D_2^2 &= 2^{-1/2}(k_a^2 - k_b^2) \qquad (A_{2g}), \end{aligned}$$

respectively. The transition to the state characterized by the function D_1^2 is permitted and possesses the polarization of an electric vector along the long axis of the molecule (axis y in Figure 25).

The transition to the third, doubly degenerate level E_{1u} in the benzene molecule is permitted. In the benzene molecule, two wave functions correspond to it:

$$\Psi_3 \text{ and } \Psi_4 = \Psi_3^* \qquad (E_{1u}).$$

In lieu of these functions, it is more convenient to take the linear combinations

$$\begin{aligned} \Phi_a^3 &= 2^{-1/2}(\Psi_3 + \Psi_3^*) \qquad (B_{1u}), \\ \Phi_b^3 &= 2^{-1/2}(\Psi_3 - \Psi_3^*) \qquad (B_{2u}). \end{aligned} \tag{10.33}$$

In the biphenyl molecule, two wave functions will correspond to the benzene function Φ_a^3 [(10.33)]:

$$\begin{aligned} D_1^3 &= 2^{-1/2}(k_a^3 + k_b^3) \qquad (B_{2u}), \\ D_2^3 &= 2^{-1/2}(k_a^3 - k_b^3) \qquad (A_{1g}). \end{aligned} \tag{10.34}$$

The functions given by (10.34) correspond to the energies

$$\begin{aligned} \Delta E_1^3 &= \Delta E_a^3 + M^3 \qquad (B_{2u}), \\ \Delta E_2^3 &= \Delta E_a^3 - M^3 \qquad (A_{1g}). \end{aligned} \tag{10.35}$$

The transition to the level ΔE_1^3 is permitted and possesses a polarization of an electric vector along the long axis of the molecule. The transition to the level of ΔE_2^3 is forbidden.

In the biphenyl molecule, two functions will correspond to a benzene function Φ_a^4 [(10.33)]:

$$\begin{aligned} D_1^4 &= 2^{-1/2}(k_a^4 + k_b^4) \qquad (B_{1u}), \\ D_2^4 &= 2^{-1/2}(k_a^4 - k_b^4) \qquad (A_{2g}); \end{aligned} \tag{10.36}$$

these have energy values

$$\begin{aligned} \Delta E_1^4 &= \Delta E_a^4 + M^4 \qquad (B_{1u}), \\ \Delta E_2^4 &= \Delta E_a^4 - M^4 \qquad (A_{2g}). \end{aligned} \tag{10.37}$$

The transition to the level ΔE_1^3 is permitted and its polarization will correspond to an electric vector along the x axis of the biphenyl molecule. The transition to the level ΔE_2^4 is forbidden.

Although direct transitions from the normal state to states with the energy ΔE_2^1, ΔE_2^2, ΔE_2^3, and ΔE_2^4 are forbidden in the biphenyl molecule, they may occur in the absorption spectrum in combination with vibrational frequencies of a certain symmetry. These absorption bands must be weak, since they will disappear if the eigenfunction of the electronic-vibrational state is represented in the form of the product of the electronic and vibrational functions.

b. Calculation of Matrix Elements. The matrix elements M^l, which determine the magnitude of the splitting of energy levels in the biphenyl molecule according to (10.29), are expressed by two terms. The first term of (10.29) characterizes the exchange of excitation (excitons) between the phenyl groups a and b. It depends essentially on the character of the corresponding transition in the phenyl group. The second term determines the interaction between phenyl groups, in connection with which the exchange of pairs of electrons takes place between a and b. In order of magnitude this term will be equal to the interaction with an exchange of electrons between the two closest carbon atoms belonging to different phenyl groups. This term depends little on the character of the transition; therefore, we may write

$$\sum_{\mu} \int \Phi_a^{l*}(\mathrm{I})\Phi_a^{\circ}(\mathrm{II}) V \Phi_b^{\circ *}(\mathrm{II})\Phi_b^{l}(\mathrm{I})\, d\tau \approx \frac{e^2}{r_{\alpha\beta}} S^2 + A - 2SB \approx -0.18 \text{ ev}, \tag{10.38}$$

where

$$S = \int U_\alpha^*(1) U_\beta(1)\, d\tau = 0.224,$$

$$A = \int U_\alpha^*(1) U_\beta(1) \frac{e^2}{r_{12}} U_\alpha(2) U_\beta^*(2)\, d\tau_1\, d\tau_2 \approx 0.68 \text{ ev},$$

$$B = \int U_\alpha^*(1) U_\beta(1) \frac{e^2}{r_{1\beta}}\, d\epsilon_1 = 3.01 \text{ ev}.$$

$U_\alpha(1)$ and $U_\beta(1)$ are the wave functions of the first π electron in the α and β carbon atoms, respectively (see Figure 25), with a screening constant $z = 3.18$; $r_{\alpha\beta} = 1.48 \times 10^{-8}$ cm is the distance[106] between the atoms α and β. The value of the exchange integral A is taken from the tables given by Sklar and Lyddane.[107] The integral B has been investigated by H. H. Hellman (Ref. 108, p. 510).

If we now use the values Φ^1 and Φ^2, corresponding to the forbidden transitions in the benzene molecule,

$$\Phi^1 = \frac{1}{\sqrt{2}}(\Psi_1 - \Psi_1^*),$$

$$\Phi^2 = \frac{1}{\sqrt{2}}(\Psi_1 + \Psi_1^*),$$

where

$$\Psi_1 = \varphi_0(1)\varphi_0(2)\varphi_1(3)\varphi_1(4)\varphi_{-1}(5)\varphi_2(6),$$

$$\varphi_l = 6^{-1/2}\sum_k e^{i2\pi lk/6}U_k,$$

and

$$\Phi^\circ = \varphi_0(1)\varphi_0(2)\varphi_1(3)\varphi_1(4)\varphi_{-1}(5)\varphi_{-1}(6),$$

we obtain

$$\frac{e^2}{R^7}\left|\int \Phi^{l*}(r^3)\Phi^\circ\,d\tau\right| = \begin{cases} 0, & \text{if } l = 1, \\ 0.01 \text{ ev}, & \text{if } l = 2. \end{cases}$$

Thus

$$M^1 = 0.18 \text{ ev}, \qquad M^2 = 0.17 \text{ ev}. \tag{10.39}$$

In order to calculate M^3 according to formula (10.29), we must first of all determine

$$\int \Phi^{3*}(\mathbf{r})\Phi^\circ\,d\tau.$$

Substituting the value Φ_α^3 from (10.33) into this integral and using the wave functions of the benzene molecule,

$$\Psi_3 = \Psi_1^* = \varphi_0(1)\varphi_0(2)\varphi_1(3)\varphi_1(4)\varphi_{-1}(5)\varphi_{-2}(6), \tag{10.40}$$

we obtain

$$\int \Phi^{3*}(\mathbf{r})\Phi^\circ\,d\tau = \frac{4\rho}{3\sqrt{2}}\mathbf{r}_{1y}, \tag{10.41}$$

where $\rho = 1.39 \times 10^{-8}$ cm and $\mathbf{r}_{1y}$ is the unit vector in the direction of the y axis.

After substituting (10.41) and (10.38) into (10.29) we obtain

$$M^3 \cong -0.46 \text{ ev}. \tag{10.42}$$

M^4 is expressed through the transition integral $\int\Phi^{4*}(\mathbf{r})\Phi^\circ\,d\tau$. Substituting Φ_α^4 from (10.33) and using (10.40), we obtain

$$\int \Phi^{4*}(\mathbf{r})\Phi^\circ\,d\tau = i\frac{\sqrt{2}\,\rho\mathbf{r}_{1x}}{\sqrt{3}}, \tag{10.43}$$

where $\mathbf{r}_{1x}$ is the unit vector in the direction of the x axis of the biphenyl molecule. Using (10.43) and (10.38), we obtain from (10.29)

$$M^4 = 0.42 \text{ ev.} \tag{10.44}$$

c. Comparison with Experiment. There are few experimental studies on the absorption spectra of biphenyl pairs. Carr and Stücklen[109,110] discovered a strong absorption in the region of 6.4 ev, as well as a wide

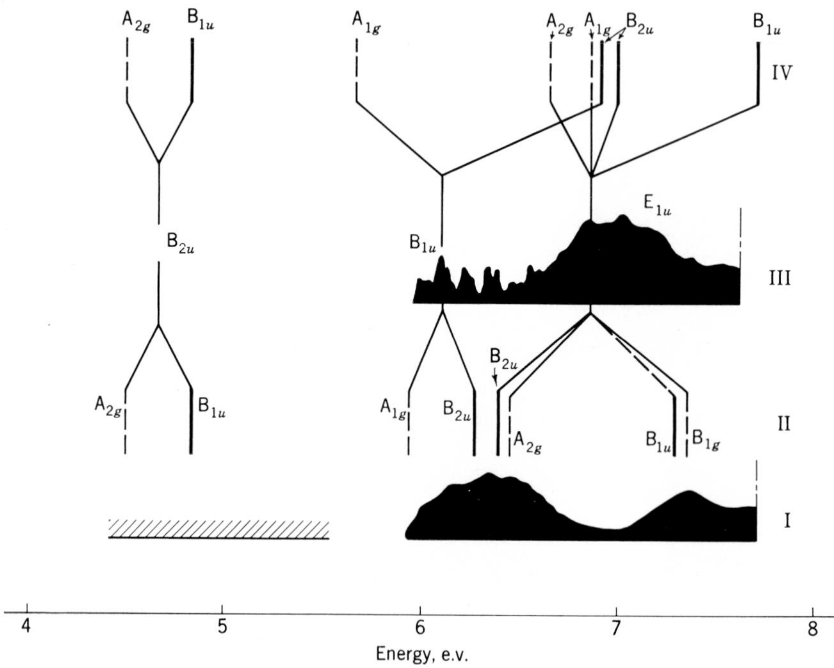

FIG. 26. Schematic representation of the ultraviolet absorption bands of biphenyl (I) and benzene (III) vapors correlated with calculated energy terms.

absorption maximum from 7.3 up to 7.6 ev. Because of the conditions of the experiment, the higher frequency portion of the spectrum was not investigated. Besides, A. London, shows in his work[58] that Beck at the University of California discovered in biphenyl pairs a wide absorption band in the region 2200 to 2800 A (5.6 to 4.4 ev). Dickson[111] also gave indications of an absorption band in the vicinity of 4.4 ev.

Figure 26 (curve I) represents the experimental absorption spectrum according to the work of Carr and Stücklen.[109] The crosshatched region corresponds to Beck's data. We do not have data on the distribution of absorption intensity in this portion of the spectrum.

Curve III represents the benzene absorption spectrum corresponding to transitions to the levels B_{1u} and E_{1u}, according to the works of Carr and Stücklen.[109,110] Consequently, for benzene levels, we may adopt the values

$$\Delta E_a^2 = 6.1 \text{ ev} \qquad (B_{1u}),$$
$$\Delta E_a^3 = \Delta E_a^4 = 6.9 \text{ ev} \qquad (E_{1u}).$$

The frequency 38,089 cm^{-1} corresponds to the first transition in benzene (according to A. Y. Eichis' data); consequently,

$$\Delta E_a^1 = 4.6 \text{ ev} \qquad (B_{2u}).$$

Using these values for the differences (above the normal level) of energy levels in the benzene molecule, we obtain, with the aid of (10.31), (10.32), (10.35), (10.37), (10.39), (10.42), and (10.44), the energy levels (relative to the normal one) of the biphenyl molecule. The position of these levels is shown in Figure 26 on line II.

The terms corresponding to the forbidden transitions from the normal level are shown by broken lines, while the permitted ones are indicated by solid lines.

Line IV gives the splitting of the terms for the benzene molecule according to A. London's theory.[58] We must note that, for the benzene levels, London adopted the levels calculated in the work of Goeppert-Mayer and Sklar[57] (5, 5.6, and 8 ev). This seems inconsistent to us, since the improved calculation of the benzene molecule, as London himself notes, leads to energy levels of 7.3, 8.8, and 11.1 ev. By virtue of the better agreement with the experiment, London justifies the use of the values 5, 5.6, and 8 ev from an older work. However, in order to be more consistent, one should then simply take the experimental values, as we do here. Besides, London's selection does not improve the agreement with the experiment, since all terms obtained from the splitting of the permitted 8 ev then go to the far ultraviolet. The strong absorption in the 6.4-ev region is, according to London, explained by the splitting of the forbidden benzene level (5.6 ev).

According to our theory, this absorption band mainly originates from the splitting of the permitted term of the benzene molecule. As a result of this splitting, a displacement of the permitted transition to the red side by 0.46 ev takes place. The second split component of this same transition (displacement of 0.42 ev) apparently corresponds to the absorption band of biphenyl in the 7.2-ev region.

CONCLUSION

The purpose of the present work was to investigate the spectra of light absorption by molecular crystals. It was assumed here that the corresponding spectra of light absorption by free molecules (spectra of rarefied gases) were completely known. The solution of the problem had to link absorption spectral changes upon transition from a gaseous to a crystalline state with the crystalline structure of a solid and with the forces of interaction between molecules.

Initially, the problem was solved under the assumption that all molecules of a crystal are rigidly fixed in the points of the crystal lattice. Classical mechanics was used in studying the influence of forces of interaction between the molecules in a molecular lattice upon intramolecular vibrations (Chapter II). Then we developed the quantum theory of these changes, as well as the theory for the change of energy states which include electronic excitation. The classical and quantum theories yield identical qualitative results, which essentially amount to the following:

1. In a crystal, each excited state of a molecule is transformed into a series of quasi-continuous zones of excited states. The number of zones is equal to the number of molecules in the crystalline unit cell. The number of sublevels in each zone is equal to the number of unit cells in the crystal. The sublevels inside each zone differ in the values of the wave vectors for the excitation waves (excitons) that spread in the crystal (Sections 7, 9, and 12).

2. Upon interaction with light only excitons with a wave vector equal to the wave vector of a light wave are excited. With the aid of group theory we established those quasi-continuous zones of excited states to which transitions take place under the action of light; the latter is propagated in a given direction and has a given polarization (Sections 8, 13, and 14).

3. As a result of the emergence of several zones of excited states corresponding to one excited state in the isolated molecule, there occurs a displacement and splitting of the crystalline absorption band in comparison with that of a gas. The number of split components and their polarization are determined by the number of molecules per unit cell and by their mutual orientation.

Until recently, the opinion generally held was that the splitting of absorption bands in a crystal could only be caused by (*a*) polymerization or association of molecules or (*b*) removal of degeneracy if the molecule possessed degenerate levels. We have shown, however, that the splitting of absorption bands may take place in a crystal even when these two reasons are lacking. The magnitude of splitting depends mainly on the resonance interaction of the molecules in a crystal. It has the greatest value for dipole transitions (proportional to the oscillator strengths) and decreases rapidly with the increase of the multipole index for the transitions (Sections 9 and 12).

4. When the theory is applied to combinational scattering (Raman scattering) of light, it leads to the conclusion that, with regard to the influence of a crystalline state on intramolecular vibrations, the latter may be divided into two groups: (*a*) vibrations noticeably influenced by crystalline structure (these vibrations must be simultaneously active in the infrared spectrum) and (*b*) vibrations not noticeably influenced by crystalline structure. Both these groups of vibrations may be simultaneously present in one molecule (Section 10).

5. We developed the general absorption spectral theory, which takes into consideration the possibility of displacements of molecules from their equilibrium positions. We pointed out the inadequacy of generally accepted conditions with respect to the accuracy of the adiabatic approximation when the latter is applied to a system with many degrees of freedom. In this case, an essential role is played by the temperature of the body and by the correlation between time of molecular displacement from equilibrium positions and time of excitation transfer from one molecule to another. Excited states of a crystal (with one excited molecule) prove to be nonstationary. Only in the case in which excitation spreads over the crystal so rapidly that there is no time for a local crystalline deformation to take place may we speak about quasi-stationary excited states (with respect to transformation of molecular excitation energy into lattice vibrational energy). If, however, excitation spreads slowly, a local crystal deformation occurs (the exciton is "localized"). In this case, the probability of molecular excitation energy transformation into lattice vibrational energy is great (Sections 15 and 16).

6. We analyzed the possibility for excitation in a crystal of two limiting types of excitons: (*a*) free excitons, which spread rapidly through the crystal and do not cause crystalline deformation, and (*b*) "localized" excitons, which move slowly because their movement is linked to the movement of the local crystal deformation (Section 17).

7. Equations were obtained which determined the movement of molecules in a crystal upon free exciton formation. Their solutions in the zeroth approximation result in a crystal excitation energy value, which coincides with the case of fixed molecules in lattice points. This estab-

lishes the limits for the applicability of the solutions which were obtained in Chapter III when studying fixed molecules (Sections 18 and 19).

8. The group velocities of excitation waves for different excited-state zones, but for identical wave numbers, were shown to be not identical. For certain excited-state zones, these velocities (for $\mathbf{k} = \mathbf{Q}$) may prove so small that excitation by light of this type of free exciton becomes impossible (localized excitons will be excited) (Section 22).

9. The proposed theory explains the pleochroism of molecular crystals and constitutes the first attempt to form a molecular theory of pleochroism in contrast to the usual phenomenological description of this phenomenon. Pleochroism of a molecular crystal is caused by a property (arising upon interaction in a specific manner of oriented molecules) of the crystal as a whole, and not by a property of separate molecules (Sections 22 to 24).

10. The solution of equations, determining the movement of molecules in a crystal upon formation of free excitons, in the first approximation permits us to describe the processes of free exciton excitation simultaneously with lattice vibrational excitation. Formulas determining absorption band structure and its dependence on temperature are deduced. It is shown that the absorption-band width increases with the temperature. As a result of interaction with lattice vibrations, absorption may attain several maximum values in the absorption band, which corresponds to one excited state of a molecule. However, the distances from these maxima to the primary band (excitation of a crystal without lattice vibrations) may not coincide with the lattice vibrational frequencies. In certain cases, upon lattice vibrational excitation, maxima may appear on the long-wave side (for $T \approx 0$) of the primary absorption band. On the contrary, in luminescence spectra of crystals at low temperature, one may directly observe lattice vibrational frequencies, which will occur in the form of satellites near the basic lines (Sections 25 to 27).

11. We have pointed out possible changes in absorption spectral structure upon temperature rise and upon translational symmetry violation in a crystal. Temperature increase leads to a general intensity increase for absorption bands, which are caused by excitation of molecules in a crystal upon simultaneous excitation of lattice vibrations. It also leads to the appearance of additional absorption bands, conditioned by the excitation of a crystal from already-excited vibrational states of a lattice. The violation of ideal periodicity of a lattice by the presence of admixtures and isotopes and, finally, by thermal fluctuations of density will lead to the following: A portion of the "quasi impulse" will be transmitted to the corresponding heterogeneity. The absorption-band width will increase as a result. This broadening effect of absorption bands must play an essential role in absorption of light by a liquid (Section 27).

12. Upon formation of "localized" excitons, the corresponding excited states of a crystal are not stationary. Owing to a local deformation of the crystal, the connection between intramolecular excitation and lattice vibrations increases. The excitation of molecules is transmitted to lattice vibrations. On the one hand, this explains the wide absorption bands upon excitation of localized excitons; on the other hand, it results in the transformation of absorbed energy into heat. In this case, the widening of absorption bands also takes place, because in addition to a "localized" exciton, there may be simultaneous excitation by light of a few phonons as well. Upon formation of localized states, the distances between various quasi-continuous zones of excited states, corresponding to one excited state of a molecule, are small and usually overlap owing to the large spread of absorption bands. Therefore, polarization effects would play a small role in these cases (Sections 29 and 30).

13. It was shown that, in a crystal, free excitons may spontaneously turn into "localized" ones if the energy of the free exciton is greater than the energy of the "localized" one; also, upon decrease in the energy of the free exciton, the velocity of the latter decreases.

Conversely, in certain cases the energy of a "localized" exciton is higher than the energy of a free exciton, and the energy decrease of a free exciton is linked with the increase of its velocity. In this case, "localized" excitons turn into free ones. This last case apparently plays an important role in a series of molecular crystals. The velocity increase (and that of the wave number) for an exciton upon decrease of its energy may (*a*) condition the presence of luminescence of a solid (in a pure state); (*b*) lead to a lifetime increase for the excited state of a crystal in comparison with the lifetime of a free molecule (for $T \approx 0$); (*c*) be the cause of an incomplete coincidence of the absorption band and of the luminescence band, which corresponds to a purely electronic intramolecular excitation (Sections 29 and 32 to 34).

14. The process of transformation of intramolecular excitation energy into heat (into lattice vibrational energy) is extremely probable for excited states of a crystal that correspond to the excitation of "localized" excitons. If, at the moment of light absorption, free excitons are formed, and if the excitation energy of the latter is greater than the excitation energy of "localized" excitons, the process of transformation of free exciton energy into heat takes place through a state which corresponds to a "localized" exciton.

The lattice vibrational frequency differs less from intramolecular vibrational frequencies than from electronic excitation frequencies. Owing to this, one must assume that the probability for the transfer of intramolecular vibrational energy to heat will be greater than the probability for a transformation of electronic excitation energy. Apparently, this explains the experimentally observed rapid transformation of the vibrational portion of molecular electronic-vibrational excitation energy to lattice vibrational energy (Sections 32 and 33).

15. An analysis was made of conditions conducive to the emission of luminescence in molecular crystals. It was shown that luminescence is basically determined by transitions from excited states, corresponding to free excitons, to the ground state of a crystal (Section 34).

16. Using certain experimental data by way of example, we have qualitatively confirmed the theoretical deductions of this work for combinational scattering (Raman) spectra, infrared spectra, and absorption and luminescence spectra in the visible and ultraviolet regions. All of the experiments described confirm beyond any doubt the presence in a crystalline state of sharply polarized absorption bands which are new in comparison with the gaseous state (Sections 36 to 38).

17. We have shown that exciton representations may be utilized to calculate the energy states of several (isolated) polyatomic molecules. We have found the dependence of the frequency for light absorption by para-polyphenyls on the number of phenyl groups in a molecule. We have calculated the spectrum of light absorption by the biphenyl molecule (Section 39).

APPENDIX I

PUBLICATIONS OF A. S. DAVYDOV

[The bibliography that follows gives the works of Davydov to December, 1961, as cited by Chemical Abstracts. Papers on nuclear physics are indicated by italic numbers.]

1. Davydov, A. S.: Calculation of the Coefficient of Internal Conversion, *J. Exptl. Theoret. Phys.* (*U.S.S.R.*), **10**: 865–873 (1940). [*C.A.* **35**: 5384^5 (1941)]

2. Davydov, A. S.: Calculation of the Lowest Excited Levels of the Naphthalene Molecule, *Zhur. Eksptl. i Teoret. Fiz.*, **17**: 1106–1113 (1947). [*C.A.* **44**: 3793*b* (1950)]

3. Davydov, A. S.: Theory of Absorption Spectra of Molecular Crystals, *Zhur. Eksptl. i Teoret. Fiz.*, **18**: 210–218 (1948). [*C.A.* **43**: 4575*f* (1949)]

4. Davydov, A. S.: Theory of the Absorption Spectrum of Biphenyl, *Zhur. Eksptl. i Teoret. Fiz.*, **18**: 201–209 (1948). [*C.A.* **43**: 4569*d* (1949)]

5. Davydov, A. S.: Dependence of the Frequency of Absorption of Light in *p*-polyphenyls on the Number of Phenyl Groups, *Zhur. Eksptl. i Teoret. Fiz.*, **18**: 515–518 (1948). [*C.A.* **43**: 3741*a* (1949)]

6. Davydov, A. S.: Consideration of the Non-orthogonality of Wave Functions in the Method of Molecular Orbitals, *Zhur. Fiz. Khim.*, **22**: 1290–1293 (1948). [*C.A.* **43**: 2503*b* (1949)]

7. Davydov, A. S.: The Theory of Light Absorption by Molecular Crystals, *Izvest. Akad. Nauk S.S.S.R., Ser. Fiz.*, **12**: 608–610 (1948). [*C.A.* **44**: 4325*c* (1950)]

8. Davydov, A. S.: Theory of the Absorption Spectra of Solutions of Metals in Ammonia, *Zhur. Eksptl. i Teoret. Fiz.*, **18**: 913–916 (1948). [*C.A.* **45**: 10035*i* (1951)]

9. Davydov, A. S.: Remarks on the Article of A. S. Davydov, "Calculation of the Lowest Electronic Levels of the Naphthalene Molecule," *Zhur. Eksptl. i Teoret. Fiz.*, **18**: 670–671 (1948). [*C.A.* **46**: 10883*b* (1952)]

10. Davydov, A. S.: Molecular Theory of Pleochroism, *Zhur. Eksptl. i Teoret. Fiz.*, **19**: 168–174 (1949). [*C.A.* **45**: 10036*c* (1951)]

11. Davydov, A. S.: Effect of Interaction Forces between the Molecules of a Molecular Lattice on the Intramolecular Vibrations, *Zhur. Eksptl. i Teoret. Fiz.*, **10**: 181–182 (1949). [*C.A.* **46**: 1325*c* (1952)]

12. Davydov, A. S.: Dispersion of Molecular Crystals in the Infrared Region, *Zhur. Eksptl. i Teoret. Fiz.*, **19**: 930–936 (1949). [*C.A.* **47**: 10994*c* (1953)]

13. Davydov, A. S.: Dispersion Theory of Molecular Crystals, *Izvest. Akad. Nauk S.S.S.R., Ser. Fiz.*, **14**: 502–507 (1950). [*C.A.* **45**: 4139*g* (1951)]

14. Davydov, A. S.: Theory of Absorption of Light by Crystalline Benzene, *Zhur. Eksptl. i Teoret. Fiz.*, **21**: 673–676 (1951). [*C.A.* **46**: 8959*d* (1952)]

15. Davydov, A. S.: Theory of Luminescence of Molecular Crystals, *Izvest. Akad. Nauk S.S.S.R., Ser. Fiz.*, **15**: 605–607 (1951). [*C.A.* **46**: 8973*b* (1952)]

16. Agranovich, V. M., and A. S. Davydov: Effect of the Surface of a Molecular Crystal on the Excitation by Light of Intramolecular Vibrations, *Zhur. Eksptl. i Teoret. Fiz.*, **21**: 677–683 (1951). [*C.A.* **46**: 9423*c* (1952)]
17. Davydov, A. S.: Theory of Light Absorption in Molecular Crystals, *Trudy Inst. Fiz. Akad. Nauk Ukr. S.S.R.*, **1** (1951), 175 pp. [*C.A.* **49**: 10045*a* (1955)]
18. Davydov, A. S.: "Teoriya pogloshcheniya sveta v molekulyarnykh kristallakh" (Theory of Light Absorption by Molecular Crystals), Izdatel'stvo Akademii Nauk Ukrainskoi S.S.R., Kiev, 1951, 175 pp. [*C.A.* **49**: 12139*g* (1955)]
19. Davydov, A. S.: Results of the Conference on the Theory of Chemical Structure in Organic Chemistry, *Trudy Inst. Fiz. Akad. Nauk Ukr. S.S.R.*, **2**: 93–101 (1952). [*C.A.* **49**: 6813*c* (1955)]
20. Davydov, A. S.: "The Question of Energy Migration in Molecular Crystals," Pamyati Sergeya Ivanovicha Vavilova, Akademiya Nauk S.S.S.R. pp. 210–219, 1952. [*C.A.* **49**: 15498*c* (1955)]
21. Davydov, A. S.: The Theory of Absorption, Dispersion and Scattering of Light by Solutions, *Izvest. Akad. Nauk S.S.S.R., Ser. Fiz.*, **17**: 523–530 (1953). [*C.A.* **48**: 5650*c* (1954)]
22. Davydov, A. S.: Theory of Non-radiative Transitions in Molecules Occurring in Solutions, *Zhur. Eksptl. i Teoret. Fiz.*, **24**: 397–408 (1953). [*C.A.* **50**: 11085*c* (1956)]
23. Borisov, M. D., and A. S. Davydov: Luminescence of Molecular Crystals Containing Impurity Molecules, *Izvest. Akad. Nauk S.S.S.R., Ser. Fiz.*, **18**: 714–715 (1954). [*C.A.* **50**: 7587*g* (1956)]
24. Davydov, A. S.: The Relation between the Oscillations of the Surface of the Nucleus and Excitation by One Nucleon, *Zhur. Eksptl. i Teoret. Fiz.*, **29**: 75–84 (1955). [*C.A.* **49**: 15511*i* (1955)]
25. Davydov, A. S.: Theory of Absorption and Dispersion of Light by Solutions II, *Nauk. Zapiski*, Kiev. Derzhav. Univ. im. T. G. Shevchenka, **14**: (8); *Zbirnik Fiz. Fak.* no. 7, pp. 5–13, 1955. [*C.A.* **51**: 9265*h* (1957)]
26. Agranovich, V. M., and A. S. Davydov: Absorption and Fluorescence Spectra of Polyatomic Molecules, *Nauk. Zapiski*, Kiev. Derzhav. Univ. im. T. G. Shevchenka, **14**: (8); *Zbirnik Fiz. Fak.* no. 7, pp. 15–20, 1955. [*C.A.* **51**: 9309*c* (1957)]
27. Davydov, A. S., and A. F. Lubchenko: The Form of the Dispersion Curves in Molecular Crystals, Which Correspond to Localized Excitations, *Ukrain. Fiz. Zhur.*, **1**: 111–119 (1956). [*C.A.* **50**: 15210*g* (1956)]
28. Borisov, M. D., and A. S. Davydov: Luminescence of Molecular Crystals Containing Molecular Admixtures, *Trudy Inst. Fiz. Akad. Nauk Ukr. S.S.R.*, **7**: 97–115 (1956). [*C.A.* **51**: 6357*b* (1957)]
29. Davydov, A. S., and A. F. Lubchenko: The Emission and Absorption of Light in Molecular Crystals, Depending on the Formation of Localized Excitations, *Ukrain. Fiz. Zhur.*, **1**: 5–13 (1956). [*C.A.* **51**: 2399*d* (1957)]
30. Davydov, A. S., and A. F. Lubchenko: The Spectral Distribution of the Intensity of Emission and Absorption of Light by Molecular Crystals under Formation of Localized Excitations, *Ukrain. Fiz. Zhur.*, **1**: 15–27 (1956). [*C.A.* **51**: 2399*f* (1957)]
31. Davydov, A. S., and G. F. Filippov: Scattering Lengths of Slow Neutrons on Deuterons, *Soviet Phys. JETP*, **4**: 267–268 (1957); *Zhur. Eksptl. i Teoret. Fiz.*, **31**: 340–341 (1956). [*C.A.* **51**: 10250*h* (1957)]
32. Davydov, A. S., and G. F. Filippov: Quadrupole Moments and Zero-point Surface Vibrations of Axially Symmetrical Nuclei, *Soviet Phys. JETP*, **5**: 773–775 (1957); *Zhur. Eksptl. i Teoret. Fiz.*, **32**: 945–947 (1957). [*C.A.* **52**: 14356*b* (1958)]

33. Davydov, A. S., and D. M. Mel'nichenko: Second Approximation in the Problem of Slow Neutron Scattering by Bound Protons, *Soviet Phys. JETP*, **5**: 769–771 (1957); *Zhur. Eksptl. i Teoret. Fiz.*, **32**: 941–942 (1957). [*C.A.* **52**: 14357*h* (1958)]
34. Davydov, A. S., and E. I. Rashba: Light Absorption in Molecular Crystals at Weak Interaction between Excitons and Phonons, *Ukrain. Fiz. Zhur.*, **2**: 226–240 (1957). [*C.A.* **52**: 2550*g* (1958)]
35. Agranovich, V. M., and A. S. Davydov: Optical Model of the Interaction of Nucleons with Nuclei in the Resonance Region of the Compound Nucleus, *Soviet Phys. JETP*, **5**: 1164–1169 (1957); *Zhur. Eksptl. i Teoret. Fiz.*, **32**: 1429–1436 (1957). [*C.A.* **53**: 75*f* (1959)]
36. Davydov, A. S., and A. A. Chaban: Rotation Bands for Even-even Axially Symmetrical Nuclei, *Soviet Phys. JETP*, **6**: 428–429 (1958); *Zhur. Eksptl. i Teoret. Fiz.*, **33**: 547–549 (1957). [*C.A.* **52**: 10737*g* (1958)]
37. Davydov, A. S., and G. F. Filippov: Collective Excitations of Even-even Atomic Nuclei, *Soviet Phys. JETP*, **6**: 555–560 (1958); *Zhur. Eksptl. i Teoret. Fiz.*, **33**: 723–729 (1957). [*C.A.* **52**: 10738*a* (1958)]
38. Davydov, A. S., and G. F. Filippov: Rotational States in Even Atomic Nuclei, *Nuclear Phys.*, **8**: 237–249 (1958). [*C.A.* **53**: 8841*a* (1959)]
39. Davydov, A. S., and B. M. Murashkin: Collective Excitation of Odd Nonspherical Nuclei, *Zhur. Eksptl. i Teoret. Fiz.*, **34**: 1619–1624 (1958). [*C.A.* **53**: 2831*a* (1959)]
40. Davydov, A. S., and G. F. Filippov: Collective Excitation States of Even-even Atomic Nuclei, *Acta Phys. Acad. Sci. Hung.*, **9**(1–2): 169–176 (1958). [*C.A.* **53**: 11008*e* (1959)]
41. Davydov, A. S., and A. F. Lubchenko: Electromagnetic Waves in a Crystal in the Region of Exciton Absorption, *Zhur. Eksptl. i Teoret. Fiz.*, **35**: 1499–1507 (1958). [*C.A.* **53**: 12004*a* (1959)]
42. Davydov, A. S., and G. F. Filippov: Rotational States for Nonaxial Nuclei, *Zhur. Eksptl. i Teoret. Fiz.*, **35**: 440–447 (1958). [*C.A.* **53**: 13807*f* (1959)]
43. Davydov, A. S., and G. F. Filippov: Magnetic Transitions between Collective Excited States for Even-even Nuclei, *Zhur. Eksptl. i Teoret. Fiz.*, **35**: 703–706 (1958). [*C.A.* **53**: 14755*a* (1959)]
44. Davydov, A. S.: "Teoriya atomnogo yadra" (Theory of the Atomic Nucleus), Gosudarst. Izdatel'stvo Fiziko-Matematicheskoĭ Literatury, Moskva, 1958, 611 pp. [*C.A.* **53**: 16751*i* (1959)]
45. Davydov, A. S., and D. A. Zaikin: The γ Vibrations of the Surface of the Atomic Nucleus, *Zhur. Eksptl. i Teoret. Fiz.*, **36**: 233–237 (1959). [*C.A.* **53**: 12863*a* (1959)]
46. Davydov, A. S., and G. F. Filippov: Shape of Even Atomic Nuclei, *Nuclear Phys.*, **10**: 654–662 (1959). [*C.A.* **53**: 14728*g* (1959)]
47. Davydov, A. S.: Collective Excited States of Atomic Nuclei, *Izvest. Akad. Nauk S.S.S.R., Ser. Fiz.*, **23**: 792–811 (1959). [*C.A.* **53**: 19591*i* (1959)]
48. Davydov, A. S., and V. S. Rostovskii: Relative Transition Probabilities between Rotational Levels of Nonaxial Nuclei, *Nuclear Phys.*, **12**: 58–68 (1959). [*C.A.* **53**: 21213*a* (1959)]
49. Davydov, A. S.: Rotational States of Nonaxial, Odd Nuclei, *Zhur. Eksptl. i Teoret. Fiz.*, **36**: 1555–1559 (1959). [*C.A.* **54**: 1091*d* (1960)]
50. Davydov, A. S., and G. F. Filippov: Form of Even-even Nuclei, *Zhur. Eksptl. i Teoret. Fiz.*, **36**: 1497–1502 (1959). [*C.A.* **54**: 1091*e* (1960)]
51. Davydov, A. S.: Intensity Rules for β-transitions to Various Rotational States of Daughter Even-even Nuclei, *Zhur. Eksptl. i Teoret. Fiz.*, **37**: 137–142 (1959). [*C.A.* **54**: 8313*e* (1960)]

52. Davydov, A. S.: "Kollektivnye vozbuzhdennye sostoyaniya atomnykh yader" (Collective Excited States of Atomic Nuclei), Redakts.-Izdatel. Otdel, Dubna, 1959, 28 pp. [*C.A.* **54:** 22085*f* (1960)]

53. Davydov, A. S.: Rotation-Vibration Interaction in Nonaxial Even Atomic Molecules, *Proc. Intern. Conf. Nuclear Structure* (C. A. Bromley and E. W. Vogt, eds., University of Toronto Press), pp. 801–813, Kingston, Canada, 1960. [*C.A.* **55:** 2293*c* (1961)]

54. Davydov, A. S.: Coupling of Nuclear Rotation and Motion of the Outer Nucleon, *Nuclear Phys.*, **16:** 597–607 (1960). [*C.A.* **55:** 9074*d* (1961)]

55. Davydov, A. S.: Rotational Energy for Even-even and Odd Atomic Nuclei, *Izvest. Akad. Nauk S.S.S.R., Ser. Fiz.*, **24:** 820–832 (1960). [*C.A.* **55:** 9075*i* (1961)]

56. Davydov, A. S., N. S. Rabotnov, and A. A. Chaban: Rotational Energies and Moments of Inertia of Nonaxial Nuclei, *Nuclear Phys.*, **17:** 169–174 (1960). [*C.A.* **55:** 10104*d* (1961)]

57. Davydov, A. S.: Collective Excitations Corresponding to Quadrupole Nuclear Surface Vibrations, *Nuclear Phys.*, **24:** 682–694 (1961). [*C.A.* **55:** 20667*b* (1961)]

APPENDIX II

SUPPLEMENTARY BIBLIOGRAPHY OF PUBLICATIONS ON EXCITONS

1. Winston, H., and R. Halford: Motion of Molecules in Condensed Systems, part V, Classification of Motion and Selection Rules for Spectra According to Space Symmetry, *J. Chem. Phys.*, **17**: 607 (1949).
2. Simpson, W. T.: Internal Dispersion Forces: The Polyenes, *J. Am. Chem. Soc.*, **73**: 5363 (1951).
3. Winston, H.: The Electronic Energy Levels of Molecular Crystals, *J. Chem. Phys.*, **19**: 156 (1951).
4. Heller, W. R., and A. Marcus: A Note on the Propagation of Excitation in an Idealized Crystal, *Phys. Rev.*, **84**: 809 (1951).
5. Dexter, D. L.: A Theory of Sensitized Luminescence in Solids, *J. Chem. Phys.*, **21**: 836 (1955).
6. Decius, J. C.: Coupling of the Out-of-plane Bending Mode in Nitrates and Carbonates of the Aragonite Structure, *J. Chem. Phys.*, **23**: 1290 (1955).
7. Craig, D. P., and P. C. Hobbins: The Polarized Spectrum of Anthracene, part I, The Assignment of the Intense Short Wavelength System, *J. Chem. Soc.*, **1955**: 539.
8. Craig, D. P.: The Polarized Spectrum of Anthracene, part II, Weak Transitions and Second Order Crystal Field Perturbations, *J. Chem. Soc.*, **1955**: 2302.
9. Craig, D. P., and P. C. Hobbins: The Polarized Spectrum of Anthracene, part III, The System at 3800 A, *J. Chem. Soc.*, **1955**: 2309.
10. Fox, D., and O. Schnepp: Theory of the Lower Excited Electronic States of the Benzene Crystal, *J. Chem. Phys.*, **23**: 767 (1955).
11. Simpson, W. T.: Resonance Force Theory of Carotenoid Pigments, *J. Am. Chem. Soc.*, **77**: 6164 (1955).
12. Longuet-Higgins, H. C., and J. N. Murrell: The Electronic Spectra of Aromatic Molecules, part V, The Interaction of Two Conjugated Systems, *Proc. Phys. Soc.* (*London*), **A68**: 601 (1955).
13. Merrifield, R. E.: Exciton Multiplicities, *J. Chem. Phys.*, **23**: 402 (1955).
14. Longuet-Higgins, H. C.: The Electronic States of Composite Systems, *Proc. Roy. Soc.* (*London*), **A235**: 537 (1956).
15. Craig, D. P., and J. R. Walsh: Intermolecular Effects in Naphthalene Crystal Spectra, *J. Chem. Phys.*, **24**: 471 (1956).
16. Craig, D. P., and J. R. Walsh: Exciton Shape Dependence and Davydov Splitting in Aromatic Crystals, *J. Chem. Phys.*, **25**: 588 (1956).
17. Moffitt, W.: Optical Rotatory Dispersion of Helical Polymers, *J. Chem. Phys.*, **25**: 467 (1956).
18. Moffitt, W.: The Optical Rotatory Dispersion of Simple Polypeptides, *Proc. Natl. Acad. Sci., U.S.*, **42**: 736 (1956).

19. Moffitt, W., D. D. Fitts, and J. G. Kirkwood: Critique of the Theory of Optical Activity of Helical Polymers, *Proc. Natl. Acad. Sci., U.S.*, **43**: 723 (1957).
20. Simpson, W. T., and D. L. Peterson: Coupling Strength for Resonance Force Transfer of Electronic Energy in Van der Waals Solids, *J. Chem. Phys.*, **26**: 588 (1957).
21. Levinson, G. L., W. T. Simpson, and W. Curtis: Electronic Spectra of Pyridocyanine Dyes with Assignment of Transitions, *J. Am. Chem. Soc.*, **79**: 4314 (1957).
22. McClure, D. S.: Energy Transfer in Molecular Crystals and in Double Molecules, *Can. J. Chem.*, **36**: 59 (1958).
23. McRae, E. G., and M. Kasha: Enhancement of Phosphorescence Ability upon Aggregation of Dye Molecules, *J. Chem. Phys.*, **28**: 721 (1958).
24. Merrifield, R. E.: Propagation of Electronic Excitation in Insulating Crystals, *J. Chem. Phys.*, **28**: 647 (1958).
25. Lyons, L. E.: First-order Calculation of Factor Group Splittings in the Electronic Spectra of Durene, Ovalene, and Phthalocyanine Crystals, *J. Chem. Soc.* (*London*), 1958, 1347–1351.
26. Trlifaj, M.: The Diffusion of the Excitation Energy in Molecular Crystals, *Czech. J. Phys.*, **8**: 510 (1958) (in English).
27. Kasha, M.: Relation between Exciton Bands and Conduction Bands in Molecular Lamellar Systems, *Rev. Modern Phys.*, **31**: 162 (1959).
28. McClure, D. S.: Electronic Spectra of Molecules and Ions in Crystals, part 1, Molecular Crystals, in "Solid State Physics," vol. 8, pp. 1–47, Academic Press, Inc., New York, 1959.
29. Tanaka, J.: Electronic Absorption Spectra of Molecular Crystals, *Supplement of the Progress of Theoretical Physics*, **12**: 183–210 (1959).
30. Broude, V. L., A. F. Prikhotko, and E. I. Rashba: Luminescence of Organic Crystals, *Uspekhi Fiz. Nauk*, **67**: 99 (1959).
31. Hexter, R. M.: Intermolecular Coupling of Vibrations in Molecular Crystals: A Vibrational Exciton Approach, *J. Chem. Phys.*, **33**: 1833 (1960).
32. Förster, T.: Excitation Transfer, in M. Burton, J. S. Kirby-Smith, and J. L. Magee (eds.), "Comparative Effects of Radiation," p. 300, John Wiley & Sons, Inc., New York, 1960.
33. Witkowsky, A., and W. Moffitt: Electronic Spectra of Dimers: Derivation of the Fundamental Vibronic Equation, *J. Chem. Phys.*, **33**: 872 (1960).
34. Magee, J. L., and K. Funabashi: Dissociation Processes in Electronically Excited Molecules: Linear Chain Model, *J. Chem. Phys.*, **34**: 1715 (1961); cf. J. L. Magee, Elementary Processes in Action of Ionizing Radiation, in M. Burton, J. S. Kirby-Smith, and J. L. Magee (eds.), "Comparative Effects of Radiation," p. 130, John Wiley & Sons, Inc., New York, 1960.
35. Agranovich, V. M.: The Problem of the Defects in the Process of Exciton Luminescence of Molecular Crystals, *Uspekhi Fiz. Nauk*, **71**: 141 (1960).
36. Kasha, M., M. Ashraf El-Bayoumi, and W. Rhodes: Excited States of Nitrogen Base-pairs and Polynucleotides, *J. chim. phys.*, **58**: 916 (1961).
37. Rhodes, W.: Hypochromism and Other Spectral Properties of Helical Polynucleotides, *J. Am. Chem. Soc.*, **83**: 3609 (1961).
38. Sternlicht, H., and H. M. McConnell: Paramagnetic Excitons in Molecular Crystals, *J. Chem. Phys.*, **35**: 1793 (1961).
39. McRae, E. G.: Molecular Vibrations in the Exciton Theory for Molecular Aggregates, *Australian J. Chem.*, **14**: 329, 344, 354 (1961).
40. Craig, D. P., and S. H. Walmsley: The Crystal Spectra of Very Weak Transitions. II. Theoretical, *Mol. Phys.*, **4**: 113–124 (1961).

REFERENCES

[Russian translations of books cited are indicated by the presence of the name of the Soviet publishing house after the title.]

1. Born, M.: "Theory of Solids," O.N.T.I., 1938.
2. Landsberg, G. S., and L. I. Mandelshtam: *Zhur. Russ. Fiz.-Khim. Obshchestva,* **60:** 335 (1928); *Naturwiss,* **16:** 557, 772 (1928).
3. Gross, E., and M. Vuks: *J. Phys. Radium,* **7:** 113 (1936); *Nature,* **135:** 100 (1935).
4. Bethe, H.: *Ann. Physik,* **3:** 133 (1929).
5. Becquerel, J.: *J. Phys.,* **4:** 328 (1907).
6. Kurbatov, V. Y.: *Zhur. Russ. Khim. Obshchestva,* **39:** 11, 134 (1907).
7. Obreimov, I. V.: *Zhur. Russ. Fiz.-Khim. Obshchestva,* **59:** 548 (1927).
8. Obreimov, I. V., and W. J. de Haas: *Commun. Kamerlingh Onnes Lab. Univ. Leiden,* no. 191 (1928).
9. Obreimov, I. V., and W. J. de Haas: *Commun. Kamerlingh Onnes Lab. Univ. Leiden,* no. 204*c* (1929).
10. Henri, V.: *Izvestia Gosudarst. Opt. Inst.,* **2**(2).
11. Pringsheim, P., and A. Kronenberger: *Z. Physik,* **40:** 75 (1926).
12. Obreimov, I. V., and A. F. Prikhotko: *Physik. Z. Sowjetunion,* **1:** 203 (1932).
13. Prikhotko, A. F.: *J. Phys. U.S.S.R.,* **8:** 257 (1944).
14. German, V. L.: *J. Phys. U.S.S.R.,* **8:** 276 (1944).
15. Obreimov, I. V., and K. G. Shabaldas: *J. Phys. U.S.S.R.,* **7:** 168 (1943).
16. Obreimov, I. V., and A. F. Prikhotko: *Physik. Z. Sowjetunion,* **9:** 34 (1936).
17. Obreimov, I. V., and A. F. Prikhotko: *Physik. Z. Sowjetunion,* **9:** 48 (1936).
18. Obreimov, I. V., A. F. Prikhotko, and K. G. Shabaldas: *Zhur. Eksptl. i Teoret. Fiz.,* **6:** 1062 (1936).
19. Frenkel, J. I.: *Phys. Rev.,* **37:** 17 (1931).
20. Frenkel, J. I.: *Phys. Rev.,* **37:** 1276 (1931).
21. Frenkel, J. I.: *Zhur. Eksptl. i Teoret. Fiz.,* **6:** 647 (1936).
22. Peierls, R.: *Ann. Physik,* **13:** 905 (1932).
23. Blokhintsev, D. I.: *Zhur. Eksptl. i Teoret. Fiz.,* **5:** 470 (1935).
24. Blokhintsev, D. I.: *Physik. Z. Sowjetunion,* **7:** 641 (1935).
25. Blokhintsev, D. I.: *Zhur. Eksptl. i Teoret. Fiz.,* **6:** 1053 (1936).
26. Vavilov, S. I.: *Doklady Akad. Nauk S.S.S.R.,* **35:** 110 (1942).
27. Vavilov, S. I., and P. P. Feofilov: *Doklady Akad. Nauk S.S.S.R.,* **34:** 243 (1942).
28. Vavilov, S. I.: *Zhur. Eksptl. i Teoret. Fiz.,* **13:** 13 (1943).
29. Vavilov, S. I., M. D. Galanin, and F. M. Pekerman: *Izvest. Akad. Nauk S.S.S.R., Ser. Fiz.,* **13**(1–2) (1949).
30. Riehl, N. V.: *Uspekhi Fiz. Nauk,* **35:** 186 (1948); "Migration of Energy," O.G.I.Z., 1948.
31. Bowen, E. J.: *J. Chem. Phys.,* **13:** 306 (1945).
32. Prikhotko, A. F.: *Izvest. Akad. Nauk S.S.S.R., Ser. Fiz.,* **12:** 499 (1948).
33. Gross, E. F., and A. I. Raskin: *Doklady Akad. Nauk S.S.S.R.,* **24:** 125 (1939).
34. Gross, E. F., and A. V. Korshunov: *Zhur. Eksptl. i Teoret. Fiz.,* **16:** 53 (1946).

35. Vuks, M. F.: *Zhur. Eksptl. i Teoret. Fiz.*, **16**: 410 (1946).
36. Raskin, A. I.: *Izvest. Akad. Nauk S.S.S.R., Ser. Fiz.*, **9**: 367 (1947).
37. Nedungadi, T. M.: *Proc. Indian Acad. Sci.*, **13**: 161 (1941).
38. Rousset, A.: *J. Phys.*, **9**: 100 (1948).
39. Davydov, A. S.: *Zhur. Eksptl. i Teoret. Fiz.*, **19**: 181 (1949).
40. Ladenburg, R.: *Z. Physik*, **4**: 151 (1921).
41. Elliott, A., and E. J. Ambrose: *Nature*, **159**: 641 (1947).
42. Buchheim, W.: *Physik. Z.*, **36**: 694 (1935).
43. Volkenstein, M. V.: *Uspekhi Fiz. Nauk*, **18**: 153 (1937).
44. Nedungadi, T. M.: *Proc. Indian Acad. Sci.*, **15**: 376 (1942).
45. Davydov, A. S.: *Zhur. Eksptl. i Teoret. Fiz.*, **18**: 210 (1948).
46. Davydov, A. S.: *Zhur. Eksptl. i Teoret. Fiz.*, **17**: 1106 (1947).
47. Schaefer, C., and F. Matossi: "Infrared Spectra," O.N.T.I., 1935.
48. Schaefer, C., C. Bormuth, and F. Matossi: *Z. Physik*, **39**: 648 (1926).
49. Schaefer, C., F. Matossi, and F. Dane: *Z. Physik*, **45**: 493 (1927).
50. Herzberg, G.: "Infrared and Raman Spectra of Polyatomic Molecules," D. Van Nostrand, Inc., Princeton, N.J., 1946.
51. Kitaigorodsky, A. I.: *Uspekhi Khim.*, **17**: 287 (1948).
52. Bragg, W. L.: *Proc. Roy. Soc. (London)*, **105**: 16 (1924).
53. Prikhotko, A. F., V. L. Broude, and V. S. Medvedev: *Zhur. Eksptl. i Teoret. Fiz.*, **21**: 665 (1951).
54. Pauling, L.: *J. Am. Chem. Soc.*, **53**: 1367 (1931).
55. Hückel, E.: *Z. Physik*, **70**: 204 (1931); **76**: 628 (1932).
56. Mulliken, R. S.: *Phys. Rev.*, **40**: 55 (1932).
57. Goeppert-Mayer, M., and A. L. Sklar: *J. Chem. Phys.*, **6**: 645 (1938).
58. London, A.: *J. Chem. Phys.*, **13**: 396 (1945).
59. Volkenstein, M. V., M. Elyashevich, and B. Stepanov: *Zhur. Eksptl. i Teoret. Fiz.*, **15**: 35 (1945).
60. Mayants, L. S.: *Izvest. Akad. Nauk S.S.S.R., Ser. Fiz.*, **11**: 353 (1947).
61. Landau, L. D.: *Physik. Z. Sowjetunion*, **1**: 88 (1932).
62. Born, M., and J. R. Oppenheimer: *Ann. Physik*, **84**: 457 (1927).
63. Pauli, W.: "General Principles of Wave Mechanics," O.G.I.Z., 1947.
64. Robertson, J. M.: *Proc. Roy. Soc. (London)*, **142**: 674 (1933).
65. Robertson, J. M.: *Proc. Roy. Soc. (London)*, **140**: 79 (1933).
66. Davydov, A. S.: *Zhur. Eksptl. i Teoret. Fiz.*, **19**: 168 (1949).
67. Volkenstein, M. V.: "Structure of Molecules," Izdatel'stvo Akademii Nauk S.S.S.R., 1947.
68. Blokhintsev, D. I.: "Introduction to Quantum Mechanics," O.G.I.Z., 1944.
69. Agranovich, V. M., and A. S. Davydov: *Zhur. Eksptl. i Teoret. Fiz.*, **21**: 677 (1951).
70. Lifschitz, I. M.: *Zhur. Eksptl. i Teoret. Fiz.*, **12**: 117, 137, 156 (1942).
71. Weisskopf, V., and E. Wigner: *Z. Physik*, **63**: 54 (1930).
72. Seitz, F.: "The Modern Theory of Solids," McGraw-Hill Book Company, Inc., New York, 1940.
73. Seitz, F.: *Trans. Faraday Soc.*, **35**: 2 (1939).
74. Randall, J. T.: *Trans. Faraday Soc.*, **35**: 2 (1939).
75. Vavilov, S. I.: *Physik. Z. Sowjetunion*, **5**: 369 (1934).
76. Terenin, A. N.: "Photochemistry of Dyes," Izdatel'stvo Akademii Nauk S.S.S.R., 1947.
77. Levshin, V. L.: *Izvest. Akad. Nauk S.S.S.R., Ser. Fiz.*, **9**: 355 (1945).
78. Hettner, G.: *Z. Physik*, **89**: 234 (1934).
79. Colby, W. F., C. F. Meyer, and D. W. Bronk: *Astrophys. J.*, **50**: 7 (1923).

80. Imanishi, S.: *Nature*, **135:** 396 (1935).
81. Leberknight, C. E.: *Phys. Rev.*, **43:** 967 (1933).
82. Rodnikova, I. V.: *J. Phys. U.S.S.R.*, **10:** 236 (1946).
83. Keesom, W. H., and K. W. Taconis: *Physica*, **2:** 463 (1935).
84. Richards, R. E., and H. W. Thompson: *Proc. Roy. Soc. (London)*, **195:** 1 (1948).
85. Henri, V., and H. G. de Lazlo: *Proc. Roy. Soc. (London)*, **105:** 66 (1924).
86. de Lazlo, H. G.: *Z. physik. Chem. (Leipzig)*, **118:** 369 (1925).
87. Coulson, C. A.: *Proc. Phys. Soc. (London)*, **60:** 257 (1948).
88. Obreimov, I. V., A. F. Prikhotko, and I. V. Rodnikova: *Zhur. Eksptl. i Teoret. Fiz.*, **18:** 409 (1948).
89. Scheibe, G., and L. Kandler: *Naturwiss.*, **26:** 412 (1938).
90. Sheppard, S. E.: *Rev. Modern Phys.*, **14:** 303 (1942).
91. Sponer, H., and E. Teller: *Rev. Modern Phys.*, **13:** 76 (1941).
92. Pringsheim, P., and A. Kronenberger: *Z. Physik*, **40:** 75 (1926).
93. Kronenberger, A.: *Z. Physik*, **63:** 494 (1930).
94. Reimann, A.: *Ann. Physik*, **80:** 43 (1926).
95. Purvis, J. E.: *J. Chem. Soc. (London)*, **99:** 2318 (1911).
96. Henri, V.: "Structure des Molecules," Paris, 1925.
97. Klingstedt, F. W.: *Z. physik. Chem. (Leipzig)*, **B20:** 125 (1933).
98. Davydov, A. S.: *Zhur. Eksptl. i Teoret. Fiz.*, **18:** 515 (1948).
99. Davydov, A. S.: *Izvest. Akad. Nauk S.S.S.R., Ser. Fiz.*, **12:** 664 (1948).
100. Fock, V. A.: *Trudy Gosudarst. Opt. Inst., Leningrad*, **5**(51) (1931).
101. Sverdlov, L. M., and M. A. Kovner: *Izvest. Akad. Nauk S.S.S.R., Ser. Fiz.*, **12:** 582 (1948).
102. Gillam, A. E., and D. H. Hey: *J. Chem. Soc. (London)*, 1170 (1939).
103. Davydov, A. S.: *Zhur. Eksptl. i Teoret. Fiz.*, **18:** 201 (1948).
104. Dhar, J.: *Indian J. Phys.*, **7:** 43 (1932).
105. Mulliken, R. S.: *Phys. Rev.*, **43:** 279 (1933).
106. Pauling, L.: "Nature of the Chemical Bond," Goskhimizdat, 1947.
107. Sklar, A. L., and R. H. Lyddane: *J. Chem. Phys.*, **7:** 374 (1939).
108. Hellman, H. H.: "Quantum Chemistry," O.N.T.I., 1937.
109. Carr, E. P., and H. Stücklen: *J. Chem. Phys.*, **4:** 760 (1936).
110. Carr, E. P., and H. Stücklen: *J. Chem. Phys.*, **6:** 55 (1938).
111. Dickson, E.: *Z. wiss. Phot.*, **10:** 181 (1911).

INDEX